# Muslim Feminism *and* Feminist Movement

IN

• NAMIBIA • NIGERIA • SIERRA LEONE
• SOUTH AFRICA • SUDAN • WEST AFRICA
• YUGOSLAVIA

VOL. 9

# Muslim Feminism
## *and*
# Feminist Movement

IN

• NAMIBIA • NIGERIA • SIERRA LEONE
• SOUTH AFRICA • SUDAN • WEST AFRICA
• YUGOSLAVIA

VOL. 9

ABIDA SAMIUDDIN
R. KHANAM

GLOBAL VISION PUBLISHING HOUSE
20, Ansari Road, Daryaganj, New Delhi-110002 (INDIA)

**GLOBAL VISION PUBLISHING HOUSE**
F-4, 1st Floor, 'Hari Sadan' 20, Ansari Road,
Daryaganj, New Delhi-110002 (INDIA)
Tel.: 011-23261581, 23276291
E-mail: globalgvph@gmail.com, info@globalvisionpub.com
Website: www.globalvisionpub.com

*Muslim Feminism and Feminist Movement in Namibia, Nigeria, Sierra Leone, South Africa, Sudan, West Africa, Yugoslavia*



First Edition, 2017

ISBN: 978-81-8220-920-6 (Set)
978-81-8220-929-9 (Vol. 9)



PRINTED IN INDIA

*Published by* Dr. N.K. Singh for Global Vision Publishing House, New Delhi-02 and *Printed at* R.K. Digital Print, Naveen Shahdara, Delhi-32.

# PREFACE

The present edition of *"Muslim Feminism and Feminist Movement in Africa"* deals with the conceptual development of Muslim feminism and motive of feminist movement in African countries— Algeria, Djibouti, Egypt, Eritrea, Ethiopia, Gambia, Ghana, Ivory Coast, Jordon, Kenya, Liberia, Mali, Morocco, Namibia, Nigeria, Sierra Leone, South Africa, Sudan, West Africa, and Yugoslavia. The focus has been given on the development of feminist culture and fundamentalists resistance in African countries. All these articles basically deal with the nature and motivation of feminist movement and its impact on the socio-political and legal reforms in family law and the status of African Muslim women.

Since the colonial period, African feminist movement have been involved as a object of social reform efforts, rather than participating as actors. The pace of change was initially slow. It increased in the 1980s due to women participation in public life. This change has not been uniform, and there are wide variations between and within countries, across social classes, and also within political movements.

Early nationalist groups of the French that controlled Algeria (1830–1962), Tunisia (1818–1956), and Morocco (1912–1956), favoured secular reform, but education for women had limited support. In the 1950s, an Algerian political party recruited women, but they met separately. Some of the more popular religious reformists during the 1920s to 1950s advocated primary school education for girls, as well as a limited overlap of the separate gender spheres. A few Algerian and French women also discussed women's veiling, education, and the conditions of marriage and divorce in newspapers or books. French women's league of Tunisia (all members are male) debated women's rights. But Tunisia's *'ulama* blocked secular reform and condemned its supporters.

Women made great contribution in all three anti-colonial struggles. Nearly eleven thousand women participated in Algeria's war of independence (1954–1962), and 20 percent were jailed or killed. The majority played traditional roles, providing food and shelter for resistance fighters. However, a few participated in combat and strategic actions, and were imprisoned and tortured, including Djamila Bouhired and Djamila Boupacha. Revolutionaries deferred the process of changing female roles until after independence, but women's war heroism remains an important symbol of their potential. Their revolutionary roles are often most powerfully described in literary works, such as Moroccan Leila Abouzeid's semi-biographical account, *Year of the Elephant* (Austin, 1989).

After independence (Morocco, 2 March 1956; Tunisia, 20 March 1956; and Algeria, 3 July 1962), each country carved its own path to social reform, including the establishment of a constitution, legal codes, and government agencies to promote changes. In order to build viable national political constituencies, and to reconcile the competing interests of Islam and nationalism, however, reforms concerning women were limited. (Yet American women finally voted in 1920, 144 years after their "independence," Tunisian women voted in 1957, Algerian women in 1962, and Moroccan women in 1963.)

Despite early constitutional reforms such as enfranchisement, Maghribi women are subject to contradictory legislation governing their status. While Maghribi constitutions support the principle of equal rights and duties of males and females, national codes actually legalize gender inequality as they are based on the Maliki version of Islamic law. These personal status codes concern the regulation of individuals before, during, and after marriage, as well as the institution of marriage itself. Under Maliki law, which has traditionally given male relatives control over key decisions in women's lives, the bride's consent to marriage is expressed via her father or male guardian. A man may marry up to four wives. Men may repudiate their wives at will, while women may request a divorce only under specific and limited conditions. Inheritance provisions overwhelmingly favour men.

Likewise, under the 1984 Algerian Family Code, most legal prerogatives of men, including polygyny and preferential inheritance, remain intact. Divorce, replacing repudiation (a verbal dismissal of the wife by the husband), must now be conducted in the courts. A widowed mother becomes the children's guardian. Yet, as a woman, she legally remains a minor throughout her life, requiring a male tutor for any legal transaction. The 1956 Tunisian Code of Personal Status provides greater rights for women and reduces somewhat the authority of man over women. The bride's physical presence and verbal consent are required to make a valid marriage, and women are entitled to initiate divorce. Polygyny, repudiation, forced marriage, and the requirement that male tutors act on behalf of women have been banned. Despite these drastic legal changes, women, often ignorant of their legal rights, remain in a position of permanent dependency as daughters and wives, as men are always legally *chef de famille.* Legal constitutional changes have not altered social reality to any great extent.

Social reform for women's right advocated by all groups– either conservative or liberals, secularists or scripturalists, but their reform agendas may be quite different. Some state-sponsored and some revolutionary groups call for the reinforcement of traditional roles, while women's organizations pursue social and legal equality. All of these groups present models for women's identities. But change for any individual woman has complex determinants, including local and global economic and political conditions; in other words, one cannot simply reduce the causes of gender inequality to Islam.

On the state level, government sponsor national women's unions focused on nation-building. These unions and also ministry programs often reinforce traditional sewing and embroidery skills. State-provided education has benefited women most. While few attended school before independence, in 1986 the primary school enrollment for girls was 62 percent in Morocco, 85 percent in Algeria, and nearly a hundred percent in Tunisia. Many state bureaucracies employ women, though not in highly influential positions. A number of political parties have affiliated women's groups or address women's issues, but with few results. Women may run for office and have won Moroccan municipal elections and two parliamentary seats (Fall 1993); women took 3 percent of the seats in Algeria's National Assembly.

Women's own increasing public advocacy of their rights represents a new historical movement for reform in gender relations and women's status. Having paid employment increases women's leverage within the family, and often in society at large. Since 1988 nearly thirty Algerian women's associations have formed, most advocating change in the 1984 Family Code. As Moroccan feminist Fatima Mernissi says, women are now "designing a future instead of growing old." A specifically North African feminist discourse also develops through scholarship in which Mernissi identifies the misogyny behind certain *hadiths* traditionally used to support male privilege and finds evidence for early Islam's egalitarianism.

Yet calls for reform among women are not inviolate. An increasing number of Maghribi women, including many educated professionals, are electing to wear the *hijab*. This modern-day version of the Muslim veil leaves the face uncovered and is worn with an ample gown. Islamists advocate separate public spheres for men and women, demanding segregated educational and public facilities. Their campaign has been only partially successful. But such a phenomenon cannot be solely ascribed to social pressure exercised by Islamists, particularly in countries where they lack an official power base.

Women adopt the *hijab* for complex and manifold reasons, not simply as an acquiescence to male power. Although perceived by most Westerners as a symbol of female oppression, for many Maghribi women, wearing the *hijab* represents a commitment to Islamic authenticity. The concept of authenticity is religious and cultural in nature, based essentially on indigenous cultural norms and a rejection of Western values. But the veil has taken on contemporary meanings and functions, to meet the demands of the new situations in which women find themselves. It allows women easier, less controversial access to public space, while at the same time reemphasizing their traditional primary role as dependent, domesticated keepers of the private sphere. The *hijab*, novel in shape as well as meaning, meets the need for an overt expression of Islamic religious and cultural identity, while providing a solution to the spatial dilemma, accommodating women's expanded social presence within an Islamic framework.

Women are defining their identity both as Muslims and as women within new social and economic realities, in which traditional boundaries of role and space are no longer clear-cut. Professional women are increasingly penetrating public space, hitherto reserved for men, while the boundaries between traditional public space and women's private sphere in the home are shifting. Against this current of change have emerged strong individual and social desires for permanence and stability. The end of the twentieth century is clearly a period of rapid and varied change for the Muslim women of Africa.

# CONTENTS

## SIERRA LEONE



## SOUTH AFRICA



## SUDAN



## WEST AFRICA



## YUGOSLAVIA

# NAMIBIA

- Many Faces of Namibian Feminist Movement

# 31

# MANY FACES OF NAMIBIAN FEMINIST MOVEMENT

As a Starting Point, it is difficult to determine whether there is something that can validly be called a feminist movement in Namibia at present. On the one hand, it is possible to speak of a Namibian feminist movement in two senses. First, although there is no single organisation that speaks for all Namibian women, various non-governmental organisations (NGOs) and governmental bodies concerned about women have on occasion been able to put aside their differences to work together to achieve common aims. Second, there is a growing perception among Namibian women that many of their social and economic problems are related to their position as women, and they are showing an increasing interest in organizing to address such problems jointly.

On the other hand, it may be misleading to speak of 'a' women's movement in a nation divided by race, ethnicity, class, political affiliation, geography, and historical experience. Most formal women groups are dominated by black, urban, educated women, who cannot be viewed as representing the needs of the majority of Namibian women. Namibian women have not yet discovered how to utilize their combined political strength effectively to advance the position of women. Past attempts at achieving organisational unity have been unsuccessful, and there is now a trend toward looser alliances around specific issues.

Despite the existence of a government body to coordinate the efforts of women's groups, the most dynamic forces for the advancement of women are independent non-governmental and community organisations with their own issues and agendas. We take the view that there is a sufficient degree of networking and mutual support among these groups to warrant the use of the term *women's movement*. In this chapter we provide an analytical description of the evolution of the Namibian women's movement. While clear strengths and weaknesses can be identified, the major developments that have taken place do not yet seem to fit into a single pattern.

Historically, discrimination against women was compounded by the racial discrimination and underdevelopment of the colonial era. Gender was first used as a framework for analysis by the women's wings of the liberation movements, which were fighting first and foremost for national self-determination. Grassroots organisations of women around bread-and-butter issues intensified within the country in the latter years of the liberation struggle.

In 1990 Namibia became an independent, democratic state with a constitutional commitment to eradicate all sex discrimination. The early years of independence have given impetus to action around issues of special concern to women, as patterns of life under colonial rule are slowly being reshaped. It is a time of opportunity for women.

The decision to abandon the vision of an all-embracing unity in favour of the idea of strategic 'unity-in-diversity' seems to be a wise one. The women's movements has been fairly successful in ensuring that women's concerns are articulated at a national level and in increasing gender sensitivity in public policy. However, action on matters of concern to women is moving slowly, and the groups that promote women's issues are not yet adequately representative of the broad spectrum of women in Namibian society. In short, the women's movement has not yet managed to mobilize the full power of Namibia's women.

**Points of Diversity and Unity**

In order to understand the challenges faced by the Namibian feminist movement in Namibia, it is necessary to examine the complex divisions and diversity that characterize this small nation. The population of approximately 1.5 million (according to 1991 government census) is spread over a landmass more than six times the size of England and includes at least twelve major ethnic and language groups. These in turn are divided into overlapping subgroups, which sometimes speak distinct dialects.

During the colonial period, the Namibian population was stratified into three racial groups—blacks, whites, and 'coloureds', a colonially created category for mixed-race persons. As a divide-and-rule tactic, eleven 'population groups' identified by the colonial authorities were assigned second-tier governing bodies, with the black groups relegated to different geographical homelands. Namibia's rich cultural variety became the basis for profound political and economic discrimination, the effects of which are proving difficult to eradicate in the post-independence era.

As a result, the experience of sexual oppression was and still is heavily intertwined with race and class distinctions. Independence has given rise to a new black elite that shares more common interest with middle-class whites than with black members of the working class, thus blurring racial differences among the privileged classes. Meanwhile, both race and class distinctions continue to operate as divisive forces in the women's movement.

These intricate planes are overlaid with much political fragmentation. Namibia became a sovereign nation on March 21, 1990 following a twenty-three-year struggle to achieve freedom from South African rule. Although the South West African People's Organisation (SWAPO) was the clear leader in the liberation struggle (other groups that were active in the liberation struggle included the Herero Chiefs' Council and SWANU) and is now a strong majority party, more than forty political parties participated in Namibia's first free and fair elections in 1989. Political activity has since been rationalized, leaving only a handful of active parties, with SWAPO remaining predominant. SWAPO made a strong showing in the 1992 regional and local government elections, and a number of leaders from other political parties have chosen to join SWAPO in the last few years. However, party-political loyalties remain a divisive factor.

Since independence, political diversity has been supplemented by an increasing number of non-governmental organisations active in different spheres. The NGOs often acquire party-political associations, voluntarily or involuntarily (for example, the nation's largest trade union federation is formally affiliated to SWAPO, while the major students' organisation suffered a split over its decision to disaffiliate from SWAPO. There are two different umbrella bodies for NGOs, each with a different political profile, even though neither has any formal ties to any party), which have been subtle and complex and often problematic.

Another point of diversity is the differing experiences of the forty to fifty thousand people who engaged in the liberation struggle from exile compared to the experiences of the majority, who remained in Namibia. While both men and women in exile benefited from contact with other feminisms, they inevitably lost touch with practical conditions inside Namibia. Returning Namibians who benefited from educational opportunities aboard now form the backbone of a new black elite, from which grassroots women often feel alienated. This point should not obscure the fact that only a small proportion of exiled Namibians (perhaps 15 percent) underwent comprehensive post-secondary school training. Many returning Namibians have faced severe difficulties in finding employment and in reintegrating themselves into Namibian society.

Namibia is characterized by complex geographical and ethnic distinctions that complicate the nation's urban-rural divide. For example, there are crucial distinctions in organisational style and characteristics between Windhoek, the nation's capital and centre of political activity, and the smaller towns that also function as 'urban' centres in some respects.[1] There are also fundamental differences in community dynamics in both rural and 'urban' settings between the broad geographical areas of north and south. Different problems and priorities also exist for women in Namibia's thirteen political regions, which are in some cases isolated by long distances and difficult travelling conditions.[2]

Namibia's ethnic groups, which still have different geographical centres as a legacy of both history and apartheid, follow distinct customs and traditions. To cite only one example, some groups in Namibia are matrilineal, while others are patrilineal. Thus, a Namibian woman's individual experience may be shaped not only by her race and class but also by political affiliations, by whether she lives in Windhoek or a smaller town or rural area, by the characteristics unique to her region, and the ethnic identity of her community. This wide range of experience creates an enormous challenge for national organisation by women's groups.

Amidst all this diversity, there are some significant unifying factors. Approximately 90 percent of Namibia's population is Christian;[3] although the church played a role in the colonial occupation and subjugation of the indigenous people, most denominations ultimately became ardent and consistent challengers of the apartheid state.[4] The church is an important force at the community level, and Christianity provides a common moral ground on certain issues. However, Christian beliefs in Namibia are often manifested in conservative Christian doctrine that works against the interest of women. For example, biblical teaching are often cited in both personal and political settings to justify the subordination of women, particularly in the family. Therefore, the potential of the church as a vehicle for organizing women is limited.

Another point of convergence is a slowly growing sense of nationhood. There is a political commitment to encouraging a concept of Namibian nationality that will unite the diverse population and to deemphasising political assertions of ethnic identity.[5] Nevertheless, ethnic, political, racial, regional and class-based conflicts remain strong and are influential in determining divisions and alliances around women's issues.

**Pre-independent Feminist Organisation**

While it is difficult to generalize about pre-colonial gender relations in Namibia's many ethnic groups, many communities had a sex-based division of labour in which women played an important, if unequal, role in both production and reproduction. For example, in the mixed-farming Owambo communities, the harvest from the wife's plot was consumed by the household, while that from the husband's plot was disposed of by him as surplus profit. Thus, even though women were involved in production, their economic role was marginalised.

Positions of influence in precolonial communities were generally held by men, although there were some exceptions, and men usually had larger economic decision making power within extended family units, *Lobola* (bride-price) also contributed to the relatively inferior position of women; men often believed that they could exercise total control and power over their wives since they had 'paid' for them. Polygamy, while ensuring household labour and arguably reducing the workload of individual women, intensified sexual inequality by linking a woman's status to her rank as wife. While women's precolonial position was later interpreted as conferring inferior status, it has been asserted that notions of gender equality or inequality were simply nonexistent during this period and that men and women were perceived as inhabiting and controlling different and complementary spheres.[6]

During this period, the missionary influence was undermining traditional ideology and religion and holding up submission and subordination as model behaviour for women. Paradoxically, it also provided useful educational opportunities for women in some parts of the country. In the white settler communities, women generally remained in the home, while the realm of public activity was completely male dominated.

Colonial rule brought new legal, social, and economic bases for women's sub-ordination. Gender dynamics were profoundly affected by the system of migrant labour that was imposed in 1925, primarily to ensure a supply of cheap labour in the country's mines. A range of influx control laws ensured that workers' families remained in rural 'native reserves'.

This resulted in an increased workload for women, as they assumed tasks traditionally performed by men in addition to their own productive and reproductive duties. This rarely, however, gave them more decision making power, as men often continued to control the household's major economic resources during their infrequent visits home. Furthermore, men engaged in wage employment did not always send regular remittances home, thus increasing the burden on women to find alternate sources of income for the household's cash expenses.[7]

As the years passed, environmental degradation, increasing poverty, a greater reliance on a cash economy, and the dangers of the liberation war all encouraged increasing numbers of people, including women, to flee the rural areas in search of wage employment in cities and towns. Unfortunately, women were concentrated in domestic work, where they had no legal protection and were vulnerable to exploitation by employers. The majority of black women, particularly those who remained in rural areas, were forced to rely on subsistence agriculture, informal economic activities and, in some cases, prostitution. Women's economic marginalisation contributed to their overall disempowerment in the pre-independence era.[8]

Although it is difficult to pinpoint a particular time or event as the beginning of Namibia's women's movement, it clearly has important roots in the liberation struggle. Women had always been active in resistance to colonial domination. For example, during a war of resistance to German rule in 1904-1905, Herero women vowed not to bear children until German rule ended. In later years, black urban women defied the pass laws imposed on them by the colonial administration. (Pass laws required blacks and coloureds to carry identity cards at all times, which were then used to strictly segregate and control the movement and settlement of these groups). Women also played a leading role in a seminal struggle against the forced removal of blacks to ethnically segregated townships in 1959—an event that was an important catalyst for crystallizing the nascent liberation movements.

When political attempts to achieve independence were supplemented by armed struggle in 1966, women overcame initial male opposition to participate as combatants in the People's Liberation Army of Namibia (PLAN), the guerrilla force that was the military wing of SWAPO. An equally important role was played by women who remained inside the country and provided crucial material and psychological support to the freedom fighters. Women also suffered from the direct and indirect consequences of the liberation war—rape, torture and imprisonment, and health, social, and economic hardships stemming from unemployment and underdevelopment.[9]

Against this background, a SWAPO women's council was formed in 1969 and formally inaugurated as a wing of SWAPO in 1976, soon establishing an active presence both inside and outside Namibia. The South West African National Union (SWANU), a smaller liberation movement, also established a women's wing during this period. While these groups discussed steps to end the oppression of women, this goal was subordinated to the achievement of national independence, considered a prerequisite for improving the condition of women.

While black women experienced a combination of race, class and gender oppression, it was the experience of living under apartheid colonialism that most affected them. Thus, the struggle for national liberation was accorded more prominence than the struggle for women's liberation. Although this approach has been criticized by some Western feminists, it has been the reality in a number of other African countries, including Zimbabwe and Mozambique.

Namibian women were mobilized to support the liberation struggle, while the hierarchy of the liberation movements remained male dominated. Nevertheless the women's wings were an important conscientizing force, as they provided the first significant framework for discussion and analysis of gender issues. In the years immediately preceding independence, women became increasingly active in local organisations formed to address community issues that affected their daily lives and in local church groups that focused on basic needs. There was some co-ordination among local church groups through the women's desk of the Council of Churches of Namibia (CCN), an ecumenical institution that spoke out strongly against the injustices stemming from apartheid.[10] A chapter of the Young Women's Christian Association (YWCA) became active in Namibia in 1985, focusing on small income-generating projects and educational programs for women.

The most significant women's group in Namibia in the pre-independence era was another ecumenical organisation, the Namibia Women's Voice (NWV). Initiated in 1985 by women from church groups, the NWV rapidly acquired a broader identity as an alliance of women across party-political and denominational lines to address a spectrum of 'women's issues'.[11] The NWV established thirteen regional branches in its first two years. It had a strong grassroot appeal in both urban and rural areas, and its membership also included educated women in professions such as teaching, nursing and social work. Although there were a few progressive white women among the members, the NWV was predominantly a black organisation; since the apartheid regime succeeded in keeping black and white Namibian apart on all fronts, it was difficult for women of different races to identify their common interests as women.

The NWV's mechanism for organisation was small income-generating and development projects. It brought women together for workshops an topics such as literacy, health education, and leadership, providing a forum to facilitate discussion and action on community problems. The NWV also took action on national issues; for example, it organized campaigns against the use of Depo-Provera and against the 'hearts-and-minds' tactics employed by the colonial government.[12]

Although there are conflicting accounts of the reasons for the dissolution of the NWV in 1989, one frequently cited factor is the opposition engendered by its challenge to male authority in church and political party hierarchies. The autonomy and success of the group were apparently threatening. Some SWAPO leaders were concerned that the NWV was competing with the SWAPO Women's Council, even though all of the NWV leaders also belonged to SWAPO.

There were tensions between the NWV and some of the churches, which pressed the NWV to formalize its relationship with them. Other groups envied the NWV's ability to mobilize grassroots women and its success in attracting funding. Some women have also cited personal conflicts within the leadership as contributing to the NWV's ultimate demise.

The NWV was unique in its emphasis on the practical problems faced by grassroot woman. It played a seminal role in alerting women to the political dimension of the gender-related problems they faced daily and in mobilizing women around the integration of gender issues into the liberation struggle. It was also significant because, as the first major women's group to operate independently of party-political, church, or other superimposed structures, it provided a forum where gender issues were not subordinated to other priorities.[13]

**Post-independence Feminist Issues**

Since Namibia became independent on March 21, 1990 there has been a wide spread sense of building anew. This has included a receptivity to changes relating to gender issues. Women's issues were discussed in campaigns leading up to the country's U.N.- supervised elections in November 1989 but did not prove influential, as the election was dominated by party loyalties.[14]

The framework created by the new constitution and the ratification of the Convention on the Elimination of All Forms of Discrimination Against Women (CEDAW) in 1992 gave the women's movement important tools. The constitution employs a gender-inclusive formulation of 'he and she' throughout. It explicitly forbids discrimination on the grounds of sex and authorizes affirmative action 'with regard to the fact that women in Namibia have traditionally suffered special discrimination and they need to be encouraged and enabled to play a full, equal and effective role in the political, social, economic and cultural life of the nation".[15] The constitution also guarantees that men and women of full age 'shall be entitled to equal rights as to marriage, during marriage and at its dissolution.'[16] Customary law is still recognized, but only to the extent that it does not violate the constitution.[17]

However, the constitution also provides that all laws in force at independence remain in place until altered by Parliament or declared unconstitutional by a court.[18] Women have not yet challenged in court any existing laws that are in conflict with the constitution or developed political skills sufficient to become a powerful lobby for change through the political process. Thus, while the legal tools for change are available, discriminatory laws on many gender-related issues remain.

The first post, independence legal reforms specific to women have been primarily aimed at the small proportion of women in formal employment. Gender inequalities in civil and customary laws on marriage and inheritance, which have a profound impact on the status of all women, have yet to be addressed. It is likely to be much more difficult for the state to take effective action to improve the status of women in private family settings than in the public sphere.

Shortly after independence, the Department of Women's Affairs (DWA) was established in the President's Office to facilitate liaison between women and the government and to help identify priorities for action. While some women feared that channelling gender issues through a single department might have a marginalising effect, the establishment of the DWA was viewed as a symbol of the government's commitment to gender issues.

Since independence, recognition of gender issues has increased at policy levels. Nevertheless, there is still a tendency to compartmentalise women's issues instead of integrating gender concerns into overall policy making. Many government initiatives designed to benefit women have been donor driven and have not garnered sustainable momentum. The DWA and the government's National Planning Commission recently established an interministerial gender network to monitor gender issues in government policy. As of 1993, there were plans to expand the role of this network as well as to incorporate more input from the NGOs.

Independence has also brought a new level of participation by women in government structures. Women constituted almost one-third of all local government representatives in 1993, due partly to a statutory affirmative action provision requiring political parties to include a specified number of women on their lists of candidates.[19] Women still constitute only a tiny minority of the representatives at national and regional levels.[20] However, at the national level the presence of even a small number of women has been significant, as they have used their influence to draw attention to gender issues.[21] Still, the political arena and the major political parties remain male dominated.

Since independence, Namibia has moved from an era of relative isolation into a period of intense international contact. This has given stimulus to the treatment of gender issues by both state and non-governmental organisations, although international networking is not yet carried out as strategically as it might be. In general, independence has brought high and often unrealistic expectations for rapid change that have inspired both energy and frustration. People have looked to the new government to bring change to every aspect of their lives, while the government faces the task of rebuilding the nation while being hampered by severe economic constraints. Gender issues must compete for attention on a crowded national agenda. It is in this climate that the women's movement has taken new forms and directions.

### The Dynamics of the Post-independence Women's Movement

In recognition of the strategic importance of unity for effective lobbying and political action, efforts were made around the time of independence to create an umbrella body to speak on behalf of all Namibian women. Shortly after independence, a steering committee composed of two delegates from each of thirteen interested women's groups began lengthy deliberations aimed at forming this body.[22]

While it was not difficult to reach agreement on aims and objectives—demonstrating a certain unity of purpose among the groups—there was strong disagreement over the form the group should take. The women's wings of political parties tended to favour an organisation that women would join as individuals to avoid the constraints of their party structures. The NGOs preferred a federation of groups on the grounds that this would be the most powerful form of alliance.

Before this debate was resolved, the effort fell apart, primarily because of splits along party-political lines exacerbated by personal competitiveness.[23] The result was the emergence of two different umbrella bodies operating on a national level: one federation of women's organisations and one national organisation open to individual women. Partly because of their origins in the failed efforts at a more comprehensive umbrella, each group acquired political connotations, with one being characterized as a SWAPO grouping, while the other had its base among the opposition parties.

In fact, both umbrella bodies drew their members from more than one political affiliation, but the party-political identities endured. The more apolitical NGOs withdrew from the efforts at unification altogether and have remained independent. There have been several subsequent initiatives to draw women together across party lines, primarily in Windhoek, but these have remained informal and ad hoc in nature.

Since the failure of this effort to establish a single women's group, there seems to be more acceptance of the notion of unity-in-diversity. The process of attempting to achieve unity, acrimonious though it was, seems to have been a maturing process that helped key individuals and groups work together strategically to achieve common aims.

As of 1993, there were several different types of women's groups active in the country. First, women's wings of political parties are still active. Although several facilitate ongoing projects, their primary focus is mobilizing women for elections and the advancement of women within the parties. It is difficult to gauge the degree of committed involvement in these groups. For example, every woman who becomes a member of SWAPO is automatically made a member of the SWAPO Women's Council.

Second, after the attempt at unification, there were for a time two national organisations that attempted to speak for "women" on a broad range of issues. The federation associated with Namibia's opposition parties is now dormant, but the Namibia National Women's Organisation is active and growing. This group is still perceived by many as being aligned with the ruling party. While it tries to reach out to a broad cross section of women, at present it remains dominated by an educated elite.

Third, there are special interest groups that focus on particular issues. Examples include a group that provides education and counselling around the issue of violence against women and a group that publishes a feminist magazine in accessible language. Both of these groups have a small membership, which includes black and white women, but they are primarily composed of educated, middle-class women who attempt to provide services that will benefit women on a broader scale. A small organisation of business and professional women has been one of the few initiatives to attract a significant proportion of white women.

Fourth, there are grassroots-based groups. The strongest among these are church based, operate locally, and focus on practical community needs rather than women's issues as such. For example, many members are active in local choirs, Bible study groups, or small income-generating projects. The only grass-roots-based women's group known to operate in towns both north and south of Windhoek is Concerned Women Against Violence Against Women, which has relatively autonomous local groups in eight locations. Their focus is not only sexual violence but also all violent crimes that impact women.

More recently, they have included other areas such as education on legal rights, income-generating projects, and the development of improved organisational skills. While there are a few men and educated black and white women who play a supportive and active role, control of the groups remains decisively in the hands of grassroots women. Concerned Women has been fairly successful in reaching across ethnic and political party boundaries; however, the profile of the group varies from place to place.[24] There have been some tensions between Concerned Women groups and some other women's organisations, partly because of competition for grassroots loyalty.

A number of other NGOs, while not specifically women's groups, mobilize women around specific concerns. The trade unions are also potential organizing structures. Although most of the existing trade unions, like most of the sectors of formal employment, are male dominated, a domestic worker' union and a teachers' union—both of which have a majority of female members— have taken a lead in addressing gender issues.[25]

The Namibian National Students' Organisations (NANSO) has been particularly successful at integrating gender concerns into its overall platform and structures. There are women's subcommittee with their own budgets in every branch; they hold an annual national conference on their own, in addition to NANSO's full national conference, to ensure the fullest possible participation by women. NANSO ensures that women are represented on its highest decision making bodies. Roughly half the members of NANSO are women, and careful attention to gender issues has produced a high level of gender sensitivity in both male and female NANSO leaders. In recent years NANSO has actively taken up several gender-related issues, such as teenage pregnancy and the promotion of family life education in the school curriculum.

Organisation of women in rural areas, where approximately 70 percent of the Namibian population resides,[26] centres around income-generating and church-related activities. The precarious economic position of rural households, often headed by women, makes the appeal of income-generating activities understandable.[27] Before independence, churches were the main sponsors of such projects; since then various other organisations have become involved in this arena. Many activists have realized that these projects can serve as an entry point for further mobilisation. Donor funding and assistance have also contributed greatly to the proliferation of such projects.

The empowering effect of most such initiatives has been minimal. Many income-generating projects for women focus on traditional skills—such as sewing, baking, gardening, and poultry rearing—thereby perpetuating gender stereotypes.[28] These projects are generally modest in scope and lack sustainability due to inadequate feasibility studies or lack of appropriate managerial skills. A number of Windhoek-based groups that assist small business enterprises now offer management skills training and evaluations. Lack of adequate access to productive resources such as land and credit also remains a limiting factor for women's economic activity.[29]

Church activities such as prayer groups and choirs are the other major focal point for rural women. In addition to providing moral and sometimes financial support, such groups are for many women the only source of social diversion from the routine of their daily lives. Although these church structures are not normally "woman centered", they indisputably reach the largest numbers of rural women. As a result, many mainstream women's organisations have cooperated with church structures but without substantially altering the issue taken up by the church groups.

Mobilisation of rural women is hampered by a range of constraints, including a heavy workload and resistance by male family members who fear that organisational involvement by women might threaten men's position of power and authority. In addition, some community activists have identified a 'dependency syndrome' whereby rural residents expect that improvements in their situation will come from the government or from donor agencies. This syndrome causes apathy and affects women's attitudes and their level of participation in women's organisations.

The DWA endeavours to coordinate the wide variety of groups operating in rural areas. However, it has faced serious difficulties in balancing the enormous expectations from the government and the public against the reality of a small staff and a limited budget—while being advised by numerous donor agencies, each with its own ideas about the ideal approach. After inviting a range of organisations to discuss strategy, the DWA has wisely chosen to focus on networking and facilitating, rather than implementing, projects.

The DWA thus tries to coordinate the activities and projects of existing women's groups and NGOs, to put these groups in touch with appropriate government ministries and donors, and to undertake needs assessments as a basis for project initiation.[30] It has also made the CEDAW a focal point for a communications strategy designed to encompass conscientisation and action on a range of gender issues.[31] Because the DWA is located within a SWAPO government, it is perceived as being SWAPO oriented by some, in spite of its work with a broad range of women's organisations. The DWA has also been criticized for favouring some groups while intentionally shunning others.[32] Another widespread criticism is that the DWA has failed to establish adequate mechanisms for accountability.

Such criticisms can be viewed as a sign of a healthy dialogue between a state structure and an active and vital NGO community; the government will clearly not be allowed to shape the women's movement unilaterally. The DWA itself seems to have become increasingly sensitive to such criticism and is attempting to give a greater appearance of openness and inclusiveness to its efforts to prepare for the 1995 United Nations Fourth World Conference on Women. At the same time, the DWA has had to struggle for meaningful recognition within the government. It is still not consistently consulted on legislation and policies that include critical gender components, and there is no DWA representative at the cabinet level.

While there is a general recognition that the DWA had been performing admirably under difficult circumstances, there is still a widespread view that it has not sufficiently articulated and acted upon rural concerns and priorities. Rural women are alienated from the processes that take place in the urban centres, feeling excluded from policy debates and uninformed about their outcomes. It has been suggested that the DWA adopt a more aggressive approach in rural areas in order to keep women informed about relevant matters and relay their concerns back to the government and to the rest of the women's movement.

The same criticisms of rural neglect that are levelled at the DWA can be applied to most other Windhoek-based women's groups. The majority of Namibian women are still isolated from the mainstream women's movement. For example, preliminary results of a survey of women in Windhoek indicate that most grassroots women, even in the capital, are unaware of the activities of the DWA or any of the Windhoek-based women's groups, with community activity centering around local church groups. Women who have heard of any of the women's organisations perceive them as being for educated women. Those few women who have attended meetings felt isolated and intimidated by the level of the discourse or the use of English. At the same time, an abiding racism complicated by class distinctions continues to divide women in these communities; for example, middle-class coloured women, who seem to be one of the groups most thoroughly neglected by the women's movement, were found to expect long hours of work for low wages from their black domestic workers.

With the exception of a few progressive thinkers, white women are largely absent from the women's movement. This is partly the result of the apartheid era in the sense that white women are perceived as being relatively privileged. They are reticent to assert their interest in the context of the larger women's movement, and some black women are suspicious of their involvement. Furthermore, most of Namibia's white population was traditionally intent on preserving the status quo, producing a general conservatism incompatible with fundamental changes in gender relations.

Since less than five years have passed since independence, it is perhaps understandable that the vestiges of the pre-independence racial divide still remain. There is more interracial meeting and mixing than before, which is largely confined to a small group of educated, middle-class Namibians. For the majority, racial barriers still exist, even if they are no longer legally enforced. This makes it difficult for most women to meet and organize across racial lines. Thus, the driving engine of the women's movement at this stage is a small urban elite dominated by educated black women who have achieved some impressive and well-intentioned results but who have not yet managed to transcend the barriers of race and class to extend the women's movement to the majority of the population.

**Emerging Priority Issues**

At a 1991 conference organized by the DWA, women from all parts of Namibia identified a range of women's needs that stemmed from the position of women relative to men and from the persisting social and economic impact of apartheid and underdevelopment. Conference participants found women to be primarily concerned about the general conditions that affect them and their families. The persistence of discriminatory and inadequate laws is a frequent focus of discussion.[33] One of the most frequently cited problems is the law on maintenance (child support), an economic issue as much as a legal one.

This problem reflects the frequent failure of fathers to take financial or emotional responsibility for their children. Another often-cited priority is the set of family laws that address marriage, divorce, inheritance, and domestic violence.[34] In general, violence against women—widespread rape and domestic violence as well as more generalized crime and violence— is a common problem that cuts across race and class lines and has been identified as a priority in both urban and rural areas. As one of the few issues that inspires consistent grassroots action, it functions as a key mobilizing issue and has inspired several public protests in Windhoek and other locations.

An issue of growing and widespread concern is the need for more access to family planning services. Before independence, family planning was complicated by a general political debate around population control, which was seen as government strategy to control the number of blacks. Since independence, the issue has become depoliticised. Birth rates in black communities are still high, and many men and women continue to define women as mothers. But women are now increasingly questioning the close linking of womanhood with fertility and are challenging male resistance to birth control.

As already noted, improving the economic position of women is a fundamental rural priority. Although this goal is shared by many urban women, it is even more pressing in the tenuous economy of rural households. There is also an urgent need for improved agricultural extension services for rural women who remain the primary producers in subsistence agriculture. Access to clean water and adequate sanitation is another major concern of rural women. The time and distance involved in collecting water are borne by women, and lack of water and sanitation is also a key contributing factor to the health problems of women and children.[35]

The effect of customary laws and practices is also of major concern to rural women, particularly in the north. Widows, who often lose all their land and property to the family of the deceased, are particularly vulnerable. Access to land and exclusion from traditional decision making structures such as headmen's courts are other areas of concern. In the southern regions, rural women often cite a nexus of interrelated family and social problems that include unemployment, alcohol abuse, and family violence. An additional problem is an intensified feeling of exclusion from rural development projects, which have been concentrated in the north.[36]

These priority issues specific to rural women have tended to be addressed, if at all, by government ministries and donor agencies rather than by women's groups. While the mainstream women's movement has acknowledged in principle the importance of including the concerns of rural women, there has been little concrete action to back up this assertion. As a result, it is not surprising that rural and urban poor women do not generally view the women's movement as a primary vehicle for the assertion of their needs. In order to attract a broader following, the women's movement must prove that it can produce tangible results on issues that concern a wider range of the nation's women.

**Characteristics, Strengths and Weaknesses**

The Namibian women's movement is a nascent one about which only a few generalisations can be made. For example, "feminism" is an unpopular word in Namibia, although many women apply feminist analysis without labelling it as such. Similarly, 'gender' is still an unfamiliar concept to many. Gender issues have understandably had to compete with a wide range of other issues for attention in a nation that is busy building itself anew. Namibia, has been inundated with well-meaning and generous donors, many of which have given special priority to matters relating to gender. While the aims of donor agencies have for the most part been consistent with those of women's organisations, donors often set differing priorities and a different pace.

The Windhoek-based women's movement is characterized by the high visibility of a few prominent women involved in multiple endeavours. There has not yet been a unifying issue strong enough to mobilize women more broadly. It is unlikely that preparation for Beijing will serve this function; in fact, Beijing could prove to be an interruption of the more pressing business of internal organisation and action on the ground. A few individuals have had contact with international women's organisations, but this has not yet filtered through to Namibian women's groups in any meaningful way.

Some of the difficulties faced by the women's movement have been noted. The challenge of articulating a feminism that will encompass the needs and aspirations of women ranging from subsistence farmers to urban professionals is immense. The women's movement is still searching for a way to bridge the gap between grassroots women and the educated elite as well as the gap between Windhoek and the rest of the nation. The continuing divisiveness of race, class, ethnicity, and political persuasion constitutes a serious obstacle to united action. An additional constraint is personal competitiveness and a similar sort of organisational competitiveness that encompasses competition for members, influence, and donor funds. Even the most active women are still strengthening their networking, lobbying, and strategising skills.

Despite these limitations, the women's movement also has significant strengths, such as individual women with untiring personal commitment to the advancement of women, a slowly increasing consciousness among Namibian women of the impact of gender discrimination on their daily lives, and a receptive national climate with growing level of gender sensitivity among policy makers. Younger Namibian women and men seem to be less divided by the experiences of the past than their parents, with less deeply entrenched gender stereotypes, as evidenced in NANSO.

The women's movement has clearly matured and evolved in the few short years since independence. There is still a need for more organisation around specific initiatives instead of attempts to organize women to address the entire spectrum of women's issues at once. There is an even more critical need to create spaces in which *all* Namibian women can assert their own priorities in their own ways. Even though the women's movement is reaching only a small minority of women at present, it has already had a significant impact on national politics and has the potential to become a vibrant and powerful force in Namibia.

M. KAPERE

## REFERENCES

1. Bruce Frayne, *Urbanisation in Post-Independence Windhoek*, Namibian Institute for Social and Economic Research, University of Namibia, February 1992; UNICEF/NISER, *A Situation Analysis of Children and Women in Namibia*, UNICEF, March 1991, p. 20. In 1991, the population of Windhoek was estimated at 150,000 although this figure could have grown to 200,000 by 1992 due to migration caused by drought. Windhoek is approximately eight times larger than its nearest urban rival, Rehoboth, and accounts for about one-third of the nation's entire urban population.

2. For political purposes, the nation is divided into thirteen different regions, each with its own elected regional council. Local authorities, classified as municipalities, towns, or villages, depending on their size and level of development, exist within each region.
3. It has also been estimated that some 70 percent of the population attend church regularly.
4. In rural Namibia, especially in the parts of northern Namibia that fell within the operational area during the liberation war, the church provided a safe meeting place as well as various forms of practical and symbolic support.
5. Republic of Namibia, *Report by Commission of Inquiry into Matters Relating to Chiefs, Headmen, and Other Traditional or Tribal Leaders,* Republic of Namibia, 1991, pp. 8-9.
6. Heike Becker, "From Anti-Colonial Resistance to Reconstruction: Namibia Women's Movement, 1980 to 1992," Ph.D. diss. University of Bremen, 1993, pp. 41-60 (This thesis provides an extremely useful and detailed synthesis of information about the women's movement.); Information about the changing gender dynamics in particular communities is available in a number of sources, some of the more recent of which include Megan Biesele, *Women Like Meat: The Folklore and Foraging Ideology of the Kalahari Ju/'hoan,* Witwatersrand University Press/ Indiana University Press, 1993; Gordon D. Gibson, Thomas J. Larson, and Cecilia R. McGurk, *The Kavango Peoples,* Franz Steiner Verlag, 1981; Robert J. Gordon, *The Bushman Myth: The Making of a Namibian Underclass,* Westview Press, 1992; Margaret Jacobsohn, *Himba—Nomads of Namibia,* Struik, 1980; Karla O. Poewe, *The Namibian Herero: A History of Their Pyshcological Disintegration and Survival,* Edward Mellon Press, 1985; Frieda-Nela Williams, *Precolonial Communities of Southwestern Africa: A History of Owambo Kingdoms,* 1600-1920, National Archives of Namibia, 1991.
7. Ndeutala Hishongwa, *The Contract Labour System and Its Effects on Family and Social Life in Namibia: A Historical Perspective,* Gamsberg Macmillan, 1992.
8. Although the laws supporting migrant labour were repealed in 1978, this employment pattern persists as a result of wage employment being concentrated in Windhoek.

9. Tessa Cleaver and Marion Wallace, *Namibia—Women in War,* Zed Books, 1990; Denis Herbstein and John Evenson, *The Devils Are Among Us: The War for Manibia,* Zed Books, 1989; Manfred Hinz and Nadia Gevers, *Koevet Versus the People of Namibia,* Working Group Kairos, 1989.

10. The CCN was established in 1978, with eight different denominations among its original members. The CCN women's desk, established in 1987, has focused on income-generating projects and educational programs as well as providing opportunities for women from churches from different regions to come together to discuss issue of common interest.

11. The NWV grew out of the first national women's conference in Namibia, convened in June 1985 by a number of church women who were establishing an ecumenical group. This conference drew together almost three hundred women from all parts of the country to discuss a broad range of issues. (Becker 'From Anti-Colonial Resistance", p. 156, for more details).

12. Under colonial population control policies, Depo-Provera (a long-acting hormonal contraceptive often accompanied by side effects) injections were often forced on Namibian women without their consent. The colonial regime also established a number of groups that organized cultural, religious, and sports activities at a local level to provide platforms for the spread of propaganda. The NWV helped raise community awareness of the true aims of these activities.

13. Becker "From Anti-Colonial Resistance", pp. 155ff; and Cleaver and Wallace, *Namibia,* pp. 89ff.

14. Bience Gawanas, 'Namibian Independence', Susan Bazilli, ed, *Putting Women on the Agenda,* Raven Press 1991, p. 249.

15. Namibian constitution, Article 23(3) Article 10(2) prohibits discrimination on the grounds of sex, race, color, ethnic origin, religion, creed, or social or economic status.

16. Namibian constitution, Article 14(1).

17. Namibian constitution, Article 66(1). The same is true of common law in force at the date of independence.

18. Namibian constitution, Article 140(1).

19. Dianne Hubbard and Kaveri Kavari, *Affirmative Action for Women in Local Government in Namibia*, Legal Assistance Center, 1993. The statutory provision applied only to the first local government elections that were held at the end of 1992; in subsequent local elections voters will select individual candidates rather political parties.

20. For example, there were only seven women in ninety-eight seats in Namibia's two houses of Parliament at the end of 1993. Only three out of ninety-five seats on Namibia's thirteen regional councils were filled by women in 1992.

21. For example, the affirmative action provision in the Local Government Act was sponsored by one of Namibia's woman ministers. Women parliamentarians have used their positions to encourage parliamentary debate on issues of particular interest to women.

22. The regular meetings of this steering committee took place in Windhoek. While many of the groups involved operated outside of Windhoek as well, no regional representatives were involved in the deliberations. There was a plan to invite women from all parts of the country to a launching meeting that would make final decisions on the aims and structure of the umbrella body, but the initiative fell apart before this meeting took place.

23. The catalyst for the breakdown was disagreement on how many representatives would be allocated to the various women's groups at the launch of the umbrella body.

24. The Windhoek branch was the first to be established, in 1992. It has since stimulated the formation of similar groups in other locations and provided follow-up support.

25. Although gender issues in general have not been high on the overall trade union agenda, it is noteworthy that some male-dominated unions have entered into collective agreements that include provisions for maternity leave and that the nation's major trade union federation took a strong stand on the issue of maternity leave during negotiations around the new labour act that came into force in November 1992. See International Labor Organisation, *Namibian Women and Employment: Strategies and Policies for the Promotion of Equal Opportunity and Treatment for Women and Men in Employment in Namibia*, ILO, 1992.

26. UNICEF/NISER, *A Situation Analysis*. p. 20.

27. The large number of female-headed households is another consequence of the extensive migration of male members of the family in search of wage employment. For example, a recent UNICEF survey of three rural areas in northern Namibia found that the percentage of female-headed households ranged from 40 to 49. UNICEF, *Household Health and Nutrition in Namibia*, UNICEF, 1990.

28. This is a function both of the interests of the women concerned and the availability of funds, as many donors are inclined to support such "traditional" programs rather than "risk" backing an unconventional project that might fail because it is "culturally unacceptable."

29. A national land conference organized by the government in June 1991 highlighted the need for affirmative action for women in the areas of landownership, inheritance, training, and credit and resolved that women should be fairly represented on all future bodies that administer communal land. However, these principles have yet to be translated into action. Similarly, while the government has repeatedly expressed its commitment to changing aspects of the laws on marriage that hamper women's economic capacity, such changes have not yet occurred.

30. More detailed information about the DWA's activities is available in Maria Kapere (undersecretary, DWA), "Report on the Department of Women's Affairs to the Inaugural Annual Sharing Forum of Agencies Engaged in the Promotion of the Status of Women (Mariental, November 14-19, 1993)" (DWA, 1993), mimeo.

31. DWA, *National Communication Strategy in Support of the U.N: Convention on the Elimination of All Forms of Discrimination Against Women*, 1993-1995, DWA, July 1993.

32. The DWA has a list of twenty-two different women's groups with which it regularly networks. However, other groups that attempt to play a networking role make use of a wider pool of contacts.

33. In fact, women in Namibia may be placing overly high expectations on what can be accomplished through law reform.

While legal changes will certainly be important for women, they are unlikely in themselves to bring about the desired transformations in social and family life.

34. The issue of inheritance is particularly acute for women in some communities, where a widow may be deprived of her home, her land, and virtually all of her property upon the death of her husband. In advance of comprehensive law reform in this area, Parliament passed a resolution appealing to traditional leaders to show more compassion for the plight of widows, particularly during the current drought.

35. In 1990, it was estimated that 53 percent of the population had no access to clean water and 77 percent had inadequate sanitation facilities. This situation was clearly linked to a high incidence of gastrointestinal disease, which produced high levels of infant mortality. UNICEF/NISER, *A Situation Analysis*, p. 88.

36. The majority of Namibia's population is resident in the north of the country. However, it is also possible that the northern regions receive more attention from donor agencies because they suffered the most direct forms of war damage. As noted earlier, some people also believe that the SWAPO government gives priority to Oshiwambo-speaking areas in the north because so much of SWAPO's membership is drawn from this population.

# NIGERIA

- Female Seclusion in Northern (Hausaland) Nigeria: Historical Development
- Theological Implication of Gender in Nigerian Society
- Women and Fundamentalism
- Wifeism and Activism in the Nigerian Women's Movement
- Survey of Female Circumcision in Ibadan, Nigeria
- Baba of Karo (1890–1960) Girls' Trading Expeditions, Bond-Friends, and Marriage
- The Patriarchal Bargaining in Tijaniyya Sufi Order in Northern Nigeria

# 32

# FEMALE SECLUSION IN NORTHERN (HAUSALAND) NIGERIA: HISTORICAL DEVELOPMENT

The history and practice of female seclusion in Northern Nigeria is strongly associated with the history and practice of Islam. Nonetheless there have been some who argue that the practice of female seclusion was traditionally a pre-Islamic custom in Hausaland The purpose of this paper is to begin to investigate the history and practice of female seclusion in Hausaland, and the ideological, religious, political and legal discourses around it in their socio-economic context.

## Pre-Islamic Hausaland

The area known as Hausaland (mostly within the northern part of what is now the Federal Republic of Nigeria) has been continuously settled since the late Stone Age.[1] There has been almost no work on pre-state formations and little on the pre-Islamic Habe states. Achi says that settlements were initially of independent gidaje (households), probably inhabited by a farming group with kinship ties and not recognising any central overall authority.[2] Settlements were often around hills, as it was believed that these were the abode of *iskoki* (spirits) who were responsible for the fertility of the soil below.

The indigenous religion, the worship of general anthropomorphised spirits, is thought to have developed from ancestor worship as settlements become more dense.[3] Through this religion (known and surviving today as Bori) leaders acted as mediums between the spiritual and temporal worlds, accommodating nature and cultivation. At various points in the farming cycle libations would be offered to the major spirits, Iya or Inna (the Mother), Uwar Dawa (Mistress/Mother of guineacorn—Sorghum Vulgare, the main staple), and Uwar Gona (Mistress/Mother of the farm).

There were prominent and institutionalised female adepts as well as men in Bori.[4] Bori seems to have had no centralised overall authority, but particular individuals could be recognised as having greater powers than others and over large territories, like Barbushe the blacksmith who settled at Dalla hill—the original settlement which expanded to become Kano City.[5] This seems to be strongly linked with the spread of iron smelting technology, from the seventh century on. The use of iron implements meant larger areas of cultivation, increased production, an agricultural surplus and therefore time to develop crafts—it also made for superior weapons in warfare. The decentralised gidaje were superseded by a political system based in territorial authority.

These incorporated farming groups into cities and later states, i.e. the development of lineage settlements into wards, then villages, then cities, then states.[6] Certainly the beginnings of state formation can be traced to around 1000 A.D. (The Kano Chronicle). Early legends and chronicles mention women rulers, such as in Daura and Abuja, Tawa as the founder of Gobir, and the most famous, Amina of Zazzau (to whom tribute was paid from as far afield as Nupeland) and her sister Zariya (after whom the town of Zaria is named). There is thus some evidence that in early Hausaland women could and did have institutionalised roles with political and religious power.

Seclusion is clearly not compatible with women prominent in public life as rulers or religious figures. What reconstructions there are of the socio-economic organisation of early Hausa settlements suggest that female seclusion was unknown in this period. Women appear to have cultivated land, as did men. There are also traditions of women potters, spinners and weavers to suggest that women were active craftworkers. Women were also prominent musicians.[7]

**Advent and Seclusion of Islam**

It is generally accepted that there were contacts with Islam since about the eleventh century, by way of traders and itinerant preachers through the medium of the trans-Sahara caravan trade. However, Islam co-existed with Bori, although there might be tension between rulers' claims to legitimacy from Bori and/or Islam.[8] It was not until about the fourteenth to fifteenth century that significant impact was made.[9] It was during the reign of Muhammadu Rumfa, Sakin Kano (1463-1499), that Islamic influence and political power came to be strongly associated. Rumfa corresponded with the Algerian scholar Al-Maghili, and invited him to come to Kano, where he wrote a treatise on Islamic statecraft (The Obligation of Princes). According to The Kano Chronicle it was Muhammadu Rumfa also who "began the custom of kulle (seclusion)."[10] The introduction of seclusion therefore is linked to Islamic influence and there is no evidence of the practice of *kulle* (women's seclusion) in Hausaland before Islam started becoming an influential discourse.

However, to talk of Islam as a discourse is to over-simplify matters. Since the death of the Prophet Mohammed what constitutes Islam has been an arena of contested meanings and power-relations. The verses of *the Qur'ân* itself are sacrosanct. Following in authority are the hadiths (sayings of the Prophet) and happenings in his life. How these should be interrupted and institutionalised as they apply to the daily everyday life of Muslims in different places and at different times has always been contentious. Several distinct schools of Shari'ah (law/theology) have evolved—Hanafi, Hambali, Maliki and Sha'afi—but even so, there may be alternative views within a school of *Shari'ah*. The issue of female seclusion is one of the arenas of contestation in Islam. The following are the only verses of *the Qur'ân* that refer to seclusion:

> "O wives of the Prophet ! You are not like any of the (other) women, provided that you remain (truly) conscious of God. Hence be not over-soft in your speech, lest any whose heart is diseased should be moved to desire (you): but withal, speak in a kindly way. And abide quietly in your homes, and do not flaunt your charms as they used to flaunt them in the old days of pagan ignorance..." (Surat al-Ahzab 33: 32-33).
>
> And (as for the Prophet's wives) whenever you ask them for anything that you need, ask them from behind a screen: this will but deepen the purity of your heart and theirs... (Surat al-Ahzab 33:53)...
>
> (However) it is no sin for them (to appear freely) before their fathers, or their sons, or their brothers, or their brother's sons, or their sisters' sons, or their womenfolk, or such (male slaves) as their right hands may possess... (Surat al-Ahzab 33: 55)

These verses are concerned with the restriction of women's physical mobility to their places of residence and to moving freely among men only if they are close kin. They clearly and unambiguously refer directly to the wives of the Prophet. It is on the grounds that all Muslim women should aspire to be like the Prophet's wives that many of the Ulama have argued that seclusion is wajab (obligatory). Levy argues that many of the early Muslims came from Persia where "women had long been secluded and it is probable that their authority in Islam began to make itself felt after the close of the Umayyad Caliph of Damascus'[11] so that one and a half centuries after the prophet's death female seclusion had become established as part of Islam.

Others however, have disagreed that seclusion is Islamic. For instance, Wali argues that even for the Prophet's wives this restriction was only advice and not compulsory, drawing on two later *hadith*, that one of the Prophet's wives was met by Abu Bakr in town and he scolded her and sent her home.[12] She complained of this to the Prophet and the Prophet said:

> "It is permitted to you to go out for your own needs (hajah). Do not prevent the handmaids of *Allâh* from going to the mosques of *Allâh*" (if they ask specifically).[13]

Wali argues that furthermore this was revealed at a time when the Umma were not secure and there was a particular risk to the Prophet's wives of physical assault from non-Muslims if they should be recognised when outside their homes, so that it was not an all-time recommendation.

Many of the Ulama counter this, however, by arguing that even if seclusion is not wajab (mandatory), it is manduban (recommended) or mubaham (correct) because not to do so is a potential source of fitnah and a temptation to men to sin. Thus they rely on another *hadith*:

> "Do not stop your women from going to the mosque but their houses are better for them."[14]

This view also has been contested on the grounds that the avoidance of fitnah was specified in *the Qur'ân* as being through chaste behaviour by both men and women, and, modest dressing by women:

> "Tell the believing men to lower their gaze and to be mindful of their chastity. This will be most conducive to their purity—(and), verily God is aware of all that they do. Abd tell the believing women to lower their gaze and to be mindful of their chastity, and not to display their charms (in public) beyond what may be (decently) apparent thereof, hence let them draw their head-coverings over their bosoms. And let them not display (more of) their charms to any but their husbands, or their fathers, or their husband's farthers or their brothers' sons, or their sisters' sons, or their womenfolk, or

> those whom they rightfully possess, or such male attendants as are beyond sexual desire, or children that are as yet unaware of women's nakedness; and let them not swing their legs (in walking) so as to draw attention to their hidden charms. And (always), O You believers—all of you—turn unto God in repentance, so that you might attain a happy state."[15]

Unlike the previously cited verses, these are addressed to all Muslims. There is thus an argument that if there is an Islamic female seclusion it is in modest dressing and chaste behaviour, and not in restrictions on mobility and social interaction between men and women *per se*. But what constitutes modest dressing has itself been a bone of contention. The dominant view has been that it consists of wearing loose and non-transparent garments that cover all but the face, hands and feet. Asad (amongst others) says that this restrictive view is incorrect, and that the phrasing is deliberately vague connoting (following some of the earliest Islamic scholars) 'that which a human being may decently show in accordance with prevailing custom'.[16]

Asad goes on to argue that the injunction to use the headcovering to cover the breast referred to the custom at the time of the Prophet of wearing a scarf on the head which was left to trail down the back, and leaving the wide opening at the front of the tunic open so that the breasts were bare. Thus 'decent dressing' cannot include bare breasts but is otherwise not specific about which parts of the body must be covered.[17] Similarly, liberal excegesists have interpreted the following surah:

> "O Prophet! Tell thy wives and thy daughters, as well as all (other) believing women, that they should draw over themselves some of their outer garments (when in public): this will be more conducive to their being recognised (as decent women) and not annoyed. But (withal), God is indeed much-forgiving, a dispenser of grace" (Surat al-Ahzab 33: 59)

as meaning that one purpose of decent dressing was to avoid sexual harassment. They draw attention again to the vagueness of the injunction, and to the reference to God's mercy that follows immediately after, to buttress their argument that this is merely a guideline to be interpreted in particular contexts. On the other hand, proponents of the more restrictive view also refer to this same surah in order to argue that wearing the burkha is not restrictive or hampering to women, but for their own protection.

There are thus three main positions in the debate over seclusion within Islam. The first and most restrictive holds that women should be physically restricted to their dwelling places and can interact freely only with their husbands, other women, close male kin, children and slaves or servants. A second position holds that women may go out if strictly necessary and if dressed decently which involves covering loosely all but face, hands and feet. The third view holds that women may go out as they deem necessary and that 'decent' dressing, though necessary, may vary according to social conventions in each times and place. All three lay claim to Islamic legitimacy. That which becomes hegemonic in any particular situation depends not so much on the absolute 'truth' of this claim, as on the complex of power-relations of the competing groups holding these variant views, their articulation with other available discourses, and the general socio-economic context.

## The Beginning of Seclusion in Kano

It seems likely that the form of seclusion first practised in Hausaland was of the most restrictive variety (non-mobility and no interaction with non-male kin).

> First, one of the strongest points made by Al-Maghili was that the adoption of Islam must entail a clean break with the non-Islamic past (the period of Jahiliya or ignorance) and the form of gender relations is a distinctive marker in this.
>
> Second, it was the rulers and wealthy who had no need for their wives' labour outside of the house who adopted seclusion (and it is still the wives of rulers and the upper ranks of the

masu sarauta (title-holders or aristocracy) who contemporarily practice this form of seclusion).

All commentators are agreed that seclusion was not widespread in the period from the time of Muhammadu Rumfa up to the end of the eighteenth century. The practice of seclusion was at least as much a mark of high status and wealth as of piety. It was confined to the urban and wealthy court, *masu sarauta* (office-holding aristocracy) and the mallamai (Islamic learned scholars) who were royal advisors.[18]

*Kulle* was little practised outside the cities. The majority of the population of Hausaland continued to be practitioners of the indigenous religion, Bori, especially outside the cities and towns. The requirement of residence in the cities of the masu sarauta, introduced in the fifteenth century to make easier their control by the *sarakuna* (rulers), also meant that they could not provide role models for those seeking to improve their social status or prestige by imitating elite modes of living. The Maguzawa (non-Muslim Hausa) were widespread, although gradually displaced more and more from the central region of the emirate around Kano City.[19]

Kasar Kano, was however, an expanding economy and attracted large-scale immigration by groups of people who then were largely assimilated as Hausa. The Fulani (moving east from Futa Djallon) and the Kanuri (moving west, especially following the political instability of the Kanem-Bornu Empire) were prominent in this migration,[20] and both were peoples much earlier exposed to Islamisation. Nonetheless, despite the injunction to break with animism, the seventeenth and eighteenth centuries were periods of transactionism between Islam and Bori for most of those nominally Muslim.[21]

Although there was a gender division of labour in the allocation of tasks in farmwork and of particular occupations, women continued to work freely in the fields, covering planted seeds, weeding, bundling and transporting crops to the fage (central ground/village square). Women's agricultural work included having their own gayauna plots, on the produce of which it is probable that they were individually taxed. Women also engaged in crafts and specialised occupations, including *ma'auna* (grain seller who also controls weights and establishes prices).[22] Authority and roles for women in the public arena and in religious life, however, became less and less possible, as Islam gained political influence in the state. In Kano Emirate far more than other Hausa Emirates women's titles either fell into disuse and were lost or were transformed into men's titles.[23]

**The Sokoto Caliphate: The Jihad's Influence**

By the late eighteenth century Islam had become an important ground of ideological legitimation in the struggle for political power which resulted in the establishment of the Sokoto Caliphate around 1807.[24] The rallying call was the promise of a new social order based on Islamic principles, with justice, fair taxation and moral purity. There were frequent references in the denunciations of the jihadists to lewdness, promiscuity and 'free women' (a euphemism for courtesans, as not being married and under husbands' control nor under that of their fathers'). The moral purity of Muslim women was one of the markers used to legitimate and set off the distinction between the reformer Muslims on the one hand, and, the lapsed, corrupt emirate Muslims (and, in a minor key, the animists) on the other.

It is therefore sometimes argued that the prevalence of seclusion in Northern Nigeria is due to the influence of the leader of the *Jihad*, Sheikh Uthman Dan Fodio.[25] Isa argues this is wrong since seclusion pre-dated the *jihad*, even if it was then a phenomenon associated only with the urban and aristocratic wealthy. However, when Isa says that

> "kulle is practised today, is not so much because Islam made references to it but, more so, it is community's custom and traditions. And custom and tradition of the people are

> accommodated in Islam so long as they do not contradict *the Qur'ân* and *Hadith*."[26]

He is ignoring the fact that the introduction of the custom of seclusion and the making of it into 'tradition', was due to the fact that it was considered to be an attribute of Islam. He says:

> "Dan Fodio's view was that 'kulle is not obligatory like the five daily prayers and fasting but a matter of convenience... (however) once there is no necessity for married women to go out of their matrimonial homes then they should stay at home."[27]

It was the Shehu' opinion that 'necessity' included the search for knowledge, going on pilgrimage, attending the funerals of relatives, going to the market (if there was no one to go for them) etc. The evidence for this is in Wakar Larura verses 12-14 (poem on Necessity), composed by the Shehu, his daughter Nana Asmau and his son Isa. Dan Fodio also felt it was better for you and beautiful women to pray at home so as not to be a temptation to men.

Isa states that Ogunbiyi is wrong to allege that the Shehu established, separate courts for women, but that women addressed the court from behind a wall in which a window was made. Furthermore he was denounced for allowing women to attend the sermons alongside men. Dan Fodio's brother Abdullahi was asked to reply to this charge of promoting immortality. His answer was that

> "I do not agree that their (women) being left to go free in ignorance is good, for the committing of the lesser evil has been made obligatory"[28]

Certainly, Dan Fodio felt strongly that women had a right to education, both religious and in wordly dealings. In his Nur al-Abab he condemned the practice of keeping women ignorant, saying.

Most of our educated men leave their wives, their daughters, and their captives morally abandoned, like beasts without teaching them what God prescribes should be taught to them and without instructing them in the articles of the law which concern them. Thus they leave them ignorant of the rules regarding ablution, prayer, fasting, business dealings and others which God commands they should be taught. Men treat these beings like household implements which become broken after long use and which are then thrown out on the dung heap. This is an abominable crime! Alas, how can they shut up their wives, their daughters, and their captives in the darkness of ignorance, while daily they impart knowledge to their students. In truth, they act out of egoism, and if they devote themselves to their pupils that is nothing but hypocrisy and vain ostentation on their part'.

It should be noted that the Jihadist 'liberal' discourse on seclusion largely cast it in terms of justifying exceptions from a general rule that Muslim women should not go out. It was not argued that women had a right to mobility, but that in some circumstances it would be worse not to permit them to do so, than for them to remain within their dwellings. Both variants of the Islamic discourse thus set off Muslim women from other women as those who remain at home, emerging either not at all or with permission from the men who have control of them.

The Shehu's own female relatives and their intimates were not secluded in the physical form. They were all highly educated, teaching women, children and sometimes men their religious duties, and discussing political and religious issues with men and women alike. Nana Asmau is also credited with the formation of the 'Yan Taru movement of women scholars who pilgrimage and travelled in much the same way as the male al-majirai do today.[29] Nonetheless, judging by the commentators of the time (and later) it does seem to be the case that to the extent that seclusion was practised during the period of the Caliphate it was dominantly of the more restrictive form, except in the small enclaves of scholars closely associated with the Shehu's family. During the hundred years or so that the Caliphate existed, seclusion remained largely a phenomenon of the urban aristocratic and wealthy.

**Seclusion in the Development of the Sohoto Caliphate**

The economy of the Caliphate continued to expand, with increasing specialisation in the division of labour: by region, between urban and rural areas, in craft, and by gender. Although each region produced all types of goods, within that some were famed for the quality and quantity of particular goods: for example, the Zaria region produced both cotton and guineacorn which were sent north for sale in the more densely populated emirate of Kano. In Kano Emirate, Bebeji was known for donkey breeding (increasingly in demand as pack animals as trade expanded), and the area around Birnin Kudu took pride in the production of indigo dyed cloth, while Sumaila area was known for silk production.

Similarly, both farming and crafts were carried out by both rural and urban dwellers. But the extension of urban settlements and the unprecedented increase in the sedentarisation of the Fulani meant land pressure, particularly around the close-settled zones of the birane (walled towns) and together with the increase in opportunities for trade meant that the development of full-time craftwork was encouraged in urban areas. In addition, some crafts, like beating indigo into cotton cloth to produce a shiny patina and deep blue-black hue, were undertaken mostly in towns.

The tasks in craft production were divided into many distinct specialisations. In cloth production, for example, spinning the sale of yarn, wearing on narrow looms or on broad looms (and different types of cloth produced on narrow and/or broad looms), the sale of undyed cloth, dyeing with indigo in particular types of cloth style or with other dyes, the sale of dyed cloth and tailoring cloth into various garments were each recognised occupations, all of which were individual small-scale enterprises.

The increasing division of labour also developed along gender lines, Spinning was, par excellence, a female craft, undertaken by women of the masu sarauta, the mallamai, and the talakawa (commoners) alike. Women formed associations to pool yarn for sale. Sales were usually by older women. Vertical loom weaving of coarse yarn for the wide strips of cloth called gwado used for blankets and wrappers was a female craft also, although some women did use the horizontal loom. The development of food snacks and the prepared meals industry made possible by the growth of settlements and expanding economy, as well as the increase in the division of labour itself was also carried out by women. Some types of pottery and pot selling were also female areas.[30] The increase in economic opportunities and the tradition of each person keeping their own income from such sana'oi (income-generating occupations) meant that women were rarely dependent on husbands.[31]

However, one should be wary of neatly equating the increasing gender division of labour with the existence of seclusion as Mahadi appears to do when he simply states that women in the urban areas were generally secluded, withdrawing their labour from some sectors of the economy and increasing it in others.[32] First, some of the female specialisation are clearly incompatible with seclusion, like that of the *'yan rugun* who took pots from Kano City for sale in other places, or the women who prepared and sold foods at various zango (recognised caravan stops on the trading routes) —although it is possible but these occupations were undertaken by older women no longer subject to seclusion.

However, secondly, in cultivation women continued to work on-field, both as free women and particularly as slaves. The incidence of slavery is contentious, with estimates varying from 25% to over 50% of the population,[33] but all accounts agree it was substantial, that the establishment of slave agricultural estates continued throughout the 19th century, that many households had 2-3 slaves, and that women were at least 50% of slaves (and considered more valuable than male salves). Since slave women were not secluded, this means that a substantial proportion of women could not have been in seclusion.

Finally, contemporary descriptions of Hausaland make observations which would contraindicate general seclusion. For example, Mai Gashin Baki, a 19th century caravan leader, referred to women and girls standing in doorways to watch processions, and to being accompanied on caravan trading trips by his wives, although he sometimes left one wife to look after the house (this was also a punishment for quarrelling with her co-wives on the previous trip).[34] Similarly, Robinson, writing towards the end of the 19th century commented that 'with the exception of the wives of the king and one or two of his chief ministers, they (i.e., Hausa women) are not kept in seclusion, but are allowed to go about as they please."[35]

Nonetheless it is most probable that as the authority of Islamic discourses grew, seclusion did become more widespread during their period of the Caliphate and especially among urban populations. The characterisation of the Caliphate as a theocratic state is debatable,[36] but taxes were extracted on the basis of Islamic legitimacy, courts were supposed to dispense Shari'ah and, initially at least, the rulerships and distribution of offices depended on claims to Islamic piety. Being Muslim increased prestige. The desirability of being Muslim was not only felt among the ruling elites. Mai Gashin Baki described the way that even minimalist Muslims, barely able to recite the al-Fatiha (the first surah every Muslim child learns), could claim to be a brother and fellow believer "and be received by the Hasua with general friendship and kindness."[37] The ideal of seclusion, associated with both high status and piety, must also have become more widespread.

Along with the public performance of the five daily prayers by men, the seclusion of women and the Islamic code of dressing constitute the most visible everyday markers of Islamic practice. From Mai Gashin Baki again, there is an indication that the use of the *mayafi* (cloth used to drape the head and/or shoulders) had become fairly general—he describes meeting a woman he later married and not being able to see her face as "following the custom of the country she knelt, wholly covered by her cloth."[38] Two factors may account for the higher prevalence of seclusion in the urban areas than in the rural. The *masu sarauta* resided in the towns, providing role models for the *talakawa* there. And the stronger division of labour, with more full-time craftworkers and fewer full-time farmers, plus the expansion of the economy and increased demand for craft goods meant that women could withdraw (or be withdrawn) more easily from on-field farmwork, to concentrate on spinning and embroidery (both of which are easily carried out within the house).

Thus by the end of the nineteenth century Islamic discourses were imbricated in temporal authority and a definer of identity and solidarity in the emirates that paid tribute to the Sultan of Sokoto, whose other title was Sarkin Musulmi (ruler of the Muslims). Although seclusion remained practised most by the office-holding groups, the wealthy *attijirai* (merchants) and some of the urban talakawa did so also, and the ideal of wife seclusion and modest dressing for women was widespread. Nonetheless, the majority of rural dwellers especially were, at best, no more than nominally Muslim, with a healthy respect for *iskoki* (spirits) and recourse to *Bori* for problem solving if they felt it necessary.[39] Women's seclusion was also far less in evidence in the rural areas, among nominated Muslim communities as well as in Maguzawa villages. The association of Islam and temporal authority also meant for a certain level of cynicism in the face of high taxes and arbitrary demands from fief-holders of their servants. It is this latter that Bello suggests as one of the factors accounting for the relatively easy conquest of the emirates in the Sokoto Caliphate between 1904–1907, compared to the resistance of the stateless people of what became Zaria and Bauchi provinces, who took to the hills and fought the British well into the 1930s,—the talakawa and especially the bayi (slaves) did not care who ruled them or on what grounds.[40]

## Colonialism and Islam

Ironically, the conquest of Northern Nigeria by the British (Christians basing their authority on secular grounds) resulted in a new impetus for Islam. An Islamic cultural identity (including the practice of seclusion) became a means of resistance to British rule, and the effects of colonial rule, particularly through taxation, did nothing to mitigate the appeal of hearkening back to the 'Golden Age' of the early period of the Caliphate. Islam's introduction to Hausaland had been through peaceful means, via contact with Muslims through trade and conversion.

Since the fifteenth century, Islam had been the religious discourse of all rulers. Even the *Jihad* had been directed against "corrupt" Muslim rulers, rather than converting non-Muslims. Islam had spread gradually over several centuries. Its adaptability to local customs and the syncretism between Islam, Bori and custom during most of this time[41] had meant that being Muslim gradually became adopted as part of a Hausa identity. Again, although most (but not all) of the *Jihad* leaders had been ethnic Fulani,[42] they were Fulani who had been living in Hausaland over several generations at least and who spoke Hausa. Furthermore, the *Jihad* had the support, because of economic grievances, of the Hausa rural talakawa "who had not smelt the scent of Islam."[43] In fact, without their support the guerrilla war of the Jihadists could neither have been fought nor won. None of these factors applied to British colonial rule. The proselytisation of Islam (and of seclusion as an identifier and symbol of Islam) became a call to pre-colonial tradition vis-a-vis the ways of the *bature* (white man, plural Turawa), and perhaps a way of coping with the ignomonies and difficulties of being a colonised people.

Acknowledging the superior fire-power of the British the Caliphate rulers rationalised their submission to the British on the grounds that migration to Islamic countries was impossible as the British already controlled them as well as the routes to them (viz Algeria and the Sudan). In addition to this, it was the wrong season for travel. Thus, it was better to submit to and acknowledge British authority, provided that they would be allowed to practise Islam. Tacit in this was a waiting game—for when the British would leave. Nonetheless, perhaps partly because of the historical understanding of Western history of the separation between temporal power as secular and religious practice as private, the British were willing to give this undertaking. Thus, for example, the British colonial administration prevented Christian missionaries from setting up missions, schools and hospitals in Northern Nigeria in order to avoid potential trouble (although this did not prevent them from imposing unIslamic taxes and the like). In fact it appears to be the case that (after the fears of a Mahdist uprising died down) British colonial administrative policy in its effect actually helped to promote Islamisation among the Maguzawa and among non-Hausa peoples in Northern Nigeria, as well as among the Muslim Hausa.

The major factors which have been associated with this process have been the ending of warfare (following the prevention of inter-Emirate feuding and of attempts at territorial expansion into non-Muslim areas, and slave raiding) and the improvement in transport and communication networks (the building of roads and railways) which gave rise to increased feelings of physical security and enabled thousands of Muslims to travel and preach in Muslim areas and to penetrate new territories to proselytise. In addition, the colonial administration's exclusion of Christian missionaries meant that Christian preachers could not take advantage of these factors to proselytise also.[44]

Nonetheless the issue of increased physical security should not be over-stressed. The establishment of "peace and protection" was one of the planks of legitimation of the British colonial imposition, and some scholars appear to have accepted the claim somewhat uncritically. While warfare and slave-raiding did take place and at particular periods and places (such as near the south-eastern border of Kano Emirate where there was raiding of and by the Ningi every couple of years for fifty years or so) they were not the norm throughout. With an eye to the economic benefits of trade the caliphate had placed much emphasis on the establishment of security and the protection of travellers.[45]

Lugard himself acknowledged this, observing just before colonialism was imposed on Northern Nigeria that the roads were peaceful, caravans and traders were plentiful, and, "women travel alone along the road and the men are all unarmed except for a few normal herdsmen who carried their inevitable spears."[46] Other factors than increased security were also important in promoting Islamisation and the increased opportunities for Islamic proselytisation. Amongst these were cultural resistance to the Turawa (Europeans), the effects of an ever increasing burden of taxation as well as discriminatory taxation, the establishment of Shari'ah courts throughout the Protectorate of Northern Nigeria, the expansion of the malamai (Islamic literati) as clerks for the colonial administration, the lack of a policy of mass secular education in the north, and the large-scale desertion of slaves in the decades following the Anti-Slavery proclamations.

The adherence to Islam as a means of resistance to the rule of the *Nasara* (lit. Christians, but also used as a synonym for Europeans) was perhaps most evident amongst the *masu sarauta* (office holders, now displaced from power or holding office by favour of the British, but nonetheless resenting it). But it was by no means limited to that group. The conquest of the Caliphate was seen as a signal of crisis and catastrophe, out of which a Mahdi was expected to rise and deliver the people—there was a continual migration eastward (from whence the Mahdi was expected to appear), which the colonial administration made every effort to prevent, including the use of force.[47] Islamic principles were also a rationale for the resistance to the new colonial taxes. The resistance at Satirn in 1906, in which an estimated two thousand unarmed villagers were cut down and the village itself razed by the British in retaliation for the deaths of three British officers who had been attempting to impose poll tax (this was regarded as *jizya*—imposed by Muslims on non-Muslims), is but the most infamous example.[48] The colonial administration, aware of the opposition to them as Christians, took the measure of discouraging references to them as *Nasara*, in favour of the term *Turawa*.[49]

Recourse to the claim of being Muslim also had material benefits in the colonial taxation system. Throughout the colonial period taxes increased dramatically, sometimes by over 1,000% in one year, as in Madaki district in Kano Emirate between 1906-1907.[50] These increases of taxation were usually prefaced by an assessment and a population census, as the colonial tax system was based not on individuals' actual production but on the colonial officers' assessments of how much could be gained from particular occupations multiplied by the number of people in each occupation (including pre-teen children) and set for whole districts. The association of census taking and higher taxation rates was made early.

The colonial reports are peppered with references to the difficulties of conducting such census because enumerators were denied access to compounds on that grounds that it was unIslamic for strange men to enter them. The advantage to those being taxed of the consequent under-counting by these means is obvious.[51] These tactics were not always successful for the talakawa. Since the colonial administration continued to use the masu sarauta at all levels to collect tax it was not uncommon for village heads and other officials to maintain one (smaller) tax list accepted by the colonial administration, and another more accurately based on the population because of their local knowledge, the difference between which they pocketed. The colonial administration accepted the claim that Muslim women were secluded and (therefore) not economically active and thus taxation rates for Muslims were much lower than those of non-Muslims where women were also taxed.[52] There were thus definite monetary advantage to being Muslim and it is very likely that a number of the recorded conversion were influenced by this.

A significant number of conversions have also been attributed to the effects of the reorganisation of the legal systems and procedure of settling disputes by the colonial administration. "General" laws was promulgated by the colonial state and adapted by decree as that of British Common Law and statutes as standing in 1900, but otherwise customary law was to prevail. A system of 'Native Courts' was set up consisting of low level Alkali courts, then Provincial courts' and finally Sharia courts to deal with litigation.

Because the British saw 'nothing repugnant' in Islamic law relating to marriage, divorce, inheritance (i.e., personal civil law) these courts were staged by men trained in Shari'ah. Since all customary courts in the North dispensed Shari'ah, the effect of this was to give Islam precedence and authority over indigenous customary law, even in area where there were substantial non-Muslim populations. Maguzawa communities in Kano Emirate, as in Sumaila, Birnin Kudu, Wudil, Gaya, Gwaram, Tudun Wada, Ringim and Roni, were thus obliged to submit to two imposed and foreign legal systems (the British and the Islamic), whereas prior to colonialism, other than the payment of jizya, Maguzawa communities had been left to settle disputes through the authority of the Sarkin Arna or Sarkin Maguzawa (chief of the pagans) and their Councils of Elders, lineage or clan heads.[53]

Shari'ah discriminates against non-Muslims in number of ways. For instance, non-Muslims may not inherit from a Muslim relative, whose estate reverts to Muslim relatives or to the beit-el-mal (state treasury—in this case the Native Authority Treasury, still controlled by the Emir). Similarly, Muslim women are not obliged to return any bride gifts to non-Muslim husbands in the event of divorce, even if they converted after the marriage had taken place. The court records show increasing numbers of cases of erstwhile Maguzawa displacing Maguzawa relatives from claims to the estate of a deceased relative or suing for divorce from Maguzawa husbands.

The undermining of the authority of the Sarakunan Arna or elders of other ethnic communities through the reorganisation of the legal system thus added impetus to the pace of conversion to Islam. Ubah notes oral evidence that Islam made many converts from the Maguzawa after the establishment of British colonial rule—to such an extent that one colonial administrator and anthropologist, Temple, predicted in 1909 that in fifty years the Maguzawa religion would not exist.[54] The colonial records also suggest that at least some of the court personnel used their power to promote conversion and to proselytise for Islam. A. B. Yusuf also mentions the degenerations of the Muslim courts to replace customary law by the Maliki school of *Shari'ah* noting the paradox of the extension of authority of Islamic law under the British.[55] This did not go unnoticed by the colonial administration—one report noted "that in court cases between Muslims and non-Muslims no matter the strength of the case of the latter, the former invariably won,"[56] but nothing was done about it.

The establishment of the court system was not the only opportunity to proselytise created or expanded by the colonial administration. As several commentators have noted the famous 'Indirect Rule' principle was less of a principle than a pragmatic necessity where a very small number of men were trying to rule a large number of people in vast territory. Colonial administrators, for lack of British personnel, were obliged to use indigenous personnel. However, lacking the knowledge by osmosis that comes from growing up in or long familiarity with an area, and with the Colonial Office's desire to keep control this meant the colonial administration required literate personnel to write the reports and records, enumerate the population, measure the fields and crops and so on. Literacy had long been the monopoly of Islamic scholars in Northern Nigeria so initially colonial officers had no option but to use the existing mallamai.

But, the British had pledged the Caliphate rulers to respect Islam. So, as the need for literate personnel to serve the colonial administration grew, this was not provided through the promotion of general mass secular education or allowing Christian missionaries to establish schools (as was the case in Southern Nigeria). Rather, there was the expansion and formalisation of Islamic education, like the Shahuci Elementary School with its School of Law set up in Kano in 1932. The result was an expansion of the mallamai—men who were not only literate but also devout Muslims. They were sent far and wide in the Protectorate as clerks, interpreters, as judges, as enumerators, as buying agents etc. And in the course of their duties they not only had the opportunity to preach Islam, but also in representing the authority of the colonial administration could, as observed above, coerce people into Islam.

However, more influential in converting people to Islam .and revitalising Islam than the *mallamaan duniya* (those ulama associated with government, whether emirate or colonial), were the *mallaman kirgi* or *mallaman gudun duniya,* (the non-worldly ulama) whose numbers and commitment expanded during the colonial period. Particularly from the 1950s on, but even before that too, the Islamic darikoki (Sufi orders or 'brotherhoods', of which the two largest were the Tijaniyya and the Qadiriyya, both of which split into reformed versions during the colonial periods) engaged in mass evangelical campaigns, urban and rural and in southern as well as northern Nigeria. They both had village mallams coming for instruction, and initiated muqaddams in rural areas so that a chain of grassroots religious leadership was set up which stretched into almost every village in the north. In part, this was due to the mere fact of British colonial domination resulting, as Paden puts it, in 'the revitalistic behaviour of the oppressed'[57] and he concludes that 'in Kano the external pressure of non-Muslim communities (British Lebanese and southern Nigerian was clearly a factor in the consolidation of the Kano Muslim community."[58]

In part too, colonial education policies aided their influence, given the respect accorded to literacy. The colonial administration was unwilling to set up schools, other than those producing personnel for the administration. Although the lack of schools in northern Nigeria has often been attributed to opposition from the emirs, Tibenderama's research of the colonial records shows that this was by no means the whole story. Although they were unwilling to allow Christian missionaries to set up schools in the north, the emirate authorities were not only willing to accept, but sometimes enthusiastic about government schools. In 1917, for example, the Emir of Sokoto's request (which was supported by Resident Arnett) to spend £69.00 on a dormitory in order to allow more boys to attend the school was refused by the Lieutenant Governor. Frequently requests by various emirs to open more schools were rejected by the colonial administration on the grounds that there was no money or staff available.[59] This meant that the Reformed Tijaniyya and the Reformed Qadiriyya had a virtual monopoly in the provision of mass education, which they undertook increasingly as a means of acquiring a mass base of membership. As Paden says "the dramatic increase in religious writing in Kano is a reflection of the desire to read and write."[60] The parsimony of the colonial state and its lack of enthusiasm for mass education thus meant that only by joining one of the religious orders could people (mostly men but also some women) acquire literacy.

Ironically, an unintended effect of the Anti-Slavery Proclamations was also to increase the numbers of those claiming to be Muslim. The 1901, 1904 and 1907, Anti-Slavery proclamations did not abolish slavery outright. They stated that no more slaves could be bought, sold or captured and that children born of slave mothers would henceforth not be slaves themselves. Existing slaves, adults or children, remained slaves. Slaves could (and had always been able to) be bought out of slavery, whether by themselves or ransoms by relatives, or they could be manumitted by their owners (as a mark of Islamic piety). Lugard hoped through the anti-slavery proclamations to turn the slaves into a proletariat willing to work for their erstwhile owners as wage earners.

To this end, unless they could prove mal-treatment by their owners, it was difficult for slaves to use the courts to assert their freedom, and they were expected to continue to work for their owners. But although some slaves did continue to do so, most slaves did not. Instead there was large-scale desertion of slaves[61] or migration of ex-slaves.[62] Salves returned to their places of origin or joined labour camps, or, most often, turned up elsewhere, especially where arable land was available, claiming to be free-born Muslims and founding new villages.[63]

Since Muslims cannot be made slaves of by other Muslims, this claim was to forestall any attempts to use the colonial state or native authority administrations to deal with them as run-away slaves. Since, by all accounts slaves were a sizeable proportion of the population, this repressed a large number of people counting themselves as Muslim, as a result of the way in which the issue of the abolition of slavery was dealt with by the colonial administration.

**The Expansion of Seclusion**

There were therefore a number of measures undertaken by the colonial state which had the effect of promoting Islam.

Some of these and a number of others also had the effect of promoting seclusion specifically. During the colonial period it is clear that the practice of seclusion increased. When precisely this occurred and why are still issues of debate. Hill compares the extent of seclusion in Dorayi and Batagarawa in the 1920s, with that of the 1970s, and dates the increase in seclusion from after the 1939-1945 war.[64] In contrast, Watts (1983) states that mention of an increase in seclusion can be found in colonial records of the 1930s. However, in Diribo and Gangur (the area of my own research) many of the elderly and middle-aged women now secluded say they were not secluded when they first married, but were secluded a little later (fieldwork interviews). This would make Hill's dating more likely in terms of a mass move to seclusion, although it is quite possible that the beginnings of a move to seclusion started in the 1930s or even earlier.

According to M.G. Smith, the reasons, for the increase in seclusion were that women formerly of slave status withdrew from framework and woodgathering in order to assert their new status, and that women preferred seclusion because they were able then to pursue their own economic interests in independent *sana'oi* (occupations) and disliked the hard labour of farmwork, rather than because of religious injunctions and tradition.[65] However, as Hill points out, this is a matter that has never been investigated. Obviously M.G. Smith is correct to rule out tradition as an explanation for a phenomenon that developed over the course of a few decades in the recent past. But, it will be argued here, while there were definite economic impetuses for women's seclusion, at least some of these benefited men as well as women and seclusion certainly cannot be reduced to women's dislike of hard work. Furthermore the economic factors were not determinant in themselves, but were also bound up with ideological-religious discourses about ideal social relations and the proper place of women in Islam.

In the context of these discourse M.G. Smith's argument about slave women may have some validity, but as a general explanation it needs to be qualified. First, the extent to which this could have resulted in the 'near-universal' practice of seclusion must rest on the establishment of what proportion of the general population were slaves. This is a contentious and as yet unresolved issue. Second and more important, he gives no indication as to what proportion of ex-slave women actually did so. Despite both his own and Meek's assertion that free Muslim women did no framework, there is considerable oral and written evidence that this was not the case.[66] The pre-colonial situation, in which both slave and free Muslim women did undertake some tasks in farmwork, where they did not have their own *gayauna* (portion of land allocated individually to household members, the proceeds of which were individually appropriated by the allocatee, has been discussed above. Meek himself noted in 1925 (without commenting on the contradiction) that women usually joined in all the farming work, and this was a decade and a half after the anti-slavery proclamations.

Hill mentions elderly informants in Batagarawa stating that women used to work on-field within their own lifetimes. Both women and men in Diribo and Gangur (some only in their late 40s in 1989) corrorborate this of their own mothers or grandmothers (fieldwork/interviews). This evidence implies that free Muslim women working on-farm was not an isolated or rare occurrence. It is unlikely therefore that framework would have been widely used by ex-slaves as the symbol of distinction between slave and free Muslim, or that this could be the explanation for the increasing prevalence of women's seclusion.

Without speculating on the reasons for the increase of seclusion, Hill suggests that a high water table, which enables wells to be dug in compounds, and the ubiquity of the donkey as a beast of burden are among the physical factors, which permit the development and existence of rigid wife seclusion as 'without inconvenience to themselves men could excuse women from their traditional function as beasts of burden."[67] She points out that Muslim women in Borno and Niger (the latter also Hausa), where the water table is lower, were and are not secluded.

The same point can be made of the Muslim Yoruba where drinking water is most often fetched from surface streams. It is also the case that the non-availability of a well in the compound or of someone to fetch water from outside was one of the reasons advanced by women and men in Gangur as to why women were not secluded. In Diribo; however, secluded women in compounds without wells or where and when the wells were dry had to suffer their thirst and manage with the little brought in (often grudgingly), rather than be allowed or willing to fetch it themselves (fieldwork observation). Thus while the availability of well water seems plausible as a possible enabling condition for women's seclusion, a positive association between the two is rather more difficult to establish.

The discussion will now turn to the general economic impetuses towards women's seclusion. As mentioned earlier, if households had secluded women their existence could both be used to prevent enumerators from entering the compound and to reduce the taxation burden on particular households, since women seem not to have been taxed on their *sana'oi,* but only if they worked on the land. Because of the drive to increase the revenue from tax, by 1910 in the Muslim Emirates also women who 'hold property in their own right' were also separately assessed, as well as women in other areas.[68]

In both cases the husband/household head was made responsible for the tax payments of all those classed as workers living in the household. It was therefore in the interests of both women and men for women not to work on the land (or possibly not to be acknowledged as working on the land), but move into seclusion as this reduced the tax burden of the whole household. It seems likely also that this added to the pressure on women to give up their rights to land by inheritance. Holding to the their own land meant a higher taxation burden, and would be regarded as unwarrantedly greedy since in Islam women have a right to maintenance from their husbands. This was particularly so as withdrawal from on-field labour or being secluded did not necessarily imply inactivity economically. Furthermore, as women rarely owned land, it was relatively easy to simply deny that women worked on the land, whether or not this was the case.

The gender division of labour up to the beginning of the colonial period in Northern Nigeria has been discussed earlier. While some of the activities which were women's areas are not compatible with seclusion, others are. Chief among the latter are cotton spinning, groundnut and other crop processing. Ironically, colonial agricultural policy in Northern Nigeria facilitated women's withdrawal from field labour, by its exclusive focus on the production of cotton and groundnuts—the two crops from which the processing of which women gained most in their autonomous *sana'oi,* and which had very high rates of women participating. Colonial policy encouraged the growth of groundnuts and cotton. Both crops had been grown before but now they were produced in increased quantities as a necessity in order to sell for cash with which to pay taxes.

In the case of cotton, this effect was not only inadvertent but contrary to colonial objectives, which were to supply cheap cotton for the British textile industry. However, Kano Emirate especially had long had a cottage textile industry, producing cloth of high quality, traded across North and West Africa, some types of which were even used as currency. Despite the best efforts of the colonial administration and the British Cotton Growing Association (flooding Kano with cheap imported textiles, introducing new cotton strains, the insistence that cotton should be sold through licensed buying agents only, and the requirements that taxes be paid in British money as well as constantly increasing taxation) the cotton industry in Kano continued to hold its own. Colonial officers in their annual reports continued to point out that higher prices were paid for cotton and cotton yarn for the local cottage industry than exporting companies were willing to offer, that Kano cloth was less expensive and more durable than imported cloth, and that it continued to be preferred to British textiles in their explanations to the Colonial Office of why sufficient cotton was not forthcoming from Nigeria.

The statistics on cotton export also show that while cotton exports were never as high as the British would have liked, from Kano Emirate there were seldom any at all, despite the fact the Kano production of cotton continued to increase through most of the colonial period.[69] Many women were thus able to concentrate on spinning cotton into yarn, from within their compounds. The production of groundnuts, under the pressure of the colonial state,[70] rose even more dramatically than that of cotton. Much of this was exported, but enough remained to make the processing of groundnuts into oil and kullikulli (groundnut cakes—the residue from pressing for oil, eaten as a snack and cooked as a flavouring for soups) for local consumption, a major and lucrative activity for women. This too is an activity which is conveniently carried out from within the compound.

Other factors too would have contributed to the increasing withdrawal of women from activity in public space. One of these was the forced labour required of people by the colonial state for the building of roads and railways. District officers would notify village heads that so many labourers were required for so many days to work in such and such an area. The majority of these were men but women were also included to cook and provide sexual services for men.[71] The women sent were bazawarai (non-married i.e. divorced or widowed), but re-marriage is easy and with little stigma. It is likely that women arranged to be re-married and in seclusion to avoid being sent (as indeed do karuwai (courtesan/prostitutes) contemporarily, when moral panics are about to ensue).

Another factor was the increasing pressure on land and consequence diminishing of daji (bush) which made it difficult for women to caughts on with those sana'oi which depend on foraging. Land pressure came from two sources—the need to put increasing acreages under cultivation in order to plant enough both for food and for sale to pay tax, and, the establishment of experimental farms and forestry reserves (often of hundreds of acres in area) by the colonial state. This meant that it became necessary to go further and further afield to gather sylvan products (fruits, herbs, leaves, roots, wood) in sufficient quantity to make their processing for sale a viable proposition. The gathering and sale of (for example) tsada, gwandan daji, dinya, kainya, gandi, or taura fruits became less and less common. So too did the processing of shea nuts into 'butter' or of tsamiya into drinks, sweets and flavourings, or the weaving of goruba leaves and rama stalks into mats and halters respectively... The availability of other activities involving less walking, like spinning and embroidering, also made it easier for these to be abandoned.

Nonetheless, it should not be thought that women's withdrawal from public space and into seclusion was solely an economic response. Withdrawal from public economic activities like farmworks or foraging is not the exact equivalent of seclusion. What converted this withdrawal into seclusion was the ideological context in which it tookplace. The ideological space around gender relations and women's role in society was not inert. It has already been pointed out above that by the end of the nineteenth century, Islam had become part of the cultural identity of the Hausa and that women's seclusion is one of the most visible markers of Islamic practice.

The boost given to Islamic fervour as a means of resistance to colonial domination, and the increased proselytisation in rural areas discussed above meant that the issue of women's proper place in Islam also became an area preached about to rural communities (along with, for example, the anti-Islamic nature of singing and drumming at funerals or of the chewing of mildly narcotic leaves, like fure). Whereas formerly seclusion had been almost solely a phenomenon of the urban officeholders and wealthy, it now became a topic of concern in rural communities also. The example of the *masu sarauta* forced by the colonial administration actually live in their fiefs, rather than residing in the cities and sending *jakadu* (agent of office holders) to collect tax and enforce regulations as they had done since the time of Muhammadu Rumfa in the fourteenth century, also meant that it was no longer an abstract and unknown phenomenon. Their way of life, including the practice of seclusion, was then easily observed by the majority of the *talakawa* (commoners), bringing their crops to be sold and attending the market.

Up to this point the dominant discourse on seclusion had been of the most restrictive variety, whereby secluded women emerged not at all or extremely rarely from their homes. This too would have been the practice brought by the masu sarauta now living in the district headquarters of the sub-provinces. However, this form of seclusion is less feasible for small-scale cultivators than for the wealthy. In the gender division of labour women had been responsible for water provision, nearby foraging and some tasks in cultivation—particularly cotton picking and groundnut harvesting. Although, as discussed earlier, women's foraging had begun to become more difficult, the increased production of groundnuts and cotton meant a continued (and heavy) demand for women's labour at harvesting periods and women did continue to harvest these crops.

For the talakawa being evangelised by the Tijaniyya and Qadiriyya then there must have been a contradiction between their labour needs and the requirements of being a good Muslim. It seems likely that this led to the development of the form of seclusion referred to as tsari, where women may actually leave their compounds for specific purposes and yet still be counted as secluded. Elderly women and men in Diribo and Gangur were quite emphatic that in the past seclusion was far more restrictive than nowadays. Contemporarily women who harvest crops only in the farms of their husbands or close relatives may still claim that they are secluded, in tsari rather than in full kulle (fieldwork interviews and observation).

This is not to imply that tsari as a form of Islamic seclusion was elaborated as an alternative form in theological evangelical preaching. The Maliki school of Shari'ah is generally one of the most restrictive in terms of its interpretation of seclusion, and this is the school to which all Muslims born in Nigeria are assumed and expected to follow. Both the Tijaniyya and (especially) the Qadiriyya substantially follow Malikite rules. However, Tijaniyya does have a more liberal history of women's roles than Qadiriyya. Women could be muqadammas (initiators) of both men and women (though most usually of women) and some Tijaniyya literature in Kano stresses the importance of women's roles in its development. Paden briefly mentions a few of the women who were prominent in the Reformed Tijaniyya, including one Mowa who, after having studied in Kaolack in Senegal (where the then Shaykh of the order was resident and wife seclusion is not practised), returned to Kano to actively oppose seclusion.[72] But there is no indication that her views became widespread enough to have been influential in the proselytisation of the Reformed Tijaniyya. Rather tsari seems to have developed somewhat apologetically as due to necessity in the rigours of rural life.

**The Run-up to Independence**

Towards the close of the colonial period, with the establishment of NEPU (Northern Elements Progressive Union) in 1950, the issue of women's rights in Islam and how this should be interpreted in contemporary society was taken up. NEPU was the only party in the North of Nigeria to make the position of women a concern of its platform at that time. Aminu Kano and then the whole of NEPU argued consistently for women's full enfranchisement and rights to education. This was couched in the language of Islamic rights (quoting, for example, surah Ash-shura 42: 38 that Muslims are those "whose rule (in all matters of common concern) is consultation among themselves" and those surahs which refer to the religious rights and duties of women as well as of men, to argue this meant that all Muslims should have a direct say in a democracy). The issue of seclusion per se was seldom directly addressed. According to Callaway Aminu Kano's position was that women's domestic seclusion did not preclude their full political enfranchisement.[73] However, Wali's series of articles in the Nigerian Citizen (July-August 1956) are more radical arguing that the physical form of seclusion is a pre-Islamic custom. Certainly Wali was one of the very few men in the North at that time who despite his social and economic status did not, out of principle, seclude his wife.

But the more conservative NPC (Northern People's Convention which with some election manipulation by the colonialists won the elections and held power from the end of the colonial period until the first coup in 1966) also couched its language in Islamic discourse. They argued that women's seclusion was not only legitimate in Islam but obligatory and drew upon appeals to tradition also (arguing versus Wali that seclusion was traditional not only in Hausaland but in Islam also). One of the concerns of NPC was to build up a power base in the north by stressing differences in culture and religion between the North (largely Muslim but treated by NPC as if it where wholly Muslim) and the south (by this time largely Christian). Women's position was one of the points de capiton in this discourse, and it was only by fiat of the military regime that northern women were enfranchised and able to vote for the first time in the 1979 elections for the Second Republic.

By the end of direct colonial rule, the practice of seclusion in northern Nigeria had changed dramatically. From an urban phenomenon it had become widespread in rural areas also. From being practised largely by the relatively small groups of the masu sarauta and the mallamai, it had become increasingly common among the largest group of the population, the talakawa. As such, the most common variant of seclusion had become, not the most restrictive form of kulle where vomen rarely if ever for any reason left the compound, but tsari in which women did emerge for work and to visit, but only apologetically and with permission. Ironically, despite Hausaland's long history of association with Islam of at least five centuries, it was during the five decades or so of colonialism that seclusion became extensively practised. As has been shown this had much to do with the way in which British colonial rule resulted in the promotion of Islamisation as a self-conscious ideology and source of group identity and resistance, as well as the economic changes brought about by the way in which northern Nigeria was incorporated into the world capitalist economy as a producer of certain primary commodities for export.

Even more ironically, the economic conditions which had led to the changes in the division of labour in which women could withdraw from working in public space without becoming economically dependent on their husbands had already begun to change again by the 1950s and 1960s. The production of groundnuts and especially of cotton had begun to slump. Where the colonial regime had no interest in promoting the industrialisation of textile production or groundnut processing in Nigeria, indigenous capitalists in Kano were interested and had begun to set up textile factories and oil processing mills. Women's two major sana'oi, cotton spinning and groundnut processing, were thus about to decline. But, by this time, women were already secluded.

And, by this time too, the religious-political ideologies on seclusion had already changed. At least since the time of Dan Fodio there had been a subordinate discourse in which, while seclusion was recommended, it was permitted for women to leave their homes in circumstances of necessity, which were quite widely defined. In this discourse it was even admirable for women to be out of their compounds for certain purposes—although these purposes (to acquire or spread Islamic knowledge) meant in effect it could only be practised by women associated with the mallamai. The dominant discourse, however, had been that seclusion was mandatory for true Muslims and that going out, for whatever purpose was antithetical to the proper practice of seclusion and was reprehensible (*makruh*) if not forbidden (haram).

This dominant discourse, over the course of the colonial period, shifted to include concepts of group identity and tradition. Seclusion became assimilated in political rhetoric (regardless of actual historical accuracy) as tradition and custom, which identified and set off the Muslim north of Nigeria first from the British colonialists and later also from southern Nigerians. In this way to argue against seclusion became characterised as anti-Muslim and anti-Hausa/northern.

Furthermore, the wielding of this discourse quite ignored the fact that the majority of women in seclusion did (even had to) leave their compounds, if only to fetch water and harvest crops. Thus, the development of the tsari form of seclusion, despite its extensiveness, remained religiously and ideologically unjustified. It was a form of seclusion of which the practitioners were ashamed—that women should be in full kulle remained the ideal and the aspiration. And this aspiration was now generalised among the Hausa and held to be applicable to all Muslims, regardless of wealth, class or status.

**Post-Independence**

This has remained the dominant discourse regarding seclusion since Nigeria gained political independence in 1960. More and more, women have become secluded so that it is commonly asserted that Muslim Hausa women are universally secluded from marriage (sometimes as early as nine or ten years of age). Nonetheless, this is not quite accurate. At any one moment there are women who are not secluded, even though they will be or have been at some time (i.e. never married women, divorced or widowed women, and old women) whose numbers are considerably higher than the ideology that all Hausa women are married admits.[74]

Even leaving aside these women, and considering only Kano State, there are not insignificant numbers of women who have never been and do not expect to be secluded. This includes a number of different categories of women. The best known is of young urban middle-class 'western' educated women who have or intend to have careers. By themselves this category is numerically insignificant as the literacy rate for women is less then 10% (Federal Office of Statistics). However, their importance as evidence of a possibly emerging trend, and, as high-status role models, should be not ignored.

Furthermore, non-secluded Muslim Hausa women also include: women in rural areas where seclusion is not practised, as exists in Hadejia Emirate (Hassan Fulata—personal communication) and Kazaure[75] and possibly other areas also; women in rural areas where seclusion is practised but who do not so themselves (fieldwork observation and interviews); many women from butcher and praise-singer families throughout Kano State; urban poor women (Hussei Abdullahi—personal communication, based on her fieldwork on women in industry in Kano); and, women whose freedom of movement extends to such an extent that even the term *tsari* (a form of seclusion in which women may emerge from their compounds, with permission and for limited purposes), becomes stretched to a meaningless extent.[76] Taking the dominant discourse for the reality all these categories of women have tended to be ignored, in research as in popular consciousness and public policy.

There have been some attempts since 1960 to dislodge this discourse from its hegemonic position, but these have often tended to be somewhat uneasy, if not actually contradictory. The official policy of both the Federal government and the Kano State government has been to encourage female education and work. Women have been exhorted to acquire education and participate in building Nigeria, and (less often) men to permit their daughters to do so.

By implication therefore government policy has been anti-seclusion, at least in the form of *kulle* (here meaning the more restrictive form of seclusion), as this is clearly not compatible with women working in the 'modern' sector. But no government has dared to publically condemn seclusion. Even the Peoples' Redemption Party (PRP) government of 1979-83 did not do so, although it came to power largely on the strength of women in the North (enfranchised only in 1976 and voting for the first time in the 1979 elections) voting for the PRP in recognition of NEPU's historical support for women's rights.[77] (PRP was the successor to NEPU. Following the 1966 coup and subsequent military regimes all political parties of the First Republic were banned and not allowed to reform. Nonetheless many of the Second Republic political parties had direct links, in personnel and orientation, to First Republic Parties—NEPU and PRP, NPC and the National Party of Nigeria, Action Group and the Unity Party of Nigeria.)

In the last decade, however, even these attempts to shift the paradigm on seclusion have become more tentative, retreating in the face of a rise in fundamentalism. Evident most markedly from the Buhari regime's War Against Indiscipline in 1984 and on has been a tendency to shift attention from the political and economic difficulties and policies in Nigeria to the social (bribery and corruption, delinquency, promiscuity, high divorce rates, drug-abuse etc). And in this the foci of blame have been corruption by Western values and women's desertion of their responsibilities (as mothers and to be chaste and modest).

At the same time there has been a growing cynicism about the possible efficacy of political or administrative action and a revival in fundamentalist religious and traditional values. The consequence of this has been to cast all feminist demands as Western and/or Christian and/or immoral. Seclusion has been stressed as Islamic, traditional, Hausa and pure. For those women who do leave their own homes there is strong pressure to dress by the Islamic code—now interpreted in a more restrictive way than ever before.

**The Kano State Committee on Women Affairs**

It has also meant the invention of a wholly Islamic past. The recent committee on women set up by the state government, for example, had its terms of reference defined in terms of the assumption that the population of Kano State is Muslim, ignoring both Maguzawa and Hausa converts to Christianity (or agnostics and atheists), as well as other Nigerians living in the state. The terms of Reference of the committee were:

1. explore and analyse the Shari'ah regarding marriage
2. identify the extent to which actual marriage practice conforms to this
3. assess women's legal rights in Shari'ah and the extent to which they are enforced
4. identify the causes of high divorce rates and means of protecting women from arbitrary divorce
5. identify the factors that militate against the understanding of women's role in changing society re family life, labour, educational pursuits etc. vis-a-vis rising divorce and deliquency rates
6. identify the areas where female labour is required for the well-being of society (e.g nursing, medicine, social work) and suggest ways to encourage women in these
7. identify causes of prostitution and means of eradication

8. ascertain Shari'ah position on rights in marriage and recommend ways of ensuring security of family life
9. make any other relevant recommendations

Although terms 4, 5, 6, 7, and 9 do not specifically mention Islam, in its deliberations the committee assumed Islam as the context and the goal. Hence the report is full of comments like the following:

> "Marriage becomes necessary for a woman if she has to go out to look for food and anytime she goes out men indicate interest in her, then only marriage can save her.[78] Nonetheless, while positioning themselves as good Muslims, the committee adopted a slightly liberal position in the debates. They argued that Islamic law states that: women should not be despised; women are equal to men in terms of personality; female infanticide is prohibited; women should be respected as wives, mothers and daughters; the acquisition of knowledge is enjoined equally on men and women; women have inheritance rights; wives have the same (though lesser) rights over husbands as husbands do over wives (Surah Al-Bakhara 2: 228 "And women shall have rights similar to the rights against them, according to what is equitable. But men have a degree (of advantage) over them"); and that women have the right to own property and have independent occupations and income." However, they pointed out that the very existence of the committee was an indication that women are being denied these rights.[79]

They were particularly strong on the issue of education. Government should enlighten parents about the right age to marry off their daughters, that age is 17-18. By that age it is expected that girls should have completed their post-primary education. Let it be an offence punishable with a prison term or fine or both for any parent who withdraws his daughter from school before she completes it.[80]

Recommending government encouragement of female education, free education for females, single-sex school so as to prevent fathers from refusing to send their daughters to school, and the establishment of women's educational centres in wards. They were, however, consistent in accepting that Islam requires three principles. One was of wifely subordination to the husband, arguing for instance that marriage is *mustahab* (recommended but not mandatory) for a woman who does not want to get married but wants children as long as if she marries 'she will bestow upon her husband, his rights"[81] or that "it is in order for a husband to authorise his wife to go out."[82] A second is the prohibition of interaction between male and female. Kamun amarya (catching of the bride) is acceptable if it does not involve the mixing of the sexes.[83] Government should prohibit the intermingling of men and women within, and during activities, organised by self-help and youth associations.[84]

And, the third is that women's role and position in society are defined in Islam according to her physiological make-up. Under Islamic law women have no better place than their homes, where they are expected to help their husbands, become pregnant and look after their children. This is the place where women are expected to play the leading role, since God has enjoined her to help in the making of a decent population.[85] The physiological makeup of a women which causes her to menstruate every month, to become pregnant and then a mother, etc. hinders her progress in a workplace. In addition the nature of their bodily build-up reduces the contributions that the women can make in occupations/duties that are not related to weaning and other household duties.[86]

The acceptance of these positions meant that the committee found itself holding contradictory and uncomfortable positions as regards the issue of seclusion, trying to held the discourses of Islam and of development. At some points they imply that seclusion is recommended (for example that marriage is not obligatory for a woman who 'can guard herself from committing adultery and is capable of feeding herself through lawful means without having to go out to earn a living'. At others they assert that it is not obligatory not to go out (thus that divorcees should stay their (ex)-husbands' houses during the iddah period, "however there is no offence if the divorce [sic] goes out in the day time to attend to some lawful obligation',—from a *hadith* narrated by Jabir Ibn Abdullah, cited from Muslim). They state quite explicitly that a woman's place is in home and that women are too weak to be really productive. But at the same time they also state the following as one of the factors that militate against proper understanding of the role of women.

It is the tradition of our people that women do not go out to seek for knowledge or to work and earn some money outside their matrimonial home. Traditionally women are confined to their husbands homes where they look after the children. In fact some men believed that seeking for knowledge (Islamic and western) by women was not important. Some men even believe that for women staying at home is their religion.[87] But they then go on to state that 'nonetheless, Islamic law also permits a women to work outside the home in order to contribute to the development of her society and the maintenance of her family'.[88]

Their solution therefore is to argue that women have a role to play in certain restricted areas (teaching, nursing, social work and the like) and for single-sex institutions and work-places, stating that 'therefore women could contribute their quota effectively in certain areas of life'.[89] The committee recommended single-sex schools and hospitals (i.e., serving females and staffed by women), no night-shifts for women (specifically for nurses and midwives), a change in nurses' uniforms to conform to the Islamic mode of dressing, that women should be able to take up any occupations but those in the army or police, the creation of locally-based jobs for women (in teaching, extension work etc. for women), the establishment of ward-based small-scale industries where women can 'secure jobs such as knitting, grinding, breadmaking and other manual/craft occupations', and the establishment of women's co-operative shops to sell the products of the former.[90]

Ironically, although all four of the women on the committee (which had 12 members) were in the approved professions (namely teaching and social work), none work in single-sex institutions and none had ever before (to my knowledge) expressed any desire to work in a single-sex institution. In act I know personally 3 of these women and 1 of the men—none of these feel that it is anti-Islamic for women and men to work in the same place, and at least one of the women does not wear 'the Islamic code' in the privacy of her home or in public abroad, similarly nor does the man in similar circumstances. Yet they put their names to the committee report—an indication of how strong the legitimacy of the Islamic discourses in its more conservative form has become in Northern Nigeria.

Even more ironically, given that it constituted the committee members and terms of reference, the state government's response to the committee report was far more of a secular orientation. They accepted recommendations regarding prompting girls' education, the establishment of women's centres, the prohibition of forced marriage and child-hawking, and to set up Marriage Arbitration Panels. But for the most part, they contended themselves with stating that the Ulama should enlighten the public on their religious duties, rather than enacting legislation,

> The Ulama should enlighten the public on the issue of *kamun amarya* (p.2)
>
> and Shari'ah provisions on marriage (p. 3-4).
>
> Traditional leaders and the Ulama are called on to educate the general public on women's rights in Shari'ah, (p. 4) and, simply noted other recommendations
>
> Government notes the recommendation re single-sex hospitals and schools and 'will improve working conditions' (p. 11).
>
> Government notes the recommendation that women can do any job but those in the policy or army, (p. 12)

> and that divorced women should be prohibited from going to the market (p. 13)
>
> Government notes the recommendation regarding night work for nurses and midwives (p.11)

Nonetheless that the Kano State government (an appointed cabinet under a military regime, and not politicians seeking popular approval) did constitute the committee in explicitly Islamic terms bears eloquent testimony to the authority that the conservative Islamic discourse holds. Furthermore, two points might well explain the government's response. First, they are themselves constrained by the need to operate within the terms of a Federal and secular republic. Secondly, a good many of the areas in which the Ulama is asked to educate the public and enforce Shari'ah provisions, are those which would mitigate the extent of and abuse of men's power over women (as opposed to challenging the concept of men's authority).

It is well-known that a great many of the Ulama (of the lower ranks particularly) oppose even this understanding of Islam. In asking these very men to educate and enforce women's rights in Shari'ah (however limited) the state government is in fact bowing to the effective authority of an even more conservative discourse than that of the committee.

## Recent Shifts in the Dominant Positions on Women's Seclusion

Even so, the extreme conservative discourse also takes its lead from some of the learned members of the Ulama (for example, Sheikh Mohammed Gumi, formerly the Grand Qadi of Northern Nigeria, an Izala leader with great influence in Nigeria). There has been little discussion of women in *purdah* per se in Nigeria recently. Rather the discussion has tended to focus round the participation of women in politics in the proposed Third Republic of 1992. But from these discussion can be extrapolated their implications for the practice of seclusion.

The opinion that women should neither vote nor be voted for, which was that expressed by the NPC and its allies and most of the Ulama throughout the 1950s and 1960s is clearly compatible with the most restrictive form of seclusion. The argument that women should vote (and especially if separate voting booths are arranged for women—as was the case in much of the North in 1979) involves only a minor breach of physical seclusion, since voting occurs infrequently and permission can be given by husbands for this. But the opinion that women may also be voted for, involving as it does the necessity for active campaigning in public, necessarily means that seclusion cannot be practiced as restriction on mobility and interaction with male kin only.

Pre-1979, Gumi had said that women should neither vote nor be voted for as politics was not a suitable activity for women. But for the 1979 presidential elections he tried to mobilise Muslim women to vote for Shehu Shagari as the Muslim candidate—saying that this was part of their *jihad* duty as Nigeria is not an Islamic state. (It might be noted here, however, that there were two other candidates who were also Muslim—one of whom was the radical and supporter of (some) women's rights, Aminu Kano). In 1989, following the (first ever) election of a (Christian) women as a local government councillor in Kano Metropolitan, Gumi soft-pedalled further and refused to comment on whether Muslim women could stand for office and participate in political campaigns (reported by Bilkisu Yusuf, personal communication).

Thus it is evident that even for one of the most conservative and fundamentalist of the Ulama, the discourse on women has been shifting. Almost all scholars now accept the Muslim women in Nigeira must vote, though there is no absolute consensus on the conditions and extent to which they think that women can be politically active and be good Muslims. Justice Bashir Sambo, (Grand Qadi of the Shari'ah Court of Appeal, Abuja Federal Capital Territory) is of the opinion that Muslim women like Muslim men have a responsibility to participate in politics—specifically to look after the interests of Muslims as Nigeria is a secular state, and since non-Muslim women will participate. This participation, however, should not interfere with their family responsibilities and is also subject to adherence of principles about mode of dress, not mixing with men and decency (separate voting booths for men and women, for example).

Sambo is somewhat ambivalent on the question of whether Muslim women may occupy leadership positions. The *hadith* that 'a nation that takes a woman to run its affairs will never prosper' (Ahmed, Bukhari, an-Nisai and Tirmidhi as authentic—on hearing that king of Persia's daughter had succeeded her father) is used by some of the Ulama to prohibit women from positions of leadership or from being judges. Sambo points out that there are acknowledged dissenting views (Abu Hanifa holds that women can judge in civil cases of wealth and At-Tabari that women can hold any leadership position). He argues that because Nigeria is not an Islamic state women must participate (decently) at all levels and in all fields of activity, including holding any position but that of head of state. This is on the principle of choosing between the lesser of two evils—the greater evil being the effects of lack of participation of Muslim women (on Muslims in a non-Muslim state).[91]

The Grand Qadi of the Shari'ah Court of Appeal in Niger State, Justice Sheikh Ahmed Lemu, agrees that because Nigeria is not an Islamic state, and assuming that the new constitution will not discriminate between men and women on voting rights and eligibility to stand for political office, it is necessary for Muslim women to participate as do non-Muslim women in order to prevent domination by non-Muslims. In this context he, like Gumi, says it is part of their *jihad* duties (struggle for Islam), by analogy with the *jihad* of Rasulullah and with the activities of Aisha in the political crisis after the death of Caliph Uthman.

However the Islamic code of conduct in respect of relations with the opposite sex should always be borne in mind, and it is only in a state of emergency 'where the Muslim community in general is in danger of serious domination and possible persecution by non-Muslims (that) it is a joint responsibility of Muslims, male and female to compete in the spirit of *jihad* with non-Muslims in every important aspect of the life of the society'. Nonetheless, because 'of their generally delicate nature, and sometimes their domestic circumstances' he feels that specific seats should be reserved 'whereby competent and respectable women could be nominated to represent women's interests' so that they do not have to compete with men in campaigning. Like Sambo, Lemu argues that despite the *hadith* on women holding a leadership position, as Nigeria is a secular and multi-religious state 'it is against the interests of the Ummah to place restriction on women's participation because this certainly leads to imbalance and domination of politics and administration by non-Muslims, and domination of the whole range of women's activities by non-Muslim women, which is obviously the case in Nigeria today'. The situation would be different in an Islamic state.[92]

The position of Justice Abdulkadir Orire (Grand Qadi of the Shari'ah Court of Appeal, Kwara State) is at first sight more radical since he says that

> "Since Islam is all-embracing and a person will be rewarded whether his or her action is in the realm of worship, or in the realm of worldly transactions, it goes without saying that if a woman participates in politics and carries it out in the manner *Allâh* wants, she is not doing wrong and she will be rewarded by him... (Politics in Nigeria is like a house on fire and everyone is expected to participate), even women in *purdah* must come out under such circumstances."

However, he goes on to say that although women should be mobilised to vote for those who will stand for Islamic values, they should not generally stand for office but be opinion-moulders of Islamic women. Only women of over fifty-five years of age 'are those who are allowed by Shari'ah to mix in public life, that is those who are of an age to be no more a fitnah (temptation) for men'. Even this category of women should not stand unless there are no suitable men. In his view Muslim women should not join a political party, nor do party work with their members.[93]

Similarly, D.O.S. Noibi, (Head, Department of Arabic and Islamic Studies, University of Ibadan) agrees that Muslim women should participate in politics (and other spheres of human conduct). But he insists that this should take into consideration 'the limits Islam has prescribed for women in accordance with their natural disposition and ability'. Thus Muslim women may seek nomination for posts where there is a da'wah (teaching) role, but not hold sensitive posts (head of state or armed forces, governorship, head to senate, judgeship) because these 'require maximum rationality and minimum emotionality and therefore may appear too demanding for women because of the physiological and psychological make up of women in general'. Furthermore, he says, Muslim women may only join women's wings of political parties and should demand separate seating arrangements from men because 'a situation where males and females mix should be abhorred'.[94]

It is evident from these interviews that a number of influential Ulama are now of the opinion that good Muslim women may participate in political activity to the extent of both voting and being voted for. But, unlike the relatively radical position that Wali sought to establish in the 1950s, their positions are defensive and remain restrictive of women. The frequently made justification that Nigeria is not an Islamic state and that the principle of the lesser of two evil must be applied implies that really Muslim women should be restricted to physical seclusion in their homes and leave community and public affairs to men.

Similarly the insistence on separate voting booths, seating arrangements, women's wings of parties, positions reserved for women, and the like are to prevent interaction between women and men. Coupled with the arguments about women's physiological and psychological conditions and hence their prohibition from occupying the most powerful positions in the state, this means that the endpoint (for women) of this more liberal discourse is to expand their scope of activities while ensuring that they remain subordinate to men overall. Thus although women would not be secluded in the sense of being restricted to the home, their interactions would just the same be with other women and their power subject to that of men. But then, as is explicit in a number of these interviews, the goal is not to serve women's interests, but to ensure the political and economic prominence of elite Muslim men in Nigeria, and their control of the state.

A.M. IMAM

## REFERENCES

1. R.S. Soper, The Stone Age in Northern Nigeria, *Journal of the Historical Society of Nigeria,* III, 1965, p. 2; Yusuf Usman, The Transformation of Katsina circa 1876–1903: The Overthrow of the Sarauta System and the Establishments of the Evolution of the Emirate System. Ph.D. Thesis, Ahmadu Bello University Zaria, 1974, 1981.

2. Bala Achi, The development and function of City Walls in the Savanna Belt of the Northern Area of Nigeria, M.Sc. Thesis, Ahmadu Bellow University, 1985.

3. Usman, *op. cit.,* 1974, 1981.

4. Renee Pittin, Marriage and Alternative Strategies: Career Patterns of Hausa Women in Katsina City, Ph.D. Thesis, University of London, 1979.

5. The Kano Chronicle, (transl.) Palmer, 1928.

6. Abdullahi, Smith, Some Considerations Relating to the Formation of States in Hausaland, *Journal of the Historical Society of Nigeria,* Vol 3, 1971, Achi, *op. cit.,* 1985, Usman, *op. cit.,*

1981, Abdullahi Mahadi, The State and the Economy: The Sarauta System and its Role in Shaping the Society and Economy of Kano Emirate with Particular Reference to the 18th and 19th centuries, Ph.D. Thesis, Ahmadu Bello University, 1982.

7. Mahdi Adamu, The Economics of Culture Among the Hausa During the Present Millenium, A.D., *Kano Studies,* 1979.

8. Yusuf Usman, *The Transformation of Katsina (1400-1883): The Emergence and Overthrow of the Sarauta System and the Establishment of the Emirate System,* Ahmadu Bello University Press, Zaria, 1981, Mahadi, *op. cit.,* 1982.

9. Herbert Palmer, (Trans. and commentary), The Kano Chronicle, *Journal of the Anthropological Institute,* 38, 1908, pp. 57–98.

10. The Kano Chronicle, p. 112.

11. R. Levy, *The Social Structure of Islam,* Cambridge University Press, 1969.

12. Isa Wali, The True Position of Women in Islam, *Nigerian Citizen* a series of 5 articles between July 18–August 4, 1956.

13. Mansur Ali Nasif, *Ittaji al Jami Lil Usul,* Beirut, p. 236

14. *Ibid.,* pp. 236-237.

15. *The Qur'ân,* 24:30-31

16. Muhammed Asad, *The Message of the Qur'ân,* (translation of *the Qur'ân* and notes), Dar an Andaulsu, Gibraltar, 1980, p. 538 n° 37.

17. *Ibid.,* p. 539 n° 38.

18. Muhammed Ahmed Al-Hajj, The Mahdist Tradition in Northern Nigeria Ph.D. Thesis, Ado Bayero College of Ahmadu Bello University, 1973, p. 19;

20. Mahadi, *op. cit.,* 1982.

21. Al-Hajj, *op. cit.,* 1973, Ubah 1985.

22. M. Adamu, Some essential Features of the Economy of Hausaland circa 1500–1804, manuscript prepared for publication in Mahdi Adamu and Djib Hamani (eds.) *Studies of the History of Central Sudan in West Africa Before 1804;* Mahadi, *op. cit.,* 1982.

23. Pittin, *op. cit.*, 1979.
24. Murray Last, *The Sokoto Caliphate,* Longmans, London, 1967; Usman op. cit., 1981.
25. Ogunbiyi, in T.Hodgkin (ed.), *Nigerian Perspectives: An Historical Anthropology.* Chaucer Press Suffolk, 1975; Haroun al Rashid Adamu, *The North and Nigerian Unity,* Gaskiya Corporation Zaria, 1973.
26. *Ibid.*, p. 3
27. *Ibid.*, p. 9.
28. from Mervyn Hiskett's translation.
29. Last, *op. cit.*, 1967; Jean Boyd, and Murray Last, "The Role of Women as 'Agents Religieux' in Sokoto *Canadian Journal of African Studies* 19:2, 1985 pp. 283–300.
30. Mahadi, *op. cit.*, 1982, p. 31; Adamu *op. cit.*, 1982.
32. *Ibid.*, 1982, p. 578.
33. Paul Levojoy, Plantation Slavery in the Economy of the Sokoto Caliphate, *Journal of African History,* XIX, 1978, pp. 341–68, Polly Hill, From Slavery to Freedom: the Case of Farm Salvery in Kano Emirate, *Comparative Studies in Society and History,* 18, 1977a, pp. 395-426; Sharpe 1988, Mahadi, *op. cit.*, 1982, Sule Bello, The State and Economy in Kano circa 1894–1960: A Study of Colonial Domination, Ph.D. Thesis, Ahmadu Bello University, 1982.
34. M.B. Duffil, A Translation and Annotation of E.R. Flegel (1885) Biography of Madugu Mohamman Mai Gashin Baki, Paper to Fourth Seminar on the Economic History of the Central Savanna of West Africa, Ahmadu Bello University, Zaria, 1976.
35. *Ibid.*, 1876, p. 206.
36. Last, *op. cit.*, 1967, C.N. Ubah, The Administration of Kano Emirate Under the British, 1900–1930, Ph.D. Thesis, University of Ibadan, 1973, Mahadi, *op. cit.*, 1982.
37. Duffil, *op. cit.*, 1976, p. 9.
38. *Ibid.*, p. 18.
39. Michael Onwuejogwu, The Cult of the Bori Spirits Among the Hausa, in Mary Douglas and Phyllis Kaberry (eds.), *Man in Africa,* Tavistock, London, 1969, pp. 279–306.

40. Bello, *op. cit.,* 1982.
41. Dean Stuart Gilliland, African Traditional Religion in Transition: The Influence of African Tradition Religion In Northern Nigeria, Ph.D. thesis, Hartford, 1971; A. Yusuf, *op. cit.*, 1976.
42. Usman, *op. cit.*, 1981.
43 Al-Hajj, *op. cit.*, 1973.
44. Ubah, Islamic Culture and Nigerian Society in E. Ihekweazu (ed.) Readings in *African Humanities Traditional and Modern Culture,* Fourth Dimensions, Enugu, 1985, pp. 225–242; Mansur Ibrahim Mukhtar, The Impact of British Colonial Domination on the Social and Economic Structures of the Society of Kano, 1903–1950, 1985.
45. Ahmed Mohammed Midibbo, European Trading Comapnies and the Under-development of Northern Nigeria 1855–1939: The Case of the Royal Niger Company/United Africa Company, Ph.D. Thesis, Ahmadu Bello University, 1985; Mahadi, *op. cit.*, 1982, Bello, *op. cit.*, 1982.
46. Colonial Office report No 863 p. 552.
47. Al-Hajj, *op. cit.*, 1973.
48. Abubaar Sokoto Mohammed, The Satiru Revolt, M.A. Thesis, Ahmadu Bello Universality, 1986.
49. John Paden, *Religion and Political Culture in Kano,* University of California Press, Berkeley, 1973.
50. Mahmud ModibboTukur, The Imposition of British Colonial Domination on the Sokoto Caliphate, Borno and Neighbouring States: A Reinterpretation of Colonial Sources (2 volumes), Ph.d. Thesis, Ahmadu Bello University, 1979, Bello, *op. cit.,* 1982.
51. Zuwaqu Abugwon Bonat, The Colonial Phase of the Underdevelopment of Zaria Province, 1902–1945, M.A. Thesis, Ahmadu Bello University, 1985.
52. Tukur, *op. cit.,* 1979, Bonat, *op. cit.,* 1985.
53. Ubah, *op. cit.*, 1973, A.B. Yusuf, *op. cit.,* 1976, Bonat, *op. cit.*, 1985.
54. Ubah, *op. cit.*, 1973, p. 294.
55. A.B. Yusuf, *op. cit.*, 1979, p. 66.

56. NAK ZARPROF 1554, quoted in Bonat, *op. cit.*, 1985, *op. cit.*, 226.

57. Paden, *op. cit.*, 1973, p. 204.

58. *Ibid.*, 1973, p. 395.

59. P.K. Tibenderama, Emirs and the Spread of Western Education in Northern Nigeria, Centre for Social and Economic Research Seminar, Ahmadu Bello University, 1983.

60. Paden, *op. cit.*, 1973, p. 139.

61. Ubah, *op. cit.*, 1973.

62. Hill, *op. cit.*, 1977a.

63. Bonat, *op. cit.*, 1985, Mukhtar, *op. cit.*, 1983.

64. Polly Hill, 1972, *Ruraal Hausa: A Village and a Setting*, Cambridge University Press, Cambridge, 1972, and *Population, Prosperity and Poverty: Rural Kano 1900 and 1970*, Cambridge University Press, Cambridge, 1977b.

65. M.G. Smith, Introduction to M.F. Smith, *Baba of Karo: A Woman of the Muslim Hausa*, Faber, Yale, 1981.

66. C.K. Meek, *The Northern Tribes of Nigeria*, Oxford University Press, London, 1925.

67. Hill, *op. cit.*, 1972: 24.

68. Tukur, *op. cit.*, 1979.

69. Ubah, *op. cit.*, 1973; Tukur, *op. cit.*, 1979, Bello, *op. cit.*, 1982; Modibbo, *op. cit.*, 1985.

70. Mukhtar, *op. cit.*, 1982; Belloo, *op. cit.*, 1082; Watts, Michael, 1983, *Silent Violence: Food, Famine and the Peasantry in Northern Nigera*, University of California Press, Berkeley,1983.

71. Tukur, *op. cit.*, 1979.

72. Paden, *op. cit.*, 1973.

73. Callaway, Barbara, Women and Political Participation in Kano City, *Comparative Politics*, Vol. 19/4, 1987, pp. 379–393.

74. Pitin 1979, Imam 1987 and fieldwork survey.

75. Hill, *Op. cit*, 1972.

76. Ayesha Imam, Ideology, Women and Mass Media: A Case Study in Kano, Nigeria, AAWORD Research Report (mimeo), 1987.
77. Callaway, *op. cit.*, 1987.
78. Kano State Committee for Women's Affaris, *Report of the Kano State Community for Women Affairs.*, 1987, p. 20.
79. *Ibid.*, pp. 114-119.
80. *Ibid.*, p. 162.
81. *Ibid.*, p. 22.
82. *Ibid.*, P. 66.
83. *Ibid.*, p. 108.
84. *Ibid.*, p. 162.
85. *Ibid.*, p. 147.
86. *Ibid.*, p. 133.
87. *Ibid.*, p. 132.
88. *Ibid.*, p. 147.
89. *Ibid.*, p. 147.
90. *Ibid.*, pP. 147-149.
91. Sambo, Bashir, The Role of Muslim Women in Politics from 1992, *The Muslim Woman,* Vol 1/1, July 1988, pp. 5–9.
92. *Ibid.*
93. Abdulkadir Orire, The Role of Muslim Women in Politics from 1992, *The Muslim Woman,* Vol. 1/1, July 1988, pp. 5–9.
94. D.O.S. Noibi, The Role of Muslim Women in Politics from 1992, *The Muslim Women,* Vol. 1/1, July 1988, pp. 5–9.

# 33

# THEOLOGICAL IMPLICATION OF GENDER IN NIGERIAN SOCIETY

This study has been dicussed in two parts. The first part focuses on some theological and other variables associated with Islam in Nigeria and briefly examines the historical context of Islamisation within Nigerian society. The second part discusses specific social and economic dimensions of Islam with respect to gender relations and the manner in which traditional norms and Islamic injunctions have accommodated one another. This accommodation between religious belief and social reality has become particularly evident with the introduction of wide-ranging economic reforms as part of the implementation of Structural Adjustment Programmes (SAP) inspired by the International Monetary Fund (IMF) and the International Bank for Reconstruction and Development (World Bank).[1] The impact of SAP, particularly in terms of changes in the life-style and day-to-day activities of Muslim women in Nigeria, has recently been the focus of two surveys carried out in Zaria and Ilorin in the north of the country.[2] Some of the survey findings will be incorporated into the analysis in order to underline the type of choices that Muslim women in Nigeria are facing.

It should be noted that Nigeria is among more than 30 African states implementing structural adjustment programmes which have been adopted in the context of large-scale indebtedness to the World Bank and the International Monetary Fund. The programme itself involves the adoption of a largely monetarist policy which implies the removal of subsidies from health, education and other social services; continuous devaluation of the domestic currency, the naria; trade liberalisation and the general consolidation of a free market model as opposed to a state capitalist model of economic growth. The overall effects of this programme have, for example, included the increased decline in the purchasing power of the populace with the exception of those who actually benefit from the new dispensations given their class connections to the ruling elite or their participation in commodity imports in the context of the liberalised market. For general and specific reference to the on-going structural adjustment programmes.

## Theological Association of Gender in Nigerian Society

It is estimated that the proportion of the Muslim population in Nigeria is 42 per cent. Given the fact that current demographic estimates for the population as a whole range from 100 to 120 million, and pending more accurate demographic data from the recent census, this would indicate that there are some 50 million Muslims in the country. There is, of course, a spatial dimension to be taken into account, with a great density of Muslims in the northern parts of the country, a medium spread in the central and western parts and a relatively sparse population in the eastern region. Northern states such as Kano, Sokoto, Katsina and Borno have higher densities of Muslims that eastern states such as Anambra, Imo and Abia, for example.

Nigerian Muslims, as is the case of Muslims elsewhere, believe in the supremacy of the Qu'ran and the necessity to be fully acquainted with its contents, preferably learning it by rote. Opposed to a polytheistic spectrum of deities, Islam is fundamentally monotheistic and firmly committed to the belief in a single omnipotent deity. *Allâh*, whose messenger Mohammad is considered to be the last of the prophets. However, this belief is not necessarily shared by all Nigerian Muslims. In fact, between belief is not necessarily shared by all Nigerian Muslims.

In fact, between 1980 and 1985 there emerged in some of the urban and predominantly Muslim regions of Nigeria, a heretical sect collectively referred to as 'the Maitatsine' after its founder, Alhaji Mohammad Marwa Maitatsine, challenging this proposition and declaring that Mohammad was not the last of the prophets.[3]

Another issue of great significance to the Nigerian Muslim community is the belief in the wisdom and truth of the Hadiths, the sayings of the Prophet Mohammad, as well as the collective wisdom of the local community of Muslim scholars, the *'ulama'*. The obligations associated with the Islamic belief system and practice in the Nigerian case involve fasting from before dawn to sunset each day during Ramadan; annual pilgrimages to Mecca by those who are able to do so; observation of the five daily prayers; partial or total seclusion of women in the context of *purdah*; as well as *zakat* or alms giving to the poor.[4]

Islam in Nigeria is believed to date back to the eleventh century, and is primarily related to the activities of African clerics who initiated the process of conversion in Kanen-Borno in the north-east of the country.[5] They took up posts as advisers in some of the central Sudanic states, placing themselves in politically strategic positions, and thus helped to further the process of conversion. In the case of the western Nigeria, the generally accepted date is the fourteenth century, though its spread appears to have been relatively limited. In fact, the major diffusion of Islam in this region took place after the mid-nineteenth century.

Other developments related to the spread of Islam in Nigeria include the expansive commercial activities associated with the trans-Saharan trade routes over the centuries, such as those between Ghana, Mogador, Fez and Awdahast in the thirteenth century; Timbuctu to Mogador and Fez via Teghaza in the thirteenth, fourteenth, and fifteenth centuries; Timbuctu to Tunis and Tripoli via Agades, Ghat and Ghadames as well as Bornu to Tripoli via Bilma and Murzuk in the seventeenth and nineteenth centuries.[6]

In short, Islam in Nigeria in particular, and West Africa in general, cannot be historically conceived outside the context of the extensive trans-Saharan trade which from its inception in circa 1000 B.C.E. facilitated extensive interaction within the West African region and between West and North Africa. In the era before Islam, such contacts evolved in the context of intra-regional and inter-regional specialisation and a network of caravan traders. With the emergence of Islam in Nigeria in the eleventh century there would have been identifiable innovations such as the use of Arabic as a lingua franca; an infrastructure of residential quarters and food centers for itinerant Muslim traders and their interpreters; a well-organised network of caravans; accounting and record-keeping procedures; and credit and brokerage facilities, all of which would help to consolidate and strengthen the significance of Islam in the region.

The *hajj* (the annual pilgrimage to Mecca) also helped to consolidate local ties amongst Muslims and to integrate Nigerian Muslims even further into the *umma* (community) of Islam, a process which continues into the contemporary era. In the 1970s, Nigeria had the second largest annual contingent to Mecca after Indonesia, though during the last decade the number of pilgrims has been declining drastically due to the overall economic recession and the subsequent debt crisis.[7] Several explanations have been given for the rapid and extensive spread of Islam in the West African region as a whole, among them the fact that most Muslim 'missionaries' were indigenous Africans; the relatively easy mode of conversion; Islamic accommodation of a largely polygynous indigenous martial system; and the perception of exemplary conduct in role models such as Usuman dan Fodio, Nana Asma'u, Ahmadu Bello and others.[8] In the contemporary era the rate of conversion to Islam has not apparently slowed down.

## Implications of Theological Principles in Gender Relations

In the following discussion, the implications of some of these theological principles for the treatment and condition of women as it relates to marriage, divorce, seclusion and inheritance will be examined. The analysis will simultaneously incorporate some insight into the effects of structural adjustment on women's lives in contemporary Nigeria.

***Marriage***: Islam has had specific implications for traditional martial relations and marriage patterns in Nigerian society. Pre-Islamic Nigerians were generally polygynous in the context of a regulated system of household production and reproduction.[9] Islam reduced the numerical option to four wives and introduced a few new rules to the martial game.[10] Since Qu'ranic injunctions call for equitable treatment of all wives, it became a social offence for husbands to be accused of discrimination.

By contrast, in the pre-Islamic worldview and philosophy in Nigeria, discrimination between wives was sanctioned and even encouraged. A clear hierarchy of wives based on seniority and age was the norm, a pattern which was not unrelated to the division of labour in the household, whereby junior wives performed more menial duties.[11] This is not to deny the fact that the pre-Islamic custom of a hierarchy based on the seniority of wives in polygynous marriages has persisted in some areas. However, this pattern is not generally socially sanctioned and is held to be counter to Islamic prescriptions favouring equality among wives. Moreover, women who are informed of their rights are, at least theoretically, in a position to negotiate a more favourable status for themselves.

In the Zaria survey referred to earlier, 90 per cent of the women had married under the age of 15, a trend which appears to be the norm in a number of Islamic communities in Nigeria.[12] Variables such as social status and class origin are relevant in the overall appraisal of martial trends, and most of the respondents were lower middle class. Their class origin is to some extent reflected in their economic activities, which ranged from petty trade to farming, i.e. sectors where the impact of SAP has tended to be particularly unfavourable to women and their sources of livelihood. Attempts have been made to legislate against the practice of early marriage within the last decade, largely as a result of activist organisations such as Women In Nigeria and in some cases protest on the part of young girls against such marriages.[13]

It is doubtful, however, whether the on-going SAP and related state policies undermine the practice of early marriage given the real or imagined economic benefits this may hold for parents in terms of absolving them from the need to support their daughters. There is also increased 'feminisation of poverty' whereby girls and women may find themselves increasingly dependent and impoverished in the context of subsidy removal on health, education and food items—a trend which also appears to encourage early marriage.[14]

However, the Ilorin survey suggests a possible countervailing force reflected in the growing caution on the part of males of marriageable age vis-à-vis the issue of starting a family given the economic crisis. Respondents in this survey pointed to a decline in the level of festivities accompanying marriage ceremonies. From the earlier practice whereby festivities spanned a seven-day period, there was now a noticeable reduction to five days and less. Moreover, there seems to be an overall decline in the number of marriages and even an upswing in the incidence of monogamy.

There were more cases of simultaneous marriages of daughters and sons in order to reduce cost. One may also assume that economic conditions have been having a perceptible impact on the *mahr* (bride-price) which women are legally entitled to under Islam. However, the data with respect to reproductive behaviour and the size of family units were inconclusive, with evidence for the retention of large families in some cases, and reduced family size in others.

***Divorce***: While Muslim males in Nigeria are not obliged to state the reasons for divorce, women are expected to do so, but only within the context of the following parameters; a women may sue for divorce should the husband fail to provide for the economic needs of the family, or decides to change his religion, or wrongly accuses her of adultery. If the husband proves to be impotent or, in the case of early marriage, she has become disillusioned with the marriage after attaining puberty, she is also entitled to file for divorce.[15]

In spite of this trend, it was noted that most of the respondents in the Zaria survey were in stable marriages of ten years or more, and there seemed to be an overall low divorce rate. By contrast, in the case of Ilorin, most of the women indicated an increase in the rate of divorce. This supports an earlier finding of Barkow, which found that around 50 percent of the Muslim women in study were divorced.[16]

The Zaria trend notwithstanding—and further research in needed to explain these apparently contradictory findings—there generally seems to be a noticeable ease by which Muslim women in Nigeria move in and out of marriage. Equally important, divorce is generally not associated with social stigma as in pre-Islamic times, and divorced women can and are expected to remarry. Casual observation suggests that the Ilorin case cited is not unique in terms of the region as a whole.

***Seclusion***: The issue of female sexuality is generally associated with the questions of male-female interaction and female seclusion. *Purdah*, identified as one of the major pillars of male patriarchy, exhibits three variations in the Nigerian case: complete seclusion, partial seclusion and voluntary 'seclusion of the heart'.[17] In the latter case, seclusion is symbolic and not based on physical segregation. This situation appears to have evolved as a compromise sanctioning the employment of educated elite women in the civil service and other forms of public activities.

Associated with the two other forms of seclusion is a degree of withdrawal from public view, which may be either partial or total—as in the case of the wives of traditional rulers and members of the '*ulama*' who trend to serve as role models. As elsewhere in sex-segregated societies, in reality the process of seclusion is largely class-based. Thus, peasant or working-class males in particular can generally ill afford the luxury of non-working wives. A recent study focusing on Kaduna, Bauchi and Kano (with a large proportion of Muslims among their populations), showed that 65 per cent of women in these areas were active in farming and livestock rearing, marketing of grain, spinning, weaving, cooking of fast food as well as in general trade.[18]

The growing force of the Tijaniyya brotherhood is important in this context for, unlike the Qadriyya, it does not consider seclusion to be imperative. The Tijaniyya, founded by Abu al-Abbas Ahmad al-Tijani in North Africa during the second half of the eighteenth century, found adherents in Nigeria following the activities of the Senegalese cleric Al Hajj Tall in the nineteenth century.[19] It remains one of the most dominant of the Sufi orders in Nigeria, and may be contrasted with the Qadriyya brotherhood, which has its roots in twelfth century Baghdad where it was founded by Abdel Qadir al-Jilani.

They differ from one another in terms of a number of basic issues. For example, unlike the Tijaniyya brotherhood, the Qadriyya is opposed to the appointment of women in positions of leadership and adheres overall to a stricter separation in its ascription of gender roles. The brotherhoods also diverge in terms of praying positions and in their attitudes towards mysticism. However, association with one or the other brotherhood and the concomitant attitudes towards seclusion are also influenced by other variables; such as proximity to urban centers, class origin and educational level.

The recent surveys in Zaria and Ilorin suggest some of the effects which economic conditions can be presumed to be having on the observation of moral imperatives dictated by the brotherhoods. Thus, there is a trend whereby women traditionally associated with *purdah* have been abandoning the custom. Some respondents pointed to the increasing participation of women farming, with effect that the differentiation between those adhering to *purdah* and those outside of it are becoming more blurred. In the words of one informant: 'Women come out of *purdah* and mix freely with men in the market because they are looking for money.'

Another informant emphasised that in her area she could hardly tell the difference between women who were traditionally in *purdah* and those who were not. One women specified that economic difficulties have caused a lot of women to come out of *purdah* and engage in different occupations, whilst another pointed out that many women who used to be secluded were now engaged in framework. For yet another respondent, it was clear that a lot of women who were formerly in total seclusion were coming out 'to find something to do'. An older respondent stressed that times were such that 'she who waited for her husband to provide sustenance would suffer.' In the words of another, 'women in purdah have to fend for themselves and not depend on their husbands.'

It would seem therefore that a large percentage of these women outside of the elite who had until recently remained in either partial or total seclusion are now modifying their behavioural patterns to accommodate the changing economic realities affecting their lives. Those who engaged in the so-called 'silent trade' (i.e. employing another person to carry out public trading activities for them) could no longer do so successfully. They now found themselves unable to compete in the market from a position of seclusion given the increased competition from petty traders 'on the beat' hawking their goods.

This trend must also be viewed within the context of rising religious fundamentalism in parts of northern Nigeria, where edicts have been issued prohibiting younger women on moral grounds from engaging in house-to-house trade and the marketing of household products. Pittin has pointed out that there are at present various indications of the fundamentalist offensive, including specific edicts on dress for women, the trend towards the boarding of female students and other forms of physical segregation, as well as the increased emphasis on the part of the state on women's family roles. She argues that these trends must be seen in the context of emerging contradictions between rhetoric and practice and within and between levels of government.[20] One may add to this the proposition that economic imperatives and the fundamentally harsh economic variables associated with SAP, in themselves constitute significant vehicles for undermining the fundamentalist call for total seclusion and sex-segregated labour.

All the women interviewed observed that there was a marked increase in the cost of providing meals for the family. Increases ranged from 300 per cent to 1,000 per cent. Ilorin interviewees specified that items such as eggs, bread and rice were being dropped from their daily diet. They also claimed that their main diet consisted of *amala* and *gari* (yam and cassava derived food products), and meat was not eaten as frequently as before. When asked about the household budget, they claimed that they were operating on comparatively smaller allowances, since in some cases they received the same sum as before or even less.

It is in the context of these economic difficulties that modifications have been taking place in terms of what some believe is a prime pillar of Islam, namely the principle of seclusion. Of course, as pointed out by one respondent, economic difficulties have been affecting women of other religious affiliation as well. Given the nature of class relations in Nigeria both historically and at present,[21] it is not surprising that, in the words of some of the women interviewed, 'wealthy women are not suffering as much.' Most interviewees reflected a clear recognition of status and class differentiation within Nigerian society, and its implications for women's economic roles.

Many respondents were engaged in petty trade. Some sold *dawa da wake* (a processed cereal), palm oil, or fast food such as *akara* or *kosai* (fried pastry made from beans), *moi moi* (another bean-based condiment prepared by steaming), or consumer products such as detergent, kerosene, sugar or salt. Some admitted to having made as many as five product changes in recent times due to the fact that some goods became uneconomical for resale almost overnight with the intense price fluctuations in the market. Between 1984 and 1990, the introduction of SAP and other economic changes caused large price increases. For example, in 1984 a plastic kettle cost 1–1.5 naira and in 1990 it cost 10 naira. In the same period, the cost of a female head cover rose from between 3 and 5 naira to 40 naira; a rosary from 1 to 4 naria; cotton prayer mats from 13 to 80 naira.

A few of the women were involved in tailoring, the making of hats or occasional farm labour. Muslim informants from both Ilorin and Zaria attested to an increase in petty trading in their respective communities with the implementation of SAP, underlining the reality that it is the informal sector in particular which provides largely unskilled women with employment opportunities. The devaluation of the local currency seems also to have brought about a shift in trading patterns. Kano in the north has become an important wholesale trading centre and Saudi Arabia has been attracting a sizeable percentage of local merchants, which implies a trend away from western Europe in particular (This trade network is not unrelated to the annual *hajj* (pilgrimage) to Mecca). The implication of these shifting patterns for women's role in petty trading remains to be seen.

***Inheritance*** : Pre-Islamic Nigerian society generally accorded women usufruct rights to land, but actual control remained exclusively in male hands. The arrival of Islam posed a threat to the traditional patterns of male land ownership by way of introducing new inheritance rights since, according to Islamic law, wives and daughters are entitled to a share in the estate of the deceased male kin. There are four Sunni Muslim schools of jurisprudence, Maliki, Shafi'i, Hanbali and Hanafi; Shi'a Muslims have their own school. Where Maliki law applies (as is the case among Nigerian Muslims), 50 per cent reverts to the daughter and 25 per cent to the widow.

This represents a perceptible difference compared with the pre-Islamic tradition whereby inheritance was exclusively patrilineal, and where the eldest brother of the deceased inherited everything in areas such as Zaria, Tivland and Abuja, for example. Historically, in the northeast, the eldest sons and younger brothers were the legal inheritors. However, there were areas of divergence such as in the Jos Plateau area in the Middle Belt region, where at the death of her father a daughter could, if she had no brothers, take the corpse to claim all his land which then became the property of her husband and sons.[22] There are also cases in the Central Nigerian region where the property of a deceased male reverted to males from adjacent villages in cases where there were no male inheritors on the father's line.

Thus Islamic law introduced new codes of conduct and legal obligations into aspects of the pre-existing patterns of inheritance though there have inevitably been cases of violation. For example, the Report of the Land Investigation Commission which held public hearings in Kaduna in 1979, includes cases of complaints by women about the misappropriation of their inherited farmland. It has also been documented that traditional rulers, the courts as well as close relatives often connived to deprive women of their inheritance rights.[23] None the less, at least in conceptual terms, women have generally benefited from new possibilities in terms of legal rights according to Islamic law.

Diop[24] and more recently Amadiume[25] have argued the case for a matriarchal foundation for African indigenous societies, proposing that patriarchal elements were later impositions on the older matriarchal system. Amadiume further argues that there was a central female role in production, reproduction, property and status in parts of eastern Nigeria, a trend which she believes might be applicable to other parts of the continent.

It would seem though that the collective testimony of oral tradition as reflected in anthropological accounts, court records, interviews and traditional legal systems, contradicts this view in the case of western, central and northern Nigeria in particular. However, it may be that the power of patriarchy in the formation of existing perceptions of societal organisation has been overestimated, and that researchers have generally failed to discern underlying matriarchal tendencies and other indications of female power.[26]

Though hard-core evidence to support the existence of widespread matriarchal elements in various African societies including Nigeria remain elusive, one should not dismiss the research carried out on this issue. But as Amadiume herself admits, additional investigations need to be carried out to substantiate the hypothesis. Thus, the spread of Islam may well have served to reactivate ancient patterns of empowerment which, for reasons as yet obscure, became submerged with the spread of the patriarchal social system.

## Conclusion

Islam gave but it also took away. On the negative side it may be noted that, with the introduction of partial or total seclusion, there has been a relative loss of mobility and independence for some sectors of the female population, in particular those of high social status. This would also be the case with adherents of the Qadriyya brotherhood which, in contrast to the followers of the Tijaniyya inspired sect, restricts women's physical mobility and participation in public life.

Islamic injunctions as laid down in *the Qur'ân* and the *Hadith* are basically patriarchal in orientation. Muslim converts therefore became subjected to new forms of patriarchal reforms, which reinforced women's subordination and thus curtailed the relative freedom of movement they generally enjoyed during pre-Islamic times. Relative economic independence has in some cases been replaced by dependence and tutelage. Nevertheless, the gains in terms of inheritance rights have been quite significant, as has been the increased security with respect to land tenure rights.

In fact, by all accounts, the assurance of an inherited share as stipulated in the Islamic legal code—however unequal in comparison to men—has apparently been encouraging conversion among some sections of the non-Muslim female population in Nigeria. It would also seem that women have generally gained respectability in the event of divorce and a breakdown of martial relations, in contrast with the pre-existing situation where divorce was socially stigmatised.

Though women generally enjoy less flexibility than men in the initiation of divorce, they are nevertheless not hindered and even encouraged to remarry. The point to be made, therefore, is that Islamisation in Nigeria should be seen neither as the introduction of light in an area of darkness nor as a retrogressive force in absolute terms. The process has in fact been a chequered one and thus merits a balance and sober evaluation.

The analysis of some impacts of the structural adjustment programme and its concomitant economic implications for Nigerian Muslim women, further illustrates the reality that the influence of Islam has and continues to be multi-faceted. Economic imperatives, in particular the subjection of non-elite women to the harsh realities of changing market forces have induced subtle and less subtle changes in attitudes towards female seclusion and economic activities outside the home. It remains to be seen what effect these changes may have for male-female gender relations, and whether the perceptibly increasing feminisation of poverty will lead to further erosion of the level of relative female autonomy which some female segments—such as petty traders—have tended to enjoy.

G. THOMAS-EMEAGWALI

## REFERENCES

1. B. Onimode (ed.), *The IMF, the World Bank and the African Debt*, London: IFAA/Zed Books, 1989.
2. Questionnaries were administered on my behalf by R.O. Lasisi, Department of History, University of Ilorin, and Nurudeen Abubakar, Centre for Nigerian Cultural Studies, Ahmadu Bello University, Zaria between December 1990 and Feburary 1991. Most of the women involved in the survey were working class and lower middle class.
3. P. Clarke and I. Linden, *Islam in Modern Nigeria: A Study of a Muslim Community in a Post-independence State, 1960–83*, Mainz: Grunewald, 1984.
4. M. Hiskett, *The Development of Islam in West Africa*, London and New York: Longman, 1984; J.S. Trimingham, *Islam in West Africa*, Oxford: Clarendon Press, 1962.
5. Clarke and Linden, *op. cit.*, 1984; A. Kani, *The Intellectual Origins of the Sokoto Jihad, Iman*, Nigeria, 1985.
6. N. Levtzoin, *Rural and Urban Islam in West Africa*, Boulder: Lynne Reiner, 1987.
7. Clarke and Linden, *op. cit.*, 1984.

8. J. Boyd, The *Caliph's Sister*, London: Frank Cass, 1989; E. Isichei, *A History of West Africa*, London New York: Longman, 1977; Ahmadu Bello Paden, *Sardauna of Sokoto*, London: Hodder and Stoughton, 1986.
9. Women in Nigeria, *The WIN Document*, Zaria, 1985.
10. A. Ogunbiyi, 'The Position of Muslim Women' as stated by Uthman B. Fudi, *Journal of West African Studies*, Ife University, 1969; Pittin, 1979).
11. Ajayi and Ikara, 1985; Falola, 1986.
12. R. Pittin, Marriage and Alternative Strategies: Career Patterns of Hausa Women in Katsina City, Ph.D. thesis, University of London, 1979; WIN, *op. cit.*, 1985.
14. G. Thomas-Emeagwali, 'Development at Risk', *Woodstock Road Editorial*, St Antony's College, Oxford, no. 7, 1991.
15. J. Schacht, 'Islam in Northern Nigeria', *Studia Islamica*, Vol. VIII, 1957.
16. J. Barkow, 'Hausa Women and Islam,' *Canadian Journal of African Studies*, Vol. VI., 1971.
17. H. Abdullah-Olukoshi, 'Women in Islamic Societies in the Kano Setting', mimeo, University of Hull, 1990.
18. WIN, *op. cit.*, 1985.
19. Isichei, *op. cit.*, 1977.
20. R. Pittin, 'Selective Educational Issues in Gender, Class and Ideology in Northern Nigeria', *Review of African Political Economy*, no. 48, 1990, p. 23.
21. G. Thomas- Emeagwali, 'Women in Pre-colonial Nigerian Economy', paper presented at the Annual Conference of the African Studies Association, Chicago, 1989.
22. *Ibid.*
23. N. Perchonock, "Double Oppression" in S. Bappa et al. *Women in Nigeria Today*, London: Zed Books, 1985.
24. C.A. Diop, The *Cultural Unity of Black Africa*, London: Karnak, 1989.
25. I. Amadiume, *African Matriarchal Foundations: The Igbo Case*, London: Karnak, 1987.
26. *Ibid.*

# 34

# WOMEN AND FUNDAMENTALISM

As a Muslim Hausa feminist from Nigeria the form of fundamentalism that I have had most direct experience of and with its Muslim fundamentalism in Northern Nigeria. However, it should be made clear from the outset that fundamentalism, as I use the term here, is not peculiar to Islam. The Gush Eminim in Israel, the Baharatiya Janata Party (radical Hindus) and militant Sikhs in India, the Christian Right in the USA (like the Oregon Citizen's Alliance) are all fundamentalist. Fundamentalism then are widely varied in form and appear in many place.

*So what is fundamentalism?*

Fundamentalism is often defined as the 'strict maintenance of traditional, orthodox religious beliefs, such as the inherently of scripture and literal acceptance of the creeds'. However, it must be noted that there is no homogeneity within religions. The rubric of Christianity, for example, includes the Roman Catholic Church (as defined from the Vatican), the Pentacostal Churches, and Methodism. Even within one strand of religion there is no acceptance of any one 'strict adherence to the text'. There are always internal contractions and even the most 'fundamentalist' of groups exercise selectivity.

Furthermore fundamentalism can be a very creative response to contemporary circumstances, i.e., many fundamentalists are not fossilised relics, traditionalists clinging to an imagined past in stubborn and irrational resistance to chaining circumstances—the very epitome of reaction.

*Common Features of Fundamentalism*

Although there is no homogeneity in religions, fundamentalism share many characteristics. First, each fundamentalist group claims that theirs is the only true creed based on divine law. And hence fundamentalists are therefore threatened by pluralism. Second, they claim the revival of tradition or a better past vis-a-vis the corrupt present. This appeal is simultaneously a claim to legitimacy and also doing. It obscure the process of invention (re-ordering and construction of representations). It also obscures, and even seeks to reveal the material interests or socio-economic groupings of those advocating fundamentalists discourses, forcing the ideological conflict to take place on their chosen terrain and within the terms of their discourse.

Third, at the heart of fundamentalists are normative prescriptions of gender role and relations between women and men—the ordering, organisation and prescription of gender and sexualities (based on propositions regarding the essential differences between women and men).

More specifically these prescriptions tend to be control of women and their sexuality and the regulation of interaction between the sexes.

Finally, they seek power and use political means to impose their understanding of the world on 'their' communities and on others.

*Why the Recent Rise of Fundamentalism?*

The recent rise in the past decade of the membership and power of organized fundamentalist groups are a response to crisis of modernity—of social orders based on belief on principles of enlightenment, rationality, progress—and particularly of the failures for most people of the promises of capitalism, communism, development, modernisation, nationalism. In Nigeria, for instance, the deteriorating health status, increase in unemployment, food shortages, inflation, violence, politics as zero-sum gain of elites, the need to wield all possible network as matter of survival, state violence (as in the forced removal of the Maroko settlement), or response to the virtually annual anti-structural Adjustment Programme (SAP) demonstrations go with a general sense of despair and crisis. And the rise in organised fundamentalist religious groups the Muslim Maitatsine group or Christian Pentacostalism, for instance—coincides with this period of crisis exacerbated since the institution of SAP.

In this context, religion is solace and solution, stability and identity. The fundamentalist groups offer freedom from uncertainty and insecurity, because their worldview is allegedly backed by divine law. Unchangeable and fixed. But they also appeal to the sapped generation in other ways: Cultural identity, a means of political mobilisation, as well as materially (education, health clinics, food, training, network re jobs and business, scholarship, loans all organised through the groups).

*Fundamentalism as anti-Western, anti-corruption, force?*

For some, Muslim radicalism is 'a progressive force, rallying the oppressed against injustice and repression', as well as providing a non western cultural identity. Others point to the ability of religious groups to make 'apolitical critiques of state, where state violence and repression versus those who openly challenge for institutional politics (through their opposition to corruption of office holders and emphasis on the need for the moral polity of state).

However, this sanguine view of fundamentalist groups should be treated with some reserve, if not scepticism.

Analysis of the international links between and among fundamentalist movements shows that they ally consistently with right wing politics (e.g., the US Christian evangelism in Africa, the influence of the Iran revolution and/or Saudi Arabia, on groups in West Africa and in South Asia).

Second, internally there is often collusion of the state with fundamentalism groups in order to maintain state power—both where the particular fundamentalists groups are part of the majority religion (e.g, Muslim in Algeria, Egypt and Nigeria), and where they are part of a minority (e.g, Muslims in Britain or India—where there is tolerance of inegalitarian philosophies as long as they are seen as applying only to a religious/ethnic minority itself is seen as homogenous groups). In doing, so the state uses the existence of fundamentalist groups to deny power and voice to other organized groups and interests (especially those on the left). Furthermore, very often specifically women's interests are sacrificed, the state itself being patriarchal and concerned with domesticity and control of women's sexuality—as in Iran and Sudan where women are being forced back into the domestic realm through loss of their jobs, as well as state sanctioned harassment and violence over the way they may choose to dress.

Thus, it is important to consider the links of religious groups with non-specifically religious struggles, their sense of community with other oppressed categories, who are their allies, what their consideration of class, imperialism etc. is, before categorising them as progressive or reactionary. One extremely important criteria must also be their level of authoritarianism and tolerance of dissent or differences of opinion in both their own group and other groups. This process is important because the adoption of 'fundamentalism' (defined here as taking on fundamentals of religion but also alleging that with critique of capitalist exploitation and imperialism) in the context in which the West in making a spectre of third world/Muslim fundamentalism (equated with any opposition to the West and with terrorism) is also pushing practising believers into the politically fundamentalist right wing camp because of their chosen identity as Muslim.

*Fundamentalism and Women*

All fundamentalism formally preach submission of women to men, focusing on the 'natural differences' between women and men. Women are central to fundamentalist projects (as with world cosmologies generally)—as markets for community identity, as carriers and transmitters of culture (both through reproduction and through the socialising work they do with children). Hence there is a focus on the importance of women's roles in the patriarchal family and a fear that their desertion of it would lead to social disaster.

This position has several consequences for women. Women's aspirations and demands for autonomy (defined as traditionally not within culture of groups concerned) are very frequently legitimised. The non-domestic aspects of women's lives tend to be ignored through a non-recognition of women's need regarding income earning and their contribution to livelihood provision. The concern in fundamentalist politics with gender relations has always been in the direction of establishing or re-establishing ideological constraints and men's control over women.

Fundamentalists insist on stricter control of women's movements and dress, a focus on the role of women as mother/wife, a containment of sexuality. Women in Christian' Malawi and Islamic' Sudan are forced to abide by state imposed dress codes. Algerian women lost the right to marry in their own right and to legal custody of their children, while men gained the right to vote in their wives' names. Young women in northern Nigeria get abducted by gangs of young men for not staying within their homes. Women in Iran and Sudan have lost their jobs. Women in India have lost rights to maintenance after divorce. Abortion rights are being challenged and lost in the USA. The list goes on.

And yet it is apparently a paradox that women can and do collude in fundamentalist groups and find comfort, security and even a sense of empowerment also. To explain this it must be recognised that religious beliefs are not simply imposed but generated and developed in the process of appropriation and reconstruction of social and personal existence. It is necessary to look at the ways in which religious beliefs are set to work by their adherents to make sense of and empower themselves within the deteriorating social, economic and political circumstances in which they live. Importantly one must take account of the absence or repression of other social basis from which to resist.

Fundamentalist groups can provide security in having at total way of life set out, giving a focus for identity and relief or empowerment therein, as well as a welcome value placed on much of women's unrecognised labour in the domestic realm. In addition, women have sometimes been able to use fundamentalist religious discourses for their own interests. These purposes include: subverting religious discourses for their own purposes—such as access to work, education, control of sexuality, rights as a person; protesting sexual harassments and men's/husbands' infidelities, and against the representation of women as witches/whores; gaining some access to an area of not-too-threatening challenge for activity and personal accomplishment (especially for middle class women); developing a sense of community, caring, sharing (especially among women with the naturalisation of gender division of labour) and the promotion of bonding between women.

Nonetheless, the overall effect of fundamentalist group policies has been and continue to be detrimental to women. The list of rights lost and numbers of women disempowered in various ways far outweights the lists of rights gained and number of women who have benefited. Furthermore, the benefits that have been gained have been, by definition, limited and constrained within a broader framework that constructs women as minors and subordinates. And because these frameworks are allegedly to be immutable and divinely ordained, there is little space to challenge them. Furthermore, the general tendency of fundamentalist groups to authoritarianism and control of their followers (and especially as the control of women plays a key role in the constitution of these new orthodoxies) makes it very difficult for either women or men to fight them from within. The treatment of 'heretics' and non-believers (which includes expulsion, ostracism, and physical violence or the threat of it), by fundamentalist groups threatens any who might wish to engage in independence thought or struggle. Thus in the long run, to accept the immediate (even if limited) benefits of fundamentalist groups, even in the hope of accruing gains for a later struggle, is a dangerous and ultimately self-defeating course for women.

# 35

# WIFEISM AND ACTIVISM IN THE NIGERIAN WOMEN'S MOVEMENT

The Nigerian population is composed of more than three hundred distinct ethnic groups, which were brought together under British colonial rule in 1914. Long-standing ethnic and religious rivalries, reinforced by the British, remain a dominant feature of Nigerian political and social life. In general, the north is dominated by the Muslim Hausa and Fulani; the southeast, by the predominantly Christian Igbo and the southwest, by the Yoruba, who include both Christians and Muslims. Since independence in 1960, competition for control of the nation's economic and political resources has led to brief efforts at democracy interrupted by prolonged periods of military rule. Most recently, the military government spent years proclaiming its commitment to a return to civil rule. After numerous delays, presidential elections were finally held in June 1993. When the government's candidate appeared to lose, the results were promptly cancelled.

The government influences every sector of Nigerian life through layers of administrative structures that reach far into rural areas. Despite increasing urbanisation, approximately 70 percent of the population still live in rural areas, where they engage largely in agriculture and small-scale economic activities. Agriculture was traditionally the core of the Nigerian economy, a situation that dramatically changed with the discovery of oil in the 1970s. This vast oil wealth has brought some infrastructure and industry to Nigeria.

However, the country's enormous economic potential has remained largely unrealised. Much of the country's oil revenue has been concentrated among a small elite or lost to poor economic planning and corruption. Few, if any, of the benefits have reached the majority of Nigerians. These problems, combined with the severe global recession of the 1980s, led the government to adopt a mandated structural adjustment program (SAP) to increase foreign exchange earnings to service the country's foreign debt. This has dramatically curtailed funding for social programs and has had severe effects on the standard of living of Nigerians at all levels.

In many areas, the brunt of these economic problems have been felt most acutely by women as few women are steadily employed in the formal economy. In urban areas, women's work is concentrated in the informal sector, especially in food production and sale and in trading. In rural areas, women generally work in food crop agriculture, food processing, pett trading, and a host of time-consuming, unremunerated household tasks. Most household, especially those in rural areas are large and multigenerational; approximately 40 percent of Nigerian marriages are polygynous and the total fertility rate, while declining, still averages more than six births per women.[1] This rate reflects prevailing attitudes, which value large families and base women's status primarily on their roles as wives and mothers, especially of male children.

These familial roles were traditionally the basis on which Nigerian women organized within their villages and communities around activities such as circumcision, childbirth, and marriage rites. The groups organized around these activities as well as savings societies and work groups formed the basis of women's rich associational history in precolonial times. Women were also active in organisations established to protect their communities. These associations unquestionably provided women with necessary support and camaraderie. However, in keeping with the values that underlay 'tradition' and religion, these activities also tended to reinforce and reproduce the structures of patriarchy through which women were subordinated.

During the British colonial period, women continued to address their traditional socioeconomic and political concerns, while also protesting against the economic and political policies of the colonial government. Two well-known examples of women's activism are the Aba women's riot of 1929 and the Egba women's protest of 1947. In both cases, women organized and took to the streets to protest the colonial administration's most egregious taxation policies and those prohibiting assembly. Out of these anticolonial struggles emerged the first women's association that crossed ethnic, religious, and class barriers. The National Women's Union was started in 1947 by Funmilayo Ransome-Kuti, a dynamic leader who organized the Egba women's protest.[2]

**Women's Emancipation and Empowerment**

In contemporary Nigeria there is at least some general level of national awareness of the importance of women's roles in development. A host of women's organisations operate at the national and/or at the grassroots community level. Of necessity, these groups are primarily concerned with conventional issues of livelihood and welfare. However, questions of women's emancipation and empowerment are also debated, and women's organisations are posing significant challenges to patriarchal structures.

Concomitant with the onset of the ongoing Nigerian economic crisis, since the 1980s rural and urban Nigeria women—sometimes joined by men—have increasingly organized to empower women and help them devise strategies to combat the effect of the economic crisis. These organisations have tackled not just the difficulties posed by the relics of traditional cultural practices but also newer problems caused by the dynamics of 'modernisation'. Generally, rural women's groups identified with traditional activities such as initiation rites have declined in number and significance as cultural values and practices have changed.

Presently, the majority of women's organisations that have emerged to champion the rights of women and to advance gender consciousness in society are located in the principal urban centres. In Nigeria, there is general agreement that there is a women's movement comparable to other social movements with a visible presence around the county. However, sociologist Mere Kisekka in substantially right in stating that:

> "it cannot however, be accurately inferred that there is a women's movement in the country which is vociferously engaged in the exposure and challenge of gender inequality in most of its ramifications. Rather, most women 's associations have striven to operate cautiously within traditional gender boundaries articulating the theory of complementary rather than competitive roles in gender relations."[3]

Only a few activists take the view that the objectives of the women's movement are similar to those of labour, human rights, and student groups, which clamor for restructuring society. Most see the objectives of women's groups as different:

> "The Nigerian women's movement is an unarmed movement. It is non-confrontation. It is a movement for the progressive upliftment of women for motherhood, nationhood and development"[4].

Very few women leaders accept that the movement is feminist in orientation. Those objecting to the feminist label view it as Western terminology that should not be employed in Africa, as captured in the words of a woman lawyer:

> "When African women demand equality, we are only asking for our rights not to be tampered with, and the removal of laws that oppress and dehumanize women. We are not asking for equality with our husbands. We accept them as the bosses and heads of the family."[5]

The concept of feminism should thus be contextualised within each society where it applies. Yet in a certain sense, the Nigerian women's movement can be considered feminist in orientation because it is attempting to transform gender relations in society. To buttress this point, a leader of the group women in Nigeria asks:

> "What is Western feminism anyway? African men see nothing wrong in their relationship with Western governments and institutions. Why? Because they feel threatened by the prospect of feminism."[6]

The women's movement is evolving as women build coalitions. Examples of these are the establishment of the Community Development Association by grassroots women's groups, the formation of the National Task Force on Vesico-Vaginal Fistulae (VVF),[7] and the formation of the Nigeria National Safe Motherhood Movement by women's health groups.

The notion that women are bound together by a common history of oppression and a common struggle to achieve liberation does hold true in Nigeria. There are secondary divisions in any social movement that create obstacles for the realisation of group objectives, even within a single-sex movement like the women's movement.[8] In Nigeria these cleavages are based on age, religion, marital status, ethnic origin, educational level, and social class. Tensions and conflicts within the women's movement have been based in part on differences over strategy and policy and in part on leadership struggles. The Nigerian movement cannot be faulted for not being a homogenous organized body. Rather, it consists of several groups, all of which are arguing in different, and at times conflicting, ways about matters affecting women based on differing perceptions of women's interests.

Throughout Nigerian history, numerous individual women have gained national prominence in their own right. It is also the case that wives of men in certain occupations, have had ceremonial responsibilities. The roles of politicians' wives have recently been institutionalised in a manner that has far-reaching implications for an autonomous, genuine women's agenda oriented toward full emancipation. The role of the Nigerian state in relation to the women's movement can be examined in the expression of this peculiar phenomenon of 'wifeism' in women's affairs. In this chapter I examine the emergence of wifeism and the bureaucratisation of women's concerns in Nigeria through state involvement, especially since the early 1980s. I pay particular attention to the relations between state-sponsored women's programs and autonomous groups in the women's movement. Finally, I explore the implications all these issues have for developing and moving forward a truly emancipatory feminist agenda in Nigeria.

**Bureaucratisation of Women's Issues**

As part of the United National decade for Women (1975-1985), all member governments were encouraged to establish appropriate national machinery to aid women's integration into development. Nigeria's response led to the increasing bureaucratisation of women's issues. The National Committee on Women and Development (NCWD) was established within the federal Ministry of Social Development, Youth, and Sports in 1982. The NCWD was set up to liaise between women's nongovernmental organisations (NGOs) and the government to coordinate all activities relating to women, to advise the government on women's issues, and to design programs to facilitate women's integration into the development process.[9] The NCWD's activities were fairly traditional, such as training in home economics, arts and crafts, health and personal hygiene, literacy, and income-generating activities. The committee's composition reflected an urban, upper-class bias; although 90 percent of Nigeria's female population work in the agricultural or informal sectors of the economy, there was no one to represent their interests on the NCWD's twelve-member board.

After reverting to military rule in the 1980s, Nigeria began for the first time since independence to pay specific policy attention to women's issues at the highest level of state power, the presidency. This interest in women can be understood in the context of the overall objectives of the SAP. One of the SAP's provisions was to facilitate opening up the rural areas by providing incentives to male farmers to increase productivity and generate higher monetary income. This was central to the government's export promotion drive aimed at boosting foreign exchange earnings for debt servicing and repayment.

To involve women fully in development, and to counter the negative effects of these export promotion policies on rural families, the government initiated the Better Life for Rural Women Programme (BLP) in 1987, launched as an arm of the Directorate of Food, Roads, and Rural Infrastructure. This programme ushered in a new era in the development of the women's agenda in Nigeria. It heralded the twin processes of direct intervention by the state in the formation and funding of women' organisations and the systematic appointment of wives of high-ranking government officials as leaders of these organisations. I refer to these phenomena as state pseudo-feminism. By introducing the BLP, the Nigerian government brought rural women, long excluded from the capitalist nexus, directly into the capitalist arena.[10] While the BLP first targeted only rural women, eventually all rural inhabitants were included in order to encourage men to support the program.

Mrs. Maryam Babangida, wife of the then military president, Ibrahim Babangida, was the founder and national coordinator of the BLP, which she came to personify. In this capacity, she was assisted by a team made up of the wives of ranking service chiefs and a select group of professional academic women. This pattern was replicated at other government levels, with wives of state governors who were appointed military officers and local government chairman heading BLP branches to their husbands' areas of jurisdiction. Only in the few cases where a woman herself was a local government chairperson were other women appointed as leaders within the BLP organisation.

The BLP's stated aim was to create a 'new rural woman'—economically strong, politically active, socially aware, psychologically fulfilled, and thus equipped to play her role in society to the fullest.[11] To achieve these objectives, the BLP began literacy and vocational training courses, social welfare and health programs, enlightenment campaigns, and income-generating projects for women. By 1991, the BLP was claiming 9,422 cooperatives 1,435 cottage industries, 1,094 multipurpose centres, and 495 shops and markets scattered throughout the country. There were BLP branches in all thirty states and the federal distinct of Abuja, from the ward level to the national level. Their activities were covered extensively in the print and electronic media. By 1992, the BLP had built the ultramodern Center for Women's Development in Abuja, named for Maryam Babangida, appointed the BLP's national patron and the only life member of the board.

Ideologically, the BLP reinforced gender subordination in the guise of women's activism. As a state-sponsored women's group, it mirrored the state's conservative image of women as wives, mothers and secondary income earners. The BLP leadership structure was both hierarchical and completely unrepresentative of its professed constituency of poor, uneducated rural women. The automatic appointment of women to positions based on their husband's rank in the state political and military hierarchy and regardless of suitability or merit was undemocratic and reinforced the prevailing societal image of women as appendages to male power.

The BLP's cooptation of the women's agenda and use of government funds were challenged in several ways. Most notable was a legal complaint filed in 1989 by Lagos lawyer and human rights activist Gani Fawehinmi seeking a court injunction to restrain the federal military government from authorizing additional public funds to Mrs.. Babangida. Fawehinmi maintained that Babangida had "no legal and constitutional function of duty assigned to her and consequently... no legal and constitutional right or backing to use or expend public funds for any purpose."[12] While the government did not respond to Fawehinmi's suit, it decreed the institutionalisation of the BLP's activities. Shortly afterward, the government created a new body, the National Commission for Women. It was mandated to take over the activities of both the NCWD and BLP, among other functions.

Both the commission and BLP enjoyed patronage from the government in the from of yearly grants. Between 1987 and 1992, the BLP received 400 million naira ($ 18 million); the commission was allocated 77 million naira ($4 million) for its three-year plan. These funds have provided office buildings in nearly every state, staff salaries, media coverage, overseas travel, vehicle purchases, and the presence of the top government functionaries at the organisations' events. The impact on actual programs and the lives of rural women is somewhat less clear.

While at first relations between the new commission and the BLP were cordial, discernible cracks soon appeared in their facade of solidarity. In keeping with the mandate to take over the BLP's activities, the commission's board wanted to streamline the BLP and subject it to examination and monitoring. However, the BLP coordinators and advisers refused to submit to this scrutiny. This initially resulted in a standoff between the two organisations and eventually in a 1992 military decree that replaced the previous decree establishing the commission. This essentially left the BLP and its leaders unaccountable to any constituency or monitoring body.

The new decree dissolved the board of the commission and named a new national advisory council (NAC) in its place. First Lady Maryam Babangida, already the chair of the BLP, was also designated the chair of this new council. Fourteen additional members were to reflect a cross section of national interests but did not include representation of the rural women whose interests the BLP was supposed to advance. One the role of the NAC, the decree states,

> "The National Advisory Council shall be charged with the responsibility of advising, guiding, and monitoring the activities of the National Commission [for women] on national policies and programs pertaining to the objectives and functions of the National Commission and the Better life for Rural Women Programme."[13]

The government gave no explanation for these actions. Apparently, the board of the commission had tried to fulfill its mandate of monitoring the BLP by subjecting the wives of the ruling military junta to rules of accountability and the laws of civil society, and in response the board was dissolved. The BLP coordinators, like their husbands, seemed to be above the laws of society and legal procedures. The dissolution of the board of the commission further entrenched the tactics of wifeism. In the eyes of many, this dissolution embodied a thinly/disguised attempt by the military state to completely take over organizing within the female sphere.

After General Babangida was forced out of office in August 1993, the BLP's and NAC's fate appeared to be in doubt. The uncertainty surrounding the NAC's future was reinforced by the clamor in some sectors of civil society to dismantle everything the Babangidas represented. Moreover,

Mariam Abacha, wife of the present military head of state, General Sani Abacha, had not been part of the BLP but had concentrated on her own activities as president of the Nigerian Army Officers' Wives Association. The BLP anniversary parade and fairs for 1993 were concealed, and Mrs. Abacha indicated that she would launch her own initiative, the Family Support Program. Without the first lady as patron, the future of the BLP remains uncertain.

## Conflicting Viewpoints: the State and the Feminist Movement

Perceptions of the state's involvement in the women's sphere and its relationship to the women's movement differ appreciably among Nigerian women leaders. The BLP and the National Commission for Women see the state's role in their formation as an indicator of state recognition of women's centrality to development and the national interest. They expect that this will lead to women's increased participation in government and the economy. They are joined in this view by leaders of the non-governmental National Council of Women's Societies (NCWS).

The NCWS was formally established in 1959, but its history can be traced back to the early. National Women's Union which in 1953 became the Federation of Nigerian Women's Societies (FNWS). The FNWS's primary aims were to bring Nigerian women together to protect their rights under colonial rule and to raise the general status of women to win equal opportunities with men.[14] The FNWS allied with the International Federation of Women, which had links with the East European socialist bloc. It concerned itself with several international issues, such as condemning French atomic tests in the Sahara, and with local issues, such as fighting for the enfranchisement of women in the northern region of Nigeria. As a result of harassment of the FNWS leadership by the colonial state and damaging internal rivalry, it was unable to maintain a national presence, although it continued to function until the 1978 death of its radical and dynamic leader, Funmilayo Ransome-Kuti.

A breakaway faction of the FNWS formed the NCWS in 1959 with a very different ideological orientation. The NCWS was far less critical of government since it was dominated by the wives of nationalist politicians and bureaucrats. It was also much more distant from the mass base of the FNWS. It redirected women's protest strategies from mass demonstrations for action to petition writing and dialogue with government.[15] The NCWS is now recognized by the federal government as the only umbrella NGO representing women's interests. All women's groups in Nigeria are required to affiliate with the NCWS if they are to be recognized by the state.

More recently, elections at the NCWS's biennial conventions have been marred by controversy. On the surface, the reasons centre on south-north, Christian Muslim bids for control, which are common divisions in Nigeria. In reality, these divisions only partially explain the elections' contentious nature. The underlying cause centered on the state patronage the NCWS enjoys at the federal, state, and local government levels in the form of ministerial and parastatal appointments, overseas travel grant support, and other favours. In essence, elite women within the NCWS were wrangling on the platform of the state-recognised women's organisation over the state's largesse and over access to political power and available resources.

The NCWS's policy calls for having the wife of the head of state as its patron. The NCWS has thereby maintained good relations with the state, generally giving its unconditional support to the state and its policies. Consequently, the organisation has been labelled a support of the AGIP party — any government in power—by its critics.[16] Confirming this stance, the immediate past president of the NCWS describes the organisation relationship with government as follows:

"it is cordial; we owe absolute loyalty to the government irrespective of the government in power. That is the reason why we have never fallen out of grace. We criticize when necessary, but when we do, we do not publicize it. All in all, we prefer dialogue to confrontation."[17]

In recent times, the NCWS's few open criticisms of the state have been based on too few women in federal or state cabinets and the National Armed Forces Ruling Council and on objections to a provision in the national population policy recommending a limit of four children per woman without stipulating any limit for men. This close relationship between the state and the 'nongovernmental' NCWS is interpreted by many more explicitly feminist activists as direct government interference.

In contrast to the close and generally uncritical relationship the NCWS has with the state, other women's activists view the government's recent involvement in women's issues as unnecessary interference aimed at neutralizing women's autonomous actions and promoting patriarchy and male-domination within the female sphere. Proponents of this viewpoint generally take a more explicitly feminist perspective, as typified by the group Women in Nigeria (WIN). Its identification with radical antigovernment groups and condemnation of the SAP, the military junta's unfulfilled transition to civil rule, and the proscription of the democratic formations and labour unions are a far more critical stance than that espoused by the NCWS. In general, WIN's relationship with the state is strained.

The emergence of WIN in 1983 as a national women's organisation qualitatively transformed the debate on the 'woman question' in Nigeria both in form and in content. WIN's emphasis, activities, and approach with regard to gender and national issues are aimed at the entire transformation of society. WIN's socialist feminist ideology holds that women's subordination stems from both class and gender oppression. WIN is urban based and made up of lower-middle-class women and men from the universities and other professions.

Although it seeks to represent the interests of poor women and men, the organisation has not successfully recruited or maintained members from this class. This can be attributed in part to a lack of financial resources for programs or staff, conflicts within the organisation over strategy, and the fact that most of its members combine career and family responsibilities. It may also be due to analyses and perspectives that differ from those of the poor. WIN's activities have been mainly in the areas of research and documentation, dissemination of information and policy recommendations, political conscientisation (training and discussion to raise women's political awareness and/or awareness of gender discrimination), and project work.

The emergence of WIN transformed the debate on the nature of gender subordination in Nigeria, as WIN embraced a multidimensional approach to the subject of gender inequality. It moved beyond articulating the importance of income-generating projects to improve women's economic status and independence. WIN also included issues of women's reproductive rights and choice, sexual harassment and violence, and consciousness-raising programs in the broader discourse on women. With its research and documentation programs, WIN has been able to generate data for policymakers and researchers on the conditions of Nigerian women. These achievements notwithstanding, WIN's impact has been limited by its inability to broaden its membership base.

WIN's relationship with the state has been uneasy and at times confrontational. The state has attempted at one level to coopt WIN by suggesting that it affiliate with the NCWS and seek to effect change from within. WIN has steadfastly and publicly refused to join the NCWS. WIN is ideologically opposed both to the NCWS's pro-government stance and the government's insistence that all women's organisations affiliate with the NCWS. In response, the government has refused to register WIN as a legal entity and has also threatened incarceration and detention of some of its leaders.

WIN, recognizing that its ideals of democratically transforming gender and class cannot be achieved by working on its own, has cooperated and identified with other social movements and progressive organisations interested in democratic change. The only time WIN did work with the state, in a political bureau set up by the Babangida government to discuss the political future of Nigeria, it linked up with other popular democratic organisations in the country.

Other women's groups with an entirely rural base, such as the Country Women Association of Nigeria (COWAN), have also cooperated with the movement for democracy in the shared objective of popular participation. The achievements of such voluntary development organisations lie not only in providing services to grassroots women but also in articulating the principles that guide such work. Grassroots organisations are generally managed by rural women for themselves and therefore base their programs on the actual needs of their members.

In fact, their success among rural women precisely what prompted the government to establish the Directorate of Food, Roads, and Rural Infrastructure, the BLP, and people's and community banks all over the country. However, the state to date has not been able to replicate the effectiveness of grassroots organisations. COWAN's leader was in fact imprisoned for 'insubordination as a result of a clash with the BLP, which tried to appropriate and take credit for COWAN's long-standing work with rural women. COWAN's participation in the prodemocracy campaign became even more pronounced after the cancellation of the presidential election results in June 1993.[18]

For one prominent activist-scholar, the mutual relationship of these organisations to the state can be regarded in class/political terms. Groups such as the NCWS, the BLP, and the commission have never threatened the dominant classes that control the state apparatus and have generally been supported by and supportive of the state.[19] As creations of the state, the BLP and the commission have had the closest relationship with the state. This relationship has been likened to that which traditionally exists between a husband and wife, based on the love and obedience of the wife to the husband. In a recent interview, the current director of the BLP aired a desire for Nigerian women "to be grateful to the president before his wife because without his support the BLP would have been an unrealized dream of the first lady."[20]

A question that emerges is whether the activities of these more conservative women's groups are emancipatory or subordinating. In the period since independence in 1960, there has been continuity in the organisational forms in which women intervene in society. There have also been changes both in the content and mode of organisation of women's associations, indicating important progress. The combination of continuity and change in women's organisations suggests, however, that the question of whether Nigerian women are moving toward achieving emancipation or remain subordinated is not a simple one. While the women's movement is fluid and historical shifts in its class and urabn-rural composition are evident, it is clear that winning over the rural women who form the backbone of the nation is key to its continued progress. Thus, the government's selection of rural women as its target, singling them out as state beneficiaries, has the potential to split alliances within the movement.

### Women's Agenda for the 1990s and Beyond

What is the vision of the Nigerian women's agenda for the 1990s and beyond? Does it reflect our situation, which is characterised by economic adjustment policies, repression, and democratic struggles? The National Commission for Women has formulated a national women's policy, which has yet to be signed into law by the government. The policy reflects the agenda of women active in development, which is based on a vision of economic independence, self-reliance, and sustainable development for women.

The policy largely neglects other issues of importance to Nigerian women, including those related to reproductive rights such as contraception and abortion and health issues such as incest. In general, however, the women's movement in Nigeria, despite internal differences and inherent weaknesses, has been successful in putting the woman question, however defined, on the national political agenda. In all this militancy and activism, however, no viable women's agenda has been put forward to lead women into the twenty-first century.

On the surface, it appears as if the state's vision for its development projects in the mid-1980s, characterized by interest in mobilizing women for development, self-improvement, and democracy, has been fulfilled. However, while the state can point to its support for and close involvement with the NCWS, the BLP, the commission, and other groups essentially conservative in nature, the reality of any discernible impact on most Nigerian women's lives is quite different. The bureaucratisation and cooptation of women's mobilisation efforts have meant that in many cases propaganda and fanfare have tended to substitute for substance and results.

The very structure of the state's efforts, top-down and top-heavy, has meant that the projects have been subject to the whims of their initiators, who presented themselves as benefactors to the rural women. Not surprisingly, such benevolent posturing has often degenerated into a patronizing attitude. In the end, we may see that a major factor in the eventual downfall of the state's efforts at mobilizing women was the selection of a group of urban, privileged women to lead, unqualified except by accident of marriage, whose modus operandi was starkly out of tune with the realities of the poor rural women the programs were supposed to benefit.

Ironically, for all the government's efforts and publicity at mobilizing Nigerian women in general and rural women in particular, women's involvement in the government's other programs, especially those for transition to civil rule, has been minimal. This certainly does not suggest any major departure from the practice of previous regimes. Women have not emerged as a credible political force able to stamp their influence on the local and national political landscape. This can be traced, at least in part, to the bureaucratisation of women's issues and the rise of Nigerian state pseudo-feminism, the hallmark of which was the policy of wifeism. Wifeism's effect on the majority of women has been far from emancipatory. To the contrary, it has tended to reinforce the structures and ideologies that have long characterized the domination of women. Rather than emphasizing autonomy, state pseudo-feminism has emphasized incorporation and patronage. The net effect has been apathy at the grass roots.

In order to be sustainable in the long term and achieve results, any programs to mobilize women should have several characteristics. First, the program should have the ultimate objective of empowering women in order to free them from the yoke of patriarchal domination and gender discrimination. Second, it should be aimed at involving economically active women in productive activities that could assist them in increasing their independent income. Third, it should encourage women to become leaders in articulating their own interests and in tackling wider societal issues. Given these criteria, the potential for a lasting impact of the Nigerian government's initiatives on behalf of women is questionable.

The Nigerian feminist movement is at a crossroads. The movement faces at least two alternatives: It can move forward independently to challenge patriarchy and see to liberate women, or it can risk being completely co-opted by the state and by other interests. Which of these will prevail depends on how the women's movement defines its agenda and how well it succeeds in popularizing its struggle. The movement can embrace its full role in society and become more integrated into the trade union, human rights, and democratic movements. It can develop a women's platform as a basis for negotiating and forming coalitions with other mass movements and as a catalyst for supporting women to take part in party politics. A true feminist agenda challenges the state. If the Nigerian movement believes in emancipation, it must divorce itself from the grip of the state.

A.M. IMAM

## REFERENCES

1. Government of Nigeria, Federal Office of Statistics and IRD/ Macro International, *Nigeria Demographic and Health Survey, 1990,* Lagos: N.P., 1992.
2. Nina Mba, *Nigerian Women Mobilized: Women's Political Activity in Southern Nigeria, 1900–1965,* Berkeley and Los Angeles: University of California Press, 1982, p.166.
3. Mere Kisekka, "Women's Organized Health Struggles: The Challenge to Women's Associations," in Mere Kisekka (ed.), *Women's Health Issues in Nigeria,* Zaria: Tamaza, 1992, pp. 105–21.
4. Interview with Mrs. Theresa Chukwana, Mrs. Hannatu Fika, and Mrs. Theresa Oguibe at the National Commission for Women, Abuja, February 2, 1993.
5. Interview with Obiagei Nwankwo, project coordinator, the International Federation of Women Lawyers, Enugu, February 12, 1993.
6. Interview with Dr. Bene Madunagu, national coordinator (1991–1993), Women in Nigeria, Calabar, February 11, 1993.
7. Vesico-vaginal fistulae are tears in the wall between the vagina and urinary tract that result from prolonged, obstructed labor.

They are particularly common among very young women whose bodies have not sufficiently matured to accommodate passage through the birth canal. VVF result in constantly leaking urine; woman suffering from VVF are commonly ostracized by family and community and often become homeless and destitute. While VVF can usually be corrected with surgery, the cost is prohibitive for most women. The National Task Force on Vesico-Vaginal Fistulae is an unusual coalition among women's groups, lawmakers, and medical experts. It has sought to bring public attention to VVF, prevent them by advocating raising the legal age of marriage to eighteen and improving access to maternity care, and raise funds for medical and vocational rehabilitation of women suffering from VVF.

8. Amrita Cchachhi and Renee Pittin, "Multiple Strategies: Confronting State, Capital, and Patriarchy, Paper presented at the International Workshop on Women Organizing in the Process of Industrialisation, the Hague, Netherlands, April 15–26, 1991.

9. Interview at the National Commission for Women, Abuja, February 2, 1993.

10. Hussiana Abdullah, "Transition Politics and the Challenge of Gender in Nigeria," *Review of African Political Economy*, 56, March 1993, pp. 27–37.

11. Maryam Babangida, text of a speech at the 1991 Africa Prize for Leadership for the Sustainable End of Hunger, reproduced in *New Nigerian*, October 13, 1991.

12. *Tell*, April 20, 1992, quoted in Renee Pittin, "Women's Work: Parameters of Representation and Action", Paper presented to an international workshop on Women and Work: Historical Trends, Center for Basic Research, Kampala, Uganda, September 1992, p. 16.

13. Government of Nigeria, Decree no. 42, 1992.

14. Mba, "Kaba and Khaki."

15. Ifi Amadiume, "Contemporary Women's Organisations, Contradictions, and Irrelevance in the Struggle for Grassroots Participatory Democracy in Nigeria", Paper presented at the CODESRIA Workshop on Social Movements, Social

Transformations, and the Struggle for Democracy, Algiers, Algeria, July 1990.

16. Ayesha Imam, "The Dynamics of Winning: An Analysis of Women in Nigeria (WIN)," in Chandra Mohanty and Jacqui Alexander, eds., *Third World Feminism,* London: Basil Blackwell, 1993; Ahmed K. Shettima, "Engendering Nigeria's Third Republic", Paper presented at the CODESRIA conference on the Politics of Structural Adjustment in Africa, Dakar, Senegal, September 1991.
17. Interview with Emily Aig-Imokhuede, president (1988–1993), the National Council of Women's Societies, Abuja, March 22, 1993.
18. Interview with Chief Bisi Ogunleye, national coordinator, the Country Women Association of Nigeria, Akure, December 18, 1993.
19. Ayesha Imam, "The Women's Movement, State, and Democracy in Nigeria," Paper presented at the Akut workshop on Social Movements and Democracy in the Third World, Delhi, India, October 1992.
20. Interview at the National Commission for Women, Abuja, February 2, 1993.

# 36

# SURVEY OF FEMALE CIRCUMCISION IN IBADAN, NIGERIA

Nigeria is the largest black African country situated in the west coast of Africa and is bounded on the west by Togo, on the east by Cameroun, in the south by the Atlantic Ocean and in the North by Niger. It is an extremely diverse and heterogeneous country in terms of ethnic groups, culture and language, and has a population of 87 million. Literacy rate is 34%, GNP/capita per annum is low—approximately 450 U.S. Dollars. Maternal mortality rate is 3 to 6 per 1,000 total births (that is 5 to 10 times the rates reported in Europe and North America), and infant mortality rate is 150 to 200 per, 1,000 live births (that is 10 to 20 times the rates reported from the developed countries like U.K., U.S.A. and Sweden).

In Nigeria there is a lack of accurate data with regard to the current practice of female circumcision. Dr. Stephens in 1931 in the Lancet stated that "I have never seen any ill effects due to circumcision in Nigeria", yet some authors have more recently reported sporadic cases of severe complications, 2-9, while others, including a former Nigerian State Governor has clamoured for legislative law banning the archaic practice.

The study which is hereby reported was therefore designed to find out the extent to which female circumcision is still being practiced in Nigeria, to study the socio-cultural factors responsible for the perpetuation of this custom and to determine the morbidity, and mortality, if any, arising from the practice, so as to formulate guidelines which will serve as a basis for an action programme geared towards eradication of female circumcision.

The survey was carried out in Ibadan, the largest city in black Africa. Ibadan is the capital of Oyo State, situated in the western part of Nigeria and has a population of 5 million, about 2/3 of which are women and children. A questionnaire interview was carried out on samples of women attending the antenatal clinics of the largest general hospital in the city as well as a large child welfare clinic in the city.

The results of the survey have revealed that female circumcision is still widely practiced and favoured by quite a large proportion of Nigerians as well as other African countries. Over 70% of the women interviewed had themselves been circumcised; 67% of them still favour the idea of female circumcision. Almost half of the respondents had their daughters circumcised and almost a quarter (25%) of them said that they will spare no pain to see that their daughters are circumcised. It is the mild form (cutting of the clitoris) that is done in Ibadan.

It was shown from the survey that the age of the respondents did not seem to have influenced their attitude to the practice of female circumcision. Both old and young favour the practice though in our survey a high proportion of the respondents were young and below the age of 35 years, and a significant proportion of them favour female circumcision.

Although the majority (72.6%) of the respondents who favour female circumcision were illiterates, yet it is noteworthy that almost 30% of those who favour the practice are literate, and as many as 10% of the literate have had a minimum of secondary education. Thus, the fact that opposition to the practice of female circumcision comes from women who have received some education which has been reported by some workers, 12 has not been clearly demonstrated in this survey.

The pattern observed in this survey is surely a reflection of the strong cultural attitude towards female circumcision among Nigerian respondents. Furthermore, it was observed that even among the educated women who do not favour the practice, family and—social pressures are often so great that the women might eventually have to give in and submit their daughters for circumcision. In these instances, the mother-in-law or some paternal grandmother or aunt insisted that it must be done. In this study although more than 80% of the respondents were indigenes of Ibadan and its environs, it is generally known that the practice of female circumcision is ethnically linked in Nigeria.

**Ethnic Groups of Ibadan**

Ethnic groups such as Ijebus and Egbas (also in the western part of Nigeria) do not favour female circumcision, while the practice is highly prevalent among the Ibadans, Ijeshas, Ebitts in the west, the Benins and Itshekiris in the midwest, Igbos in the east and some tribes in the northern parts. This ethnic differences was also observed by other researchers from other countries, e.g. Sudan and Kenya. About 70% of the respondents who favour female circumcision are Muslims while 29 are Christians and 1% are traditionalists. Religion, per se, does not seem to play an important role in influencing the people's attitudes toward female circumcision.

The sample employed in this study is predominantly Muslim and this is reflected in the results obtained. Almost 95% or the female circumcision carried out in Ibadan was done by traditional circumcisionists. Nurse/midwives and traditional birth attendants were said to have carried out 4% and 1% respectively of the female circumcisions. The instruments used include sharp knives, scapels or blades. The operation is usually carried out in the first two weeks of life, or when the child is few months old. In Bendel State (Midwest Region) it is done on the woman at the 7th month of her first pregnancy if she was not circumcised as a child. With regard to complications, only 8% of the respondents reported complications from female circumcision performed by the native circumcisionists. The possibility of gross under reporting of the outcome of the cases performed by these circumcisionists should nevertheless not be overlooked. On the other hand, some postoperative medications are usually applied to the wound by the circumcisionists which include local herbal preparations as well as penicillin ointment. However, from clinical observation and surveys carried out in hospitals and clinics, some of the complications that have been reported among girls who have been circumcised include shock from severe pain and haemorrhage, infection, especially tetanus.

Urinary retention, damage to the urethra giving rise to urinary in continence, damage to the anus resulting in fistula-in-ane and fecal incontinence, as well as cysts of the clitoris. Other serious gynaecological and obstetrical complications such as chronic pelvic infection and calculi formation and subsequent infertility, obstructed labour as a result of labial adhesions, severe fibrosis and scarring leading to narrowing of the vaginal orifice had also been recorded. Such cases of obstructed labour could end up in ruptured uterus and severe haemorrhage, causing the death of both mother and child. Some of the reasons which the respondents gave in favour of female circumcision were:

1. 'Female circumcision which involves the cutting of the clitoris will dampen sexual desire' and thus help to prevent promiscuity and maintain chastity between the age of the puberty and the time of marriage, and it will also ensure fidelity in a married woman.
2. Female circumcision is "an essential ritual" a woman must undergo as a child (or in any case before the birth of her first child) in order to ensure a quick and easy labour during child birth. It is felt that the clitoris may swell during childbirth and thus obstruct the delivery of the head of the baby.
3. Prevention of the development of a large head (Hydrocephalys) of the baby, as the "contact between

the clitoris and the baby's head might give rise to congenital hydrocephalus, and consequent infant death".

4. Excision of the clitoris will reduce excessive vaginal secretion which is thought to cause vaginal irritation and rashes in the pelvic area.

The respondents who do not favour female circumcision gave the following reasons:

1. "It is a cultural/traditional heritage that should be discarded, as it is barbaric."
2. "It is an absolutely unnecessary procedure (which like tribal facial marks) only causes severe pain and suffering for the child".
3. "It is 'disvirgining' at childhood; tampering with a child's genitalia".
4. "It is a denial of a woman's self-fulfilment, as it greatly reduces a woman's sexual pleasure.

## Conclusions

In this study, it was generally felt by the respondents that the practice of female circumcision helps to promote sexual morality among women, and also contributes to safe delivery among them as well as to ensure infant survival. The implication of this therefore, is that any measure being planned to discourage the practice of female circumcision must be an endeavour to invalidate these two claims by intensive health education, and community motivation, whilst highlighting the apparent dangers of female circumcision.

## Actions Taken Since the Dakar Conference

Since the Dakar Conference, a National Committee has been set up in Nigeria with representatives from the 19 states of the federation and representatives from the various pressure groups in the country namely, the Islamic and Christian organisations, the Nigerian Red Cross Society the National

Council of Women's Societies, the University Women's Association, the Medical Women's Association of Nigeria, the Market Women's Association, as well as the Traditional practitioners' Association. The Committee plans to meet next month to deliberate and formulate some guidelines for policy decisions which will be submitted to the Nigerian Government for an action plan.

In the meantime, I am working towards achieving a closer link with all the circumcisionists in Ibadan City, Capital of Oyo State and knowing more about their characteristics and persons with a view to using them as change agents. In other words, if they could be made to appreciate the dangers inherent in their practice, then they may be inclined to discourage client who may bring them their daughters to be circumcised.

Madam Chairperson, distinguished guests, my dear sisters and brothers, what I would like to suggest is that may be we need to apply a three-pronged attack on the problem of female circumcision:

(1) Acceleration of Public Enlightenment: Working with the general public to discourage the people from taking their daughters for circumcision.

(2) Integrated Approach Through Closer Collaboration with the Circumcisionists: Working with the traditional practitioners themselves, not only to cease from circumcising girls, but also to act as agents for enlightening parents and discouraging them from subjecting their daughters to female circumcision.

(3) Integration of Female Cicumcision Campaign into School Health Education Program: Working on and with the younger generation in order to achieve a positive change in societal attitudes towards female circumcision so that the practice will be strongly opposed by them and eventually eradicated.

F.A. AZIZ

# 37

# BABA OF KARO (1890–1960) GIRLS' TRADING EXPEDITIONS, BOND-FRIENDS, AND MARRIAGE

Baba was a Muslim Hausa woman in her sixties when Mary Smith, a British woman accompanying her anthropologist husband, M.G. Smith, on his fieldwork in northern Nigeria in West Africa, recorded her life story. *Baba of Karo* is the first published account of the daily life of an African peasant woman that was written from the woman's point of view. Such accounts, from any area of the continent about ordinary events before incorporation into the colonial system and later into the new nation-state, are exceedingly rare.

The Hausa are the largest ethnic group in West Africa and have long attracted "the attention of travellers, Islamic scholars, colonial officials, historians, linguists, and anthropologists," for their "culture and society are complex and include many extremes of experience: urban and rural communities, agricultural systems and highly specialized craft production, Muslim and non-Muslim religious and ritual systems and a highly elaborated status system based upon occupation and birth."[1]

In Karo, the small town where Baba lived as a child at the end of the nineteenth century, indigenous Hausa culture was more dominant in daily life than either the Islamic culture that had been brought to the area centuries earlier or the new practices and policies laid down under British colonial rule. In these two excerpts, Baba recalls learning trade as a child and explains how Hausa women cooperated to manage their marriages.

Baba and her cohort of young girls learned the art of trading by engaging in small-scale endeavours modelled after those of their mothers and female relatives and encouraged by the village. The centrality of women's trading activities to the economies of many countries that produce agricultural products and trade in raw materials on the international market has been the focal point of much research on women and development.

Contemporary feminist scholars, trained to ask 'and what are the women doing?' have insisted that development experts, national governments, and international agencies recognize the fact that more than three-quarters of the agricultural work in Africa is done by women, but that almost none of the resources that go into improving agricultural work has been directed to women. Baba's trading activities build on this female agricultural tradition and place her at the centre of the economy of her region.

The economic status of Hausa women, like many women throughout Africa is one of the factors traditionally associated with their power and authority.[2] In the second excerpt, Baba recounts how the women of her village monitored their relationships with their husbands. Through a set of indigenous ritual practices, *Kawaye,* women who belonged to an age cohort, shared information about how their husbands treated them. Such practices as the one described here serve multiple functions.

Women are observing how they are treated by their husbands. They are sharing that information directly with their peers. They are notifying their husbands of their satisfactions. And they are publicly recording a social practice that is carried on between the two individuals involved, thereby reinforcing the notion that the status of a marriage is a matter of concern to an entire community. The ability to influence others is one of the bases of power; the recognition that such influence rightfully belongs to a particular person is one of the bases of authority.

As many researchers have observed, class status, wealth, age, and ritual power are among the attributes that Hausa women use to determine their positions.[3] Learned in childhood and carried out through a variety of customs, these practices of Hausa women appear to provide one example of the ways in which women express agency in compelx social systems.

## Girls' Trading Expeditions

The thing I remember best before I was married was our girls' trading expeditions. We took our money and our big calabashes, we went to Doka and bought yams, we went to Fillata and got groundnuts, we went and bought sweet potatoes from our hamlet, Karo, and from Dankusuba, Sundu, Wawaye, Guga....When we had been to a lot of different villages and bought things, we came home and cooked them. When they were ready we took them to market. This had nothing to do with our parents, we went and sold our goods and put by our money. In the dry season we traced like this. When we had been to market in the morning with our mothers' cakes, eight or ten of us, we would meet our friends, and come back, twenty of us, all singing, crowds of girls. Then we would put our heads together, we would go on an expedition. 'Are you coming?' Yes, I'm coming.' In the morning we got up early and we went along singing, twenty of us, thirty of us.

When we arrived at a village we would go to the market and see things for sale. 'Oh, look at that ! It's cheap, we'll go and make a profit'. And we bought it. One girl would buy groundnuts, one would buy yams, one sweet potatoes—each one bought her own produce. The little girls came along too with little loads, about three-pennyworth. We older ones took about a shillingsworth. The country people said 'Welcome, daughters of the village, welcome!" We said, 'M-hm'. Then the country people would laugh, 'ha! ha! ha!, they never laugh softly. We weren't exactly village children, we used to live in the town. They were country bumpkins, they hadn't got much sense, they weren't used to seeing a lot of people.

When we got back home we would cook the food we have bought, and next day we sold it in the market. The third day we returned to the hamlets. We were traders all right!

**Bond-Friends and Marriage**

We Bare-Bare women have a special custom: if your husband gives you kola-nuts and tobacco-flowers, you know that he desires you. You sit in your hut in the evening, eating kolanuts and rubbing the tobacco-flowers on your teeth, and you feel good. As you finish with the tobacco-flowers you put them in a flat basket and hang it up on your wall. You do this for seven days, you collect them. On the following Friday you send a young girl to your *kawa* with the used tobacco-flowers. If your *kawa's* husband has also been giving her tobacco-flowers and kolanuts, she hangs your little basket on the wall, and for seven days she collects her used flowers. Then when the Friday comes she puts them all together, yours and hers, and sends them back to you. Then you both know that your marriages are going well.

After dark the *kawaye* will go to visit each other, they laugh and are glad because each one knows her husband desires her. But if the husband of one of them does not give her kolanuts and tobacco-flowers, and the other one sends her a little basket full of used flowers then the neglected one will break up her marriage—that is, it is her *kawa* who has caused the marriage to break up. One wants to be treated as well as one's friend. This is a custom of Bornu women.

J. KOOPMAN

**REFERENCES**

1. Catherine Coles, and Beverly Mack, eds. *Hausa Women in the Twentieth Century*. Madison: U of Wisconsin P, 1991, p. 4.
2. Jeanne Koopman, "Women in the Rural Economy: Past, Present, and Future," *African Women South of the Sahara*. Ed. Margaret Jean Hay and Sharon Sticher, 2nd ed. New York: Wiley and Sons, 1995, p. 15.
3. Coles and Mack, *op. cit.*, p. 13.

# 38

# THE PATRIARCHAL BARGAINING IN TIJANIYYA SUFI ORDER IN NORTHERN NIGERIA

This chapter describes the rules and scripts that operate in a sub-Saharan African system, the Tijaniyya Sufi order in Kano, Nigeria. It analyses the patriarchal bargains between the women and men in the order and reveals how the actions of Muslim women with position of spiritual authority were both independent and shaped by the order's patriarchy. Deniz Kandiyoti suggested that comparative work on women's coping strategies can reveal patriarchy's different forms and lead to a more "grounded understanding of patriarchal systems."[1] I found, her use of the term patriarchal bargain helpful in my study. She defined it as "the set rules and scripts regulating gender relations, to which both genders accommodate and acquiesce."[2]

Kandiyoti sketched two patriarchal systems: the sub-Saharan African pattern and classic patriarchy. She found the clearest instances of classic patriarchy to be in North Africa, the Middle East, and South and East Asia; she did not, however, preclude the use of this term for other regions and has also discussed bargains that vary by class. Kandiyoti called for these sketches to be "expanded and fleshed out with systematic, comparative, empirical content."[3] Helen Rose Ebaugh first answered Kandiyoti's call by describing a classic patriarchal system in the United States, carrying out an empirical analysis of American nuns' patriarchal bargains with the Roman Catholic Church;[4] Gerami and Lehnerer have followed by describing Islamic fundamentalist and secular Iranian women's strategies for gaining agency in negotiation with their families and state regulations.[5]

Here, I show which rules and scripts were operating in a sub-Saharan African system, the Tijaniyya order in Kano, Nigeria. I analyse the activities across several decades of Tijaniyya *muqaddamat* (women representatives authorised to initiate and supervise members of a Sufi order), herein referred to as initiators, and the order's responses to them. I categorised these initiators in two groups: first-and second-generation initiators.

First-generation Tijaniyya initiators were women appointed to initiator status between 1937 and 1963: 1937 marks the year the first Kano woman was appointed an initiator, and in 1963 Emir Sansui of Kano was forced to abdicate by the Nigerian government. The emir was a staunch Tijaniyya member, and his abdication signalled the waning power and membership of the order. Second-generation initiators became initiators after 1963; several of these women were either daughters, granddaughters, or students of first-generation women.

While the Islamic world, the international Tijaniyya leadership, and the Nigerian state shifted their policies and set new religious and educational trends from 1937 to the present, I suggest that Tijaniyya men and women in Kano continued to abide by the same patriarchal bargains. Although they accommodate and acquiesced to the same set of rules and scripts, larger historical shifts allowed Kano second-generation women initiators to act differently and increase their spiritual authority and personal autonomy without being marginalised.

I define spiritual authority as the recognised right to perform certain religious functions and personal autonomy as the ability to determine various aspects of one's life (e.g., residence, profession, Sufi affiliation, mobility). I also use the classical Weberian definition of power as the ability to control situations and other people despite their resistance. The differences between the lives of first-and second-generation women initiators illuminate the importance of social and historical context to patriarchal bargains. This study indicates that the rules of patriarchal bargains endure across generations and survive social changes; these rules are in some ways inherited at the collective level. But historical shifts can change social context, and that changing context is influential on how individuals negotiate within the inherited rules.

## Historical Background

Kano City is the capital of Kano State located in northern Nigeria. More than 90 percent of its inhabitants are Hausa speakers and practice the religion of Islam.[6] In the nineteenth century, Kano was one of several emirates that made up the Sokoto Caliphate: Kano's emir was one of the Caliphate's most influential regional rulers. Historically, the city has been an important Islamic educational centre for West and North Africans and has had a history of cultural and religious exchange with the wider Muslim world. Since colonisation of the Caliphate in the twentieth century, social changes have shifted the social context for patriarchal bargains in Kano. Education and religion have been important arenas for bargains between Tijaniyya women and men in Kano.

The Sokoto Caliphate placed an emphasis on learning. The emirs of the Caliphate were learned men who were very knowledgeable in the scholarship and ideas of the larger

Muslim world, and there was an Islamic Arabic and Hausa educational system in place prior to British colonisation. The emirs saw no reason to replace their educational system with an English-based curriculum, so they resisted colonial attempts to establish a school system based on missionary and British models. Hausa Muslim leaders were especially concerned that colonial education would corrupt girls and lead them away from proper Muslim behaviour.[6]

The British colonial government eventually did succeed in establishing schools for both girls and boys in the emirates, including Kano. However, Hausa resistance resulted in fewer schools for girls than boys in the North; this has been the case since the colonial period.[7] Present-day Nigeria, in fact, still has a gender gap in education.[8]

Nigeria attempted to address the gender gap and other problems in its educational system in 1976, when the military-led government established universal primary education (UPE). UPE helped narrow the gender gap in education by increasing the number of girl's schools, especially in northern Nigeria.[9] UPE also resulted in an increase in women teachers in the North.

The state was not the only agent of educational reform in northern Nigeria. Religious movements and Sufi orders, including the Tijaniyya, have been agents of both educational and religious reform in Nigeria. These organisations have helped reform private education in Kano, reformed their doctrines, and challenged the doctrine of others. The Tijaniyya is one of the two leading Sufi orders in Kano, and its members have practiced in Kano since the early nineteenth century.

The Arabic term for Sufi order (*tariqa*) is often translated as brotherhood; however, this study does not employ that term because it does not reflect the reality of women's participation in these organisations. The purpose of Sufism and Sufi orders is to provide a path that Sufi adherents can follow to gain closeness to God, *Allâh*. Founding Sufi *shaykhs* (masters) blaze those paths for their adherents and then supply litanies, rites, and rules that prove efficacious in the quest for proximity to God. Members of orders who master rites are also known as *shaykhs* and lead orders after the founders' deaths. The greatest of these succeeding *shaykhs* may renew or reform an order.

Such a reform was initiated in the late 1930s and 1940s when Shaikh Ibrahim Niasse of Kaolack, Senegal, expanded and consolidated his international following among West African Tijaniyya members. Most of Kano's ruling family became his adherents, and thereafter, most of the Kano Tijaniyya shaykhs and initiators came under his influence. Shaykh Niasse's leadership ushered in a number of reforms to the practice, organisation, and doctrine of the order. Perhaps the most important reform that affected women was the greater public role that the Tijaniyya began to take in its aim to become a mass movement. This change in the leadership and the new public role of the Kano Tijaniyya facilitated the first transformation in the order's patriarchal bargains.

The order's increased public presence encouraged sectors of Kano society not traditionally affiliated with the Tijaniyya (the less educated, women, and youth) to join the order. The Tijaniyya mass movement did succeed; men's and women's membership in the order was significantly increased through mass initiation campaigns. Tijaniyya men *shaykhs* from North Africa toured northern Nigeria and initiated a surfeit of members who did not have a local initiator to whom they could turn for spiritual advice. This was especially the case for women. The Tijaniyya was one of several Islamic mass mobilisation campaigns in West Africa that recognised that recruiting more women members was necessary for the success of its efforts.[10] The norms for the Tijaniyya changed, and membership for women on a wide scale was made one of the order's goals and became compatible with its doctrine.

The 1960s brought a challenge to the popularity of all Sufi organisations in Nigeria. Anti-Sufi organisations, many of them supported financially and ideologically by Saudi Arabian interests, began gaining popularity because of their message of reform throughout Hausa society, including reform in the private educational system in northern Nigeria. The anti-Sufis pioneered the building of Islamiyya schools, which held the best of traditional religious education with the advantages of the British model for studying secular subjects. Instead of attending government schools for secular subjects, with little religious instruction during the day, and traditional Hausa religious schools in the afternoon, children now get a comprehensive education with an Islamic Hausa perspective in Islamiyya schools.

Anti-Sufis also began to affect governmental policies on Islamic matters.[11] This trend had devastating consequences for Sufi orders such as the Tijaniyya. It was during the 1960s that Emir Sanusi was forced to abdicate. Because of this trend, many Nigerian Muslims no longer join Sufi orders; instead, they choose to join the ranks of anti-Sufi movements that question the orthodoxy of Sufi orders and doctrines and view most Sufis as heretics.

## Tijaniyya Initiator: Adherent Relationship

To enjoy the spiritual benefits of the Tijaniyya order, a person must be old enough to make a conscious choice to become a member (at least reach puberty) and must be formally inducted into the order by a Tijaniyya initiator. To become an initiator, a member must know the rules of the order, be sufficiently grounded in its spiritually and doctrine, and have a good temperament and moral behaviour. Therefore, an initiator will be able to provide a good example and teach the obligations and prohibitions incumbent on its members, including the Arabic text and best times to perform the order's litanies.

The initiation of a member is just that, the initial experience in a relationship with the initiator and the first level of Sufism as practiced by the Tijaniyya. A small percentage of Tijaniyya members aspire to become initiators, and even fewer initiators reach a spiritual level that earns them the title of shaykh or Sufi master.

Once admitted, the member is in frequent contact with the initiator. An individual may call on an initiator for any number of reasons. A member may have questions of doctrine, want business advice, or need counsel on Islamic legal matters. The Islamic education of a member and his or her family will be turned over to the initiator. Some initiators have knowledge of traditional herbal and Islamic medicine, and their clients will seek them out for consultations about health or personal problems. The Tijaniyya order has two daily rites: *lazumi* and *wazifa*. Men are required to perform *wazifa* communally; an initiator must lead the rite. For all these services, the members will pay the initiator whatever amount they are able. However, their obligations to the initiator do not stop there.

Initiators and members have reciprocal obligations and responsibilities, which make for strong patron-client relationships. As patrons, initiators can garner material advantages as well as spiritual authority and power in these relationships. For example, as clients and adherents, members may do personal service for initiators. If the member is in need of housing, attending the initiator may become part of his or her chores if accepted as a resident in the initiator's household. Alternatively, an adherent might be called upon to render help occasionally. An initiator (or someone in the initiator's household) might also provide foster care for members' children. In exchange for attending to the child's education and upbringing, the initiator's family obtains use of the child's labour for household chores.

If a Tijaniyya member is especially learned in the order's doctrine or seems to overflow with *baraka* (spiritual blessing), an initiator might help the member open a school or appoint him or her from ordinary membership to the position of initiator. However, most of these relationships do not result in the appointment of a member to initiator status, and, prior to 1937, only men had access to initiator status and its power and authority in the Kano Tijaniyya. Kano Tijaniyya women had some power over younger women, especially relatives, but had no spiritual authority and little personal autonomy in terms of mobility, residence, or profession.

In 1937, the first Tijaniyya woman in Kano obtained the position of initiator. Thereafter, women initiators obtained power over their own adherents—young and old women, related or not—and gained the spiritual authority to perform all the duties described previously.[12] In the 1970s and 1980s, women initiators gained personal autonomy without having their respectability questioned.

One spiritual position that Kano Tijaniyya women have not held is that of *shaykha* or Sufi master. Sufi master is not a title that requires an official appointment within the Tijaniyya. Instead, when initiators have initiated many members, appointed many members to initiator status, and are known to have a great deal of *baraka*, most people will refer to them as *shaykh*. No Kano Tijaniyya women initiators have been widely referred to as *shaykha*.

This article shows that from 1937 through 1997, the patriarchal bargains between women and men initiators in the Kano Tijaniyya were premised on Kandiyoti's sub-Saharan pattern generally. Kandiyoti observed that in sub-Saharan African patriarchal bargains, women generally have strong ties outside of marriage and that Hausa women specifically are highly dependent on men but have relative freedom in allocating their own labour. She pointed out that the first condition exists because African polygyny is uncertain for women; they gain security not from marriage or from their husband's household but from their own kinship groups.

Hausa society has high divorce rates, and Hausa women frequently instigate divorce and maintain strong bonds with their own kin on whom they must rely when unmarried. African polygyny also compels women to cooperate with other women (cowives) with whom they have no blood relationship. These points are very important; unlike the classical pattern of patriarchy, the sub-Saharan pattern requires women to forge strong bonds outside of marriage that give women more choices in shaping their lives. Kandiyoti also posited that because the Hausa practice Islamic wife seclusion, Hausa women are highly dependent on their husbands or make kin. However, she concludes that seclusion also reduces labour demands by their husbands. Hausa patriarchal bargains accommodate women's allocation of their own labour.[13] My research on the Kano Tijaniyya illuminates four additional rules governing the order's patriarchal bargains:

(1) utility—women's activities in the order had to have a unique utility to a goal set by men in the order that men could not achieve through their own efforts;

(2) compatibility—women's motives had to be compatible with Tijaniyya and general Islamic principles;

(3) consistency—women's roles had to be consistent with Hausa family hierarchy and societal norms; and finally;

(4) prestige—women's status and actions had to be in accordance with, or increase, the order's prestige and reputation.

The general sub-Saharan pattern and the four principles specific to Kano Tijaniyya patriarchal bargains provided continuity in a dynamic period in the history of the order and the city.

**Women and the Tijaniyya**

Prior to the Tijaniyya's reforms of the late 1930s and 1940s, women had been members of the Kano Tijaniyya, but in limited numbers. They had only participated as members of the order, not as leaders. Nonetheless, some women had obtained a traditional Islamic education through the private Hausa system. To receive a thorough education, young girls had to have supportive scholarly parents. Girls had two choices for their Islamic education: Someone (a hired teacher or their parents) taught them at home, or they were sent to a neighbourhood Islamic school. Both options required some sacrifice by the parents. Hiring a teacher was expensive; local schooling meant mothers had to forgo the use of girl's labour. One second-generation woman depicts her childhood as one of a scholar in training, and she reports having an interest in learning since she was a young girl. Along with her schooling, she had to sell items in the market for her mother who had very few children.

> "I was with my mother. Her children kept dying, I was her 10th pregnancy. The rest of them all died. Only one I know, she is still living."[14]

Although she was one of her mother's only sources for acquiring an independent income, her mother let her attend the school of a first-generation woman initiator.

> "With her I began to understand the letters. If I wrote on the slate, she would say to me that I should read it. May God be good to her. Everytime I wake up and I do prayers for my parents, I do them with prayers for her."[15]

Her words indicate that her studies, her teacher, and the sacrifice of her parents were not standard experiences for Hausa girls and therefore they have special significance to her.

Once married, a woman's husband would often teach her the books beyond *the Qur'ân* privately or allow a woman Islamic teacher in the house. Tijaniyya women educated in this way could read Arabic, the *Holy Qur'ân*, books about Islamic prayer, and texts on Tijaniyya doctrine. Some of these learned women in Kano became private teachers. Women teachers could be single, married, divorced, or widowed women. However, all categories of women teachers depended on men for support in teaching and living, because most Kano women did not own their homes or other property outright. For about a 20–year period, judges in Kano would not grant women land in inheritance cases.[16]

Women lived in homes owned by men, usually a husband or other relative, and taught privately there as well. The first woman initiator was widowed and living in her brother's home just before she was appointed an initiator.[17] Women also taught in their students' homes, with the permission of their students' fathers or husbands. Men acquiesced to women's teaching because it was compatible with the greater Islamic patriarchal system in Kano; women were reproducing Islamic knowledge but were still dependent on men.

The federal government of Nigeria would later subvert this dependence by instituting UPE, thus requiring that more northern girls be educated. More women teachers, especially of IRK, had to be employed in order for this requirement to be fulfilled without transgressing the Hausa social norm of gender segregation. One Tijaniyya woman was among the first northern women to become a salaried professional, colonial government schoolteacher of IRK. But first, women used their educational and experience to become initiators.

## First-Generation Women Initiators

In 1937, the first Kano woman, Hajiya Iya, became an initiator of the order; a male West African scholar who resided in Saudi Arabia gave her initiator status while she was on a pilgrimage there. In a 1984 interview, Hajiya explained how two Arab Tijaniyya women visiting Kano helped her make the journey.

> "They were very intelligent women and read books of the Tijaniyya...... They stayed for about six months. I asked [my brother] if I could follow them to Mecca. He refused. Then, they said [to him] if they went to Mecca without [me], it would be like not packing anything."[18]

Her daughter, Hasana Sufi, a second-generation initiator, finishes the story of her mother's pilgrimage.

> "Her spiritual guide Ahmad, he was the one who gave [her initiator status]."[19]

Unlike the Kano Tijaniyya, the community in Saudi Arabia had a history of women as initiators.[20] This community of African Sufis lived within an Arab anti-Sufi environment with very strict gender segregation. Saudi gender segregation must have presented a barrier to women's membership in the Tijaniyya; they could not have men initiators as their spiritual advisers. Yet, women's membership would have been needed to increase the number if Tijaniyya followers and therefore the order's ability to withstand anti-Sufi attacks.

Despite their status as Sufi minorities, this community in Saudi Arabia was well thought of by West Africans because of its location, the Holy Land. The status of this community reinforced the rule of prestige by lending prestige to the first Kano woman initiator. The community in Saudi Arabia also showed Kano Tijanis that the concept of women initiators adhered to the rule of compatibility with Tijaniyya doctrine and practice.[21]

Soon after this event, Shaykh Niasse's reform movement changed the Tijaniyya into a more prominent order through the mass initiation of men and women by North African *shaykhs*. Although less strict than Saudi rules of gender segregation, Kano's social norms prevented many of these newly initiated women from having long-term initiator/adherent relationships with unrelated men. Without women initiators, the Kano Tijaniyya could not have sustained its mass membership and upheld the rule of being consistent with Hausa social norms. The first-generation of women initiators resolved this problem.[22]

The majority of first-generation women initiators were elite women from important Tijaniyya families. Like their male counterparts, these learned women were educated in the traditional Hausa Islamic system. Therefore, they were maintaining the Kano Tijaniyya's educational traditions and thus the rule of prestige.

Like most Kano women of the time, women initiators married at a young age (13 to 16 years old). Because they married so young, they usually became official members of the order after marriage, when they were old enough to make a conscious choice to join. A few Kano Tijaniyya women were appointed initiators while they were married, but the majority became initiators after they had been divorced or widowed. Divorced women and widows have tenuous status in Hausa society, especially if they are still child-bearing years.[23] All these women were premenopausal when they became initiators. Hausa society considers marriage to be ideal state for respectable women of this age; if unmarried, women are often thought to be promiscuous or in danger of becoming so.[24]

Despite Hausa attitudes about unmarried younger women, several of these Tijaniyya women refrained from remarrying after becoming initiators. They were not, however, the only divorced or widowed women to refrain from remarrying in order to escape seclusion and have more personal autonomy. Like other Kano women, women initiators found Hausa polygyny insecure and marriages sometimes unstable and short-lived. Therefore, women initiators forged strong, long-lasting relationships outside of marriage. Nonetheless, the initiators were unique; their relationships were with other pious women or male *shaykhs* and were based on Sufi affiliation. Spiritual authority and reputation for piety kept these women from being viewed as promiscuous and kept them from being marginalised by Kano society. Because they were divorced or widowed, they had no husbands whose authority or reputations might be challenged by women's spiritual authority over other women or women's allegiance to the order's leadership. These Tijaniyya relationships did not contravene Hausa family hierarchy—their relationships adhered to the rule of consistency.

**First-Generation Women's Men Patrons**

All the first-generation women initiators depended on men *shaykhs* as patrons. These men appointed women as initiators, taught them advanced books of Tijaniyya doctrine, provided them with room and board, set up a school in which the women taught, or engaged them as private teachers for the patron's women relatives. Despite gender segregation, most men *shaykhs* were not close relatives of these women, and many were not related by kinship at all. Instead, ties to men *shaykhs* were forged through scholarship and common Sufi affiliation.

Yet, these relationships were seen as necessary to support the rules of compatibility and unique utility because they limited the further mixing of the genders, while still increasing women's membership. When one man bestows initiator status to one woman, she has the ability to gain hundreds of women as adherents of the Tijaniyya. Because women were useful, indeed necessary, to the goal of popularising the Tijaniyya, men in Kano supported them in the new role of initiator. The support of important men in the order also helped women retain their respectability.

Like Tijaniyya men, women performed most of the services and obligations of initiators. In exchange for these services, women adherents contributed to women initiators' material and financial needs. Women initiators with schools boarded some of their students and adherents; women initiators also provided their advanced students with teaching opportunities in the houses of elite secluded women. One second-generation initiator reported that "when I finished learning *the Qur'ân*," her teacher, a first-generation woman, "[took] me to the house of the Ciroma of Kano...... there I taught school to his family. From there I was taken to be married."[25] These services for girls and women, especially those in seclusion, are further evidence of the existence of the rule of utility.

Notably, when interviewed, adherents portrayed first-generation women initiators in a different way than men initiators and *shaykhs*. Women's former students consistently told me that none of these women initiators taught for a set amount of money. Clearly, adherents were representing initiator's teachings as work done for other worldly rewards, not the cash of this world. A second-generation woman said of her first-generation teacher: "She was not given weekly school fees, sometimes she was given something, but always I know [she taught] because of *Allâh*."[26]

Students also described initiators as very fair-minded women who showed no difference between their students and their children. In an elegy for a first-generation initiator, she was described as "a just upright honest woman was sympathetic to students, her children one and all... She is a leader and a mother... mother of children of the order."[27] These traits also helped women initiators build large followings.[28] Although they set no fee for their teaching, as well-known teachers and initiators they were given gifts of cloth, livestock, and money at major Islamic feasts. In turn, women initiators would redistribute those gifts among initiates, students, visiting well wishers, and relatives.[29]

In terms of spiritual services, some women initiators were learned enough to conduct readings and exegesis of *the Qur'ân* for gatherings of women in private homes.[30] However, there was one function that men did not want women to perform, that was leading *wazifa*. Some thought the initiator's role in that rite too similar to the role of *iman* (prayer leader), which is specifically denied to women.[31] First-generation women refrained from leading *wazifa*, no doubt because of the rule of compatibility; they wanted the order's principles to comply with general Islamic ones.

Nor did first-generation women initiate or lead men. Theoretically, the order sanctioned women to initiate universally,[32] practically, women's unique utility lay in women, first-generation initiators' roles were compatible with Islamic notions about the superiority of men.

> "And women shall have rights similar to the rights against them, according to what is equitable: But men have a degree over them and *Allâh* is Exalted in Power, Wise" (*Holy Qur'ân* 2:228)

Women only initiating other women adheres to the rules of utility and compatibility.

### Second-Generation Women Initiators

Today, second-generation women initiators continue to operate under the same patriarchal bargains as the first-generation women. They uphold the same four rules, but they have helped to redefine norms for the order and Kano society. Indeed, both the circumstances and the women themselves have reshaped the context in which the rules are employed. Second-generation initiators remain predominantly elite women. Most of these women divorced or were widowed before they became initiators and refrained to remarry. One second-generation woman who was widowed in her early 30s explains why she stayed unmarried after her husband's death:

> "I decided I was grown up and I saw that I would not mind living the way I do [single in her brother's house]."[33]

Many of these women are dependent on male relatives for housing. Like first-generation initiators, the second-generation is authorised to initiate anyone into the Tijaniyya, but they continue to abide by the rule of compatibility and predominantly initiate women.[34] Most Kano Tijaniyya women I interviewed said that they refrain from initiating men voluntarily. One woman said her initiator status was important because women's teachings and initiating other women were the best ways to ensure harmony in the order. Clearly she attributed her restraint to the gender-segregated nature of proper Hausa society and Tijaniyya doctrine; she was conscious of maintaining the rules of the bargain.[35]

Second-generation men initiators consent to the same bargain their predecessors did: They recognise that women initiators' unique utility is in bolstering Tijaniyya membership among women. In exchange for this support, the men respect the women initiators' spiritual authority and their contributions to the order. However, the context for second-generation bargains has changed. Resisting Saudi-supported anti-Sufism is the chief goal of these Tijaniyya men. There is no doubt the Tijaniyya men face pressure similar to their counterparts in 1930s' Saudi Arabia and employ the utility of women initiators to build membership in the face of anti-Sufi attacks.

Women's spiritual dependence on men is another sign of continuity in the rules associated with patriarchal bargains among the Kano Tijaniyya. All the women (first and second generation) received initiator status from men and none have ever given initiator status (to women or men). Why Kano Tijaniyya women have not passed on initiator status to others is an intriguing question, especially since it would further limit contact between the genders. Unfortunately, first-generation women did not answer this question, in the records and interviews that survive. Second-generation women have said they have not yet found any of their adherents to be qualified for the position.[36] As there are no religious restrictions against women bestowing initiator status, it is clear that maintaining the rule of prestige keeps Kano women from doing so.

The *baraka* of first-generation women was not perceived to be intense as men *shaykhs* and therefore affected their prestige and practical ability to bestow initiator status. That the Tijaniyya's leading men were seen as having more *baraka* than women is not surprising. Tijaniyya men had more opportunities to read complex Islamic books, more financial freedom, more freedom of association, and more mobility to study with experts and to found schools. The patrons who bestowed initiator status on the first-generation women were extraordinary men (e.g., one was the leader of the West African community in the holy city of Medina and another was a titleholder and headmaster of a legal school). The men who appointed second-generation women to initiator status were similarly accomplished.

However, *baraka* and prestige are not gendered. They can be inherent in families such as Shaykh Niasse's family. While no Kano woman has passed her title on to another, a daughter of Shaykh Niasse from Senegal elevated one Kano woman.[37] This appointment is a clear indication that the rule of prestige is the element preventing Kano Tijaniyya women from appointing other women as initiators; the patriarchal bargains remain intact.

Continuities in Kano patriarchal bargains indicate that men's and women's attitudes are enduring and in some ways inherited. Attitudes about gender do not begin and end with individual women initiators or with the men who were their patrons; individual actors are important, but so are philosophies of the order that survive any given individual or generation. Just as analysing Kano Tijaniyya gender relations makes patriarchy less abstract, it also brings norms into sharper focus by shifting from the collective perspective to the transfer of specific attitudes at the individual level.

Tijaniyya patriarchal bargains and attitudes endure, yet the individual lives of second-generation initiators represent some significant changes in Kano Tijaniyya women's activities and status. Second-generation women have taken steps further toward personal autonomy and spiritual authority because national political and worldwide Islamic changes in educational policy have transformed Hausa societal norms and given women opportunities to redefine norms for the order.

For example, one young woman initiator is in her 20s; in 1994, she had never been married and was pursuing a teaching career.[38] Most first-and second-generation women initiators married before they joined the order, and all had been married at least once before they became initiators. But national educational policies have changed in Nigeria. The introduction of UPE in 1976 brought many more northern girls (urban and rural) into the classroom. Now, most girls marry and do not go on to secondary school, but many do finish secondary school and put off marriage until 18 or 20.[39]

This single, young Tijaniyya initiator is an example of a select group of Kano Hausa women (Tijaniyya and non-Tijaniyya) who have delayed marriage to obtain a higher educational level. She is not deviant from Hausa norms; her life is an indicator of an ongoing transformation in Hausa society that affects family life and women's opportunities to maneuver within their patriarchal bargains.

The state was not the only agent of educational reform in Nigeria; the Islamiyya school movement pioneered by anti-Sufis has reformed the private educational system in northern Nigeria. To retain students, Tijaniyya initiators and teachers opened their own Islamiyya schools. One second-generation woman owns her own house and in it runs a private Islamiyya school; her daughter, who is also an initiator, lives and teaches with her.[40] Until 1997, both of these women were divorced; the daughter was in her 30s and had been divorced for several years.[41] The dynamic of a woman-headed household gave both women more personal autonomy. The daughter remarried in 1997 and now lives in rooms built on top of her mother's house by her husband. She stays active in the community.

Although the changing forces of political Islam made these women's lifestyles possible, anti-Sufis only meant to transform education. Political Islam might see this household arrangement as deviant, but these women's activities are consistent with the rules of Kano Tijaniyya patriarchal bargains. Their school's utility is its ability to compete with anti-Sufis in the field of education, thereby maintaining the Tijaniyyas' prestige as Islamic educators. The school is not specifically for Tijaniyya girls and women, but the owner does hold Tijaniyya activities there. Finally, neither the mother nor the daughter is contravening Hausa family hierarchy: The mother is divorced and in her independent space, and the daughter officially lives under her husband's roof yet does not have to move outside of the house daily to get to work.

Financially, the majority of second-generation women initiators have a further measure of personal autonomy than most of their predecessors. The first-generation woman discussed earlier who taught in the colonial educational system led the way to this autonomy. Most second-generation women followed her into the salaried profession of school teaching. They were able to do so because educational norms have changed in northern Nigeria. The women interviewed report having found their government positions during the 1970s, after UPE was instituted.[42] One woman initiator and school teacher explains how she began teaching to make a living after her husband died and she had decided not to remarry.

> "Because I knew (women) were teaching, I knew that it was necessary for me to do it too. Then they opened up a primary school for women and they took me on there."[43]

Private Islamic educational norms have changed; the initiator who owns her own Islamiyya school has broken with her predecessors by charging set fees.

The educational background of women initiators has also changed in the second generation. None of the first generation attended colonial schools, knew English, nor could most write Hausa in roman script. Not only do most second-generation initiators teach in modern government schools, most have gone to government primary schools or received a certificate from a government school.[44] They represent an increase in the types of knowledge Kano Hausa women now have. Florencia Mallon pointed out that "sometimes the fissure between systems of rule allow(s) some personal autonomy for women."[45]

In this case, there were two fissures: one between federal government policy (UPE ensured that more attention was paid to girl's education) and the policy of the Kano emirate (which perceived British-style education for girls as corrupt), the other between the Tijaniyya and anti-Sufis. Both resulted in an increased need for women teachers at girl's schools. As government and Islamiyya school teachers, second-generation women have managed to maintain the rules of the bargain: They still have a unique utility to the order, they have updated their roles to be compatible with the modernising policies of the federal government and the anti-Sufi movement, they have not challenged Hausa social norms, and they have enhanced their types of knowledge and therefore the order's educational prestige.

Second-generation Tijaniyya women initiators have also blazed new spiritual trails for Tijaniyya women. One second-generation initiator conducts readings and exegesis of *the Qur'ân* in her school. She is one of only two Kano women certified by the emirate to hold public Qur'ânic exegesis. Since 1985, the emir's chief Islamic legal official must certify all persons who visit to hold a public reading and exegesis of *the Qur'ân*. The other certified woman is also a Sufi member, but not of the Tijaniyya.

Another woman initiator leads *wazifa* for an all-women's group.[46] This activity seems to breach the Tijaniyya patriarchal bargain because of its possible incompatibility with Islamic law and the resulting blow to Tijaniyya prestige. Although a daughter of Shaykh Niasse sanctioned this new spiritual role, there is no evidence that she wrote or requested an Islamic legal opinion to justify this within Islam. However, her prestige as a member of a family known for its Islamic scholarship and its abundance of spiritual grace has so far shielded this *wazifa* group from attack within the order. A third woman has initiated a few men.[47]

These last two actions clearly show how changing societal conditions in Nigeria have influenced these individual women's lives but have not influenced the four rules of Tijaniyya patriarchal bargains. Most second-generation women and men still uphold the rules handed down to them. Second-generation women who know about the women's *wazifa* group have chosen not to conduct *wazifa*, and they still refrain from initiating men. Therefore, these two women's activities are marginal within the Tijaniyya in Kano and may be short-lived. Ironically, these two changes can also be attributed to the weakening of Sufi orders.

Some readers might conclude that when Kano Tijaniyya women initiators are faced with larger societal changes, they react in the same manner: They manipulate options to their best advantage. One might argue that women from most societies use that strategy. Perhaps that is true, but all women's actions are not equally successful. I contend that the four principles gleaned from Kano Tijaniyya patriarchal bargains shed light on how "rules and scripts" determine whether women's strategies will succeed by gaining widespread acceptance or result in women's personal autonomy but also their cultural marginalisation. The contrast between Kano Tijaniyya initiators and the leadership in women's branches of Kano political parties in the 1960s illustrates this difference.

During the First Republic (1960–66), women in northern Nigeria could not vote, yet Kano's two political parties, the Northern Peoples Congress (NPC)—which opposed women's suffrage—and the Northern Elements Progressive Union (NEPU)—which supported women's suffrage and was loosely affiliated with the Tijaniyya—established, recruited, and financed women's branches. These branches could have represented significant steps towards including women in the political process and given women more personal autonomy and political authority.

Instead, most women officers of these branches were illiterate and were employed to dance, chant, and sing at political rallies, contravening the rule of prestige. The presidents and most active members of these two groups were prostitutes, and therefore, their lives were incompatible with Islamic principles and inconsistent with Hausa societal norms. However, women officers received money to travel, and the rallies were venues in which they could allocate their own labour.[48] Their new roles clearly gave these women more personal autonomy but no political authority, and participation in these groups carried a social stigma.

Nigerian women received universal suffrage in 1976, but the women's branches of NPC and NEPU were not revived in the Second Republic (1979–83), exactly when they could have been most effective. The marginalisation and eventual death of women's branches was not due to women's lack of interest in politics—more northern women than men voted in the 1979 elections, they voted for "the party 'supporting' women."[49]

Women's branches did offer women the advantages of money and mobility, but for most women that did not compensate for the resulting marginalisation. Because women did not acquiesce merely to providing entertainment for men politicians and did not embrace these new political roles, women's branches were not inherited and perpetuated. There was no second generation of these secular political organisations. Clearly, changing social and political context gave rise to women's branches, but individuals in these organisations broke the enduring rules of Hausa patriarchal bargains; therefore, the women's branches were short-lived.

In contrast, second-generation Tijaniyya women initiators have not only endured, they have expanded their spiritual authority beyond the order. First and foremost, in their capacity as teachers of Islamic religious knowledge, these women initiators have taught and interacted with hundreds of women and girls in various settings. The majority of their students are not members of the Tijaniyya, yet their students remember these women as pious and learned women and have helped build these women's reputations. Their reputations have brought some of their students into the order, and this recruitment has reinforced women's utility to the Tijaniyya. There are second-generation women initiators who work as Kano state government tutors helping potential pilgrims learn the duties of the pilgrimage.[50] The fact that these women were chosen for this work shows that they are considered spiritual authorities by the state government apparatus. In their capacity as tutors, they have yet another chance to establish their reputations among non-Tijaniyya members and to reinforce the prestige of the order.

Patriarchal bargains in Kano prior to 1937 were such that women who persevered could become educated in the traditional Hausa system. After 1937, some Kano Tijaniyya women obtained positions of spiritual authority because they were educated and thus qualified to become women initiators. But the opportunity to use their education in the interest of the order was only presented after changes occurred within the Kano Tijaniyya's doctrine and hierarchy. The precedents and activities of first-generation women initiators paved the way for the second generation. Rules agreed to by first-generation women and men were inherited by the second generation. However, changes in national social policies and Saudi attempts to influence worldwide Islam gave second-generation women a chance to modernise their roles in a changing society. Changing social context did not change the rules of Tijaniyya patriarchal bargains but it has influenced individual women's lives in Kano.

Saudi Arabians have made similar attempts to suppress radical Islamic fundamentalism elsewhere (like the supporters of Khomeini's Islamic Republic of Iran) and stop it from spreading throughout the Middle East and North Africa.[51] Those fundamentalist movements aim to mobilise the masses; therefore, they include women.[52] Saudi challenges to Muslim fundamentalism may have affected women's roles in fundamentalist patriarchal bargains. Research to define patriarchal bargains more precisely in these classic patriarchies of the Middle East can reveal the rules and scripts under which Arab women must labour to gain more autonomy yet avoid marginalisation.

The contrast between the classic patriarchy of the Arab world and the sub-Saharan patterns of Nigeria surely produced different sets of rules. For example, strong ties outside of marriage are not a feature of classic patriarchy, and therefore, the rules pertaining to Arab family hierarchy probably work differently than the rules for patriarchal bargains within Hausa families. However, like Tijaniyya bargains in Kano, fundamentalist Arab women no doubt have to consider whether their actions will be seen as compatible with Islamic principles, and fundamentalist men have recognised women's unique utility in the struggle to increase support for their movements.

The strategies Kano Tijaniyya women employed were founded on general conditions in sub-Saharan patriarchal bargains were bound by four rules. Both genders were insecure in polygny, maintained strong bonds outside of marriage, and were able to allocate their own labour. Women initiators provided a unique utility to the order's primary goal, their actions were compatible with Tijanniya doctrine and Islamic principles, their roles were consistent with Hausa societal norms, and their status maintained the order's prestige. Within these boundaries, women were able to vary their activities without "stepping out of line and losing their respectability." The result was an increase in both their personal autonomy and spiritual authority.

M. AHMAD

## REFERENCES


1. Deniz Kandiyoti, "Bargaining with patriarchy," *Gender and society*, Vol. 2, 1988, p. 274
2. *Ibid.*, p. 286.
3. *Ibid.*, p. 275.
4. Helen Rose Ebaugh, "Patriarchal bargains and latent avenues of social mobility: Nuns in the Roman Church," *Gender and Society*, 7, 1993, pp. 400–14.
5. Shahin Gerami, and Melodye Lehnerer. "Women's agency and household diplomacy: Negotiating fundamentalism," *Gender & Society*, 15/4, 2001, pp. 556–73.
6. Catherine Coles, and Beverly Mack, "Women in twenthieth-century Hausa society," in *Hausa Women in the Twentieth Century*, Madison: University of Wisconsin Press, 1991, p. 249; Peter K. Tibenderana, The beginnings of girls' education in the native administration schools in northern Nigeria. *Journal of African History*, 26, 1985, p. 108.
7. Albert F. Ogunsola, *Legislation and Education in Northern Nigeria*, Zaria, Nigeria: Oxford University Press, 1974, pp. 26–28.
8. Coles and Mack, *op. cit.*, 1991, p. 14.
9. *Ibid.*, pp. 155, 185.
10. Christian Coulon, "Women, Islam and *baraka*," in *Charisma and Brotherhood in African Islam*, edited by Donal Cruise O'Brien and Christian Coulon. Oxford, UK: Clarendon, 1988, pp. 121–23.
11. Muhammad Sani Umar, "From Sufism to anti-Sufism in Nigeria," *Muslim Identity and Social change in sub-Saharan Africa*, edited by Louis Brenner. Bloomington: Indiana University Press, 1993.
12. A.S. Huston, "The development of women's authority in the Kano Tijaniyya, 1894–1963," *Africa Today*, 46/3–4, 1999, pp. 43–64.
13. Kandiyoti, *op. cit.*, 1988, p. 276.
14. Ta Sidi, Interview by author, Kano, Nigeria, 7 July, 1992.
15. *Ibid.*
16. S.S. Zawiya, and T.A. Sadauki, *Jigatau Dan Bayero*, Kaduna, Nigeria: Nationhouse Press, 1991, pp. 86–87, 120.

17. Hajiya, Interview by Halilu Dantiye, Kano Nigeria, 1984.
18. *Ibid.*
19. Hasana Sufi, *Wakar ya Kamata* (A necessary poem). Unpublished poem, 1980.
20. Abubakar Atiku, *Ifadat al-murid* (Informing the disciple), Cario: Shukrat Maktabat, 1956.
21. *Ibid.*
22. Alaine S. Huston, We are many: Women Sufis and Islamic scholars in twentieth century Kano, Nigeria. Ph.D. diss., Indiana University at Bloomington, 1997, Ch. 5.
23. Enid Schildkrout, Widows in Hausa society, in *Widows in African Societies: Choices and Constraints*, edited by Betty Potash, Standford, CA: Stanford University Press, 1986.
24. Catherine Coles, Muslim women in town: Social change among the Hausa of northern Nigeria. Ph.D. diss., University of Wisconsin at Madison, 1983.
25. Maryan Ahmad, Interview by author, Kano, Nigeria, 1 July, 1993.
26. *Ibid.*
27. Muhammad Kani, *Hakuri* (Patience), Unpublished poem, n.d..
28. Aliyu Har Azumi, Interview by author Kano, Nigeria, 1 May, 1994.
29. Sufi, Husaini, *Takaitaccen tarihin Hajiya Tya* (A short history of Hajiya lya), Unpublished manuscript, 1993.
30. Zahra, Interview by Hajiya Mario Muhammed *Uwa Mabada Mama*, radio programme, July/August. Kano State Radio, 1984.
31. Joseph Kenny, trans. *The Risala: Treatise on Maliki Law of 'Abdallah Ibn Abi Zayd Al-Qayrawani*, Minna, Nigeria: Islamic Education Trust, 1992, p. 49.
32. Ahmad interview, 1993; Maryan Habibu, Interview by author Kano, Nigeria, 31 August, 1992; Hasana Sufi Interview by author Kano, Nigeria, 27 September, 1994.
33. Habibu interview 1992.
34. Hasana Sufi interview 1993; Balarabe Sule and Priscilla Straratt, "Islamic leadership positions for women in contemporary Kano society," *Hausa women in the twentieth century*, edited by

Catherine Coles and Beverly Mack Madison: University of Wisconsin Press, 1991, p. 42.

35. Habibu interview 1992.
36. Hasana Sufi interview 1993.
37. Badamasi interview 1992.
38. Raliya, Interview by author. Kano, Nigeria, 14 May 1994.
39. Katja Werthmann, "Seek for knowledge, even if it is in China!: Muslim women and secular education in northern Nigeria," Paper presented at Africa, Islam and Development conference, 26–27 May, 1997, Centre for African Studies, University of Edinburgh, Scotland, 1999.
40. Halima Sadiya, Interview by author, Kano, Nigeria. 21 October 1993; Hasana Sufi interview 1993).
41. Halima Sadiya, Interview by author, Kano, Nigeria. 21 October 1993.
42. Habibu interview 1992; Hasana Sufi interview 1993; Sadiya interview 1993; Ta Sidi interview 1992.
43. Habibu interview 1992.
44. Fulani interview 1994; Habibu interview 1992; Hasana Sufi interview 1993; Raliya interview 1994; Sadiya interview 1993).
45. Florencia E. Mallon, "The promise and dilemma of subaltern studies: Perspectives from Latin American history," *American Historical Review* 99 (December) 1994, 1510
46. Maryam Badamasi, Interview by author, Rimin Kebe, Nigeria, 20 August, 1992.
47. Sa'adatu Fulani, Interview by author, Kano, Nigeria, 9 May. 1994.
48. Barbara Callaway, and Lucy Creevey, *The Heritage of Islam: Women, Religion and Politics in West Africa*. Boulder, CO: Lynne Rienner, 1991, p. 152.
49. *Ibid.*, pp. 152–53.
50. Hasana Sufi interview 1993; Sadiya interview 1994.
51. William Ochsenwald, Saudi Arabia. In *The Politics of Islamic revivalism: Diversity and Unity*, edited by Shireen T, Hunter, Bloomington: Indian University Press, 1988, p. 106.
52. Leila Ahmed, *Women and Gender in Islam*. New Haven, CT: Yale University Press, 1992, p. 197.

# SIERRA LEONE

- Female Circumcision in Sierra Leone

# 39

# FEMALE CIRCUMCISION IN SIERRA LEONE

Sierra Leone is situated on the bulge of the West African Coast. It is bounded by the republic of Guinea on the North East and North West and by the Republic of Liberia on the South East and by the Atlantic Ocean on the West and South West. The country is divided into areas, namely the Western area in which lies the capital city of Freetown. The other areas are the Northern, Southern and Eastern areas. Literacy rate is 5–7%. Illiteracy is 90–95%. The population is 4.2 million and of this 80% live in the rural areas. The practice of female circumcision affects 90% of our female population.

There are four major ethnic groups in the country, inhabiting the 4 areas already noted. The Krio, 8% the whole female population, live in the Western area and are the only ethnic group who do not practice female circumcision. The other ethnic groups, the Mendes, Temnes, Limbas all practice the act of female circumcision. I must point out these ethnic groups consist of Muslims, Christians and Animists. Therefore the practice of female circumcision is not a religious rite, but it is a culture rite or a rite of passage from childhood to adulthood.

Female circumcision has been practiced in Sierra-Leone for over 200 years. The practice is believed to have originated because Communities required women to be virtuous until marriage, and after Marriage to remain faithful to their husbands. The communities believed that female circumcision removed the Organ responsible for sexual excitement and renders the female unresponsive to other males seeking sexual adventure. They also believed:

that it keeps the genital area clean
that it prevents promiscuity
that it increases matrimonial opportunities
that it promotes social and political integration
that it increases fertility
that it improves males' sexual performance and enjoyment
that it preserves virginity.

Although examination of all these reasons has shown that they have no real scientific or logical basis for continuing the practice, they still persists. They are 3 types of Female Circumcision:

*Type I—Clitoridectomy*: This is practiced by the Krio Muslims as a religious rite, according to Qur'ânic Law. It is practiced in the Western area of Sierra-Leone.

*Type II—Excision*: Excision is practised by the rest of the ethnic communities over the country. It is performed as part of an initiation rite in which girls are elevated from childhood to womanhood. During the past few years some communities performed the practice on younger girls and even on female babies between the age of one week and one year. The Susu tribe practice this type

*Type III—Infibulation*: Infibulation is not practiced in Sierra-Leone, except at the border with Guinea in the Northern part of the country.

Child mortality in the 3 areas where the practice is domain is between 230–250/1,000. Obstructed labour is very high in this provincial areas. Maternal mortality in this area is higher in the same area, as comparated to 40–60/1,000 in the Western area. Complications are poorly reported because of the code of the Secret Society involved. They include bleeding and shock, infections, urinary infection, tetanus

Death is not reported at all. Instead, the child who dies is proclaimed to be a devil who brings bad luck into the Society. Her parents have to pay substantial amounts of money to retrieve her name.

After the Dakar Conference those of us who attended formed a National Committee of Concerned Health Professionals, incorporating staff from the Ministries of Health, Education, Social Welfare, Development, UNICFF and WHO. We have met only once and plans are a foot to draw up strategics on how to approach the head of 'Bundu Bush' Sowes and her staff (TBA) considering its secret society and the fact that most of the National Committee are not members of the Bundo Bush, but we are going to have a workshop in December whereby the Traditional Birth Attendants, *i.e.*, circumcisers will be invited to the members and we can learn from them ways and means of eradicating the practice in Sierra-Leone, having as our goal the WHO 'Health for all by the year 2000".

I have a proposal drawn up which consists of a team of 7 health professionals to collect information and sensitise the population to the health hazards of female circumcision. The method used will be face to face interview using specially designed questionnaires and physical examination of selected patients of health centres and hospitals. From the findings we hope to develop strategies first to decrease the number of young girls being circumcised and later on to eradicate the practice altogether from Sierra-Leone.

R. FAVRET-SAADA

# SOUTH AFRICA

- Muslim Feminism and Muslim Personal Law

# 40

# MUSLIM FEMINISM AND MUSLIM PERSONAL LAW

Muslim women face the same status problems in the private and public spheres of life as their non-Muslim counterparts but it is alleged that, as members of a particular religious community, they experience another inequality. To assess this assertion, it is necessary to consider how gender issues are dealt with not only in terms of Islamic law, but also in the light of the authentic spirit of *the Qur'ân*. *The Qur'ân* is separated from the classical formulation of Islamic law or *shariah* by a process of legal development lasting more than two centuries.[1] It is common for Islamic law, which the interpretation and application of the primary sources by early Muslims, to be mistaken with Islam itself.

With an eye to how South Africa's final constitution might address the status of Muslim personal law and the related question of the position of Muslim women, this chapter examines the issue of Muslim personal law in South Africa and the constitutional provisions relating to the rights of women in a number of Muslim countries. It argues for the need to reform and codify Muslim personal law and for its recognition by the subordination to the constitution. However, it also stresses the importance of the reform project being in Muslim hands and the need for those involved "to ask afresh who we are, what we want, and if we are willing to begin to create a new order of things."[2]

## Advent of Islam in South Africa

The first Muslims arrived at the Cape from the Dutch colonies in the East Indies (now Indonesia) and the coastal regions of southern India between 1652 and 1658.[3] Although they were granted freedom to practise their religion in 1804,[4] the social and political inequalities prevailing in South Africa until recently prevented this from having full legal effect. However, it is anticipated that the rapid changes taking place in South Africa since the democratic elections of 1994 will rectify this situation. Central Statistical Services data[5] reveal that Muslims constitute an estimated 1.1 per cent of the South African population (excluding inhabitants of the former 'independent' homelands of Transkei, Bophuthatswana, Venda and Ciskei)[6] while Christians make up 66.5 per cent. South African Muslims in general belong to the Sunni[7] school of Islamic law.[8] They are more or less equally divided between the Hanafi and Shafi'i schools.

While the South African Law Commission has been engaged on a comparative study of South African and Islamic law,[9] its latest progress report records a temporary halt to the project.[10] The reasons are twofold. In the fist place, the previous minority government gave assurances, albeit at commissions level only, that the *modus operandi* of Muslim personal law would be determined by Muslims themselves. Hence, the South African Law Commission had to leave room for this kind of discretioin.[11] Secondly, the present government of national unity has not instructed the commission or any other body to investigate the possible recognition of Muslim personal law.[12]

In the interim, however, the *ulama* or Muslim religious bodies composed of experts on Islamic law have responded to a questionnaire issued by the commission, supporting the incorporation of Muslim personal law into the South African legal system.[13] These *ulama,* established in some of the erstwhile provinces of South Africa, consist of the *jamiats* of Natal and Transvaal, the Muslim Judicial Council of the Western Cape and the Madjlisul Ulama of Port Elizabeth in the Eastern Cape.[14]

Although the decisions of these bodies are theoretically binding upon the consciousness of Muslims, their competence to apply Islamic. Law is often questionable, since their members frequently lack accredited legal training. In any event, the long-standing non-recognition of Muslim personal law by the South African state has meant that the *ulama* have lacked the legal power to enforce their decisions.

This situation is almost certain to change, given the fact that the interim Constitution of the Republic of South Africa,[15] which is scheduled for finalisation by April 1999,[16] not only guarantees freedom of religion and belief (section 14(1)) but also provides for the enactment of legislation recognising religious personal law (section 14(3) (a)) and Muslim marriages (section 14(3) (b)). It may be that the establishment of the new political order underwritten by the Constitution is what persuaded the *ulama* and other local Islamic bodies to finally reach consensus on the need for state recognition of Muslim personal law.

In any event, the result was that a Muslim Personal Law Board was inaugurated in Durban on 14 August 1994 and charged with working for the incorporation of Muslim personal law into the South African judicial system.[17] Although the board is preparing draft bills aimed at providing interim relief in the areas of marriage and divorce,[18] its main task is conceived as hammering out how Muslim personal law might be applied, by 'ordinary courts or special family courts presided over by Muslim judges, and interpreted.[19]

However, some controversy surrounds the establishment and composition of the board. Although participation by the range of Muslim organisations is emphasised in the working of the board, critics point to a need for greater transparency and inclusivity, emphasising the principle that women's experiences should inform the drafting of any proposals that affect them.[20] In addition, there are differences of opinion over whether the recognition of Muslim personal law would mean that Muslims were exempted from the provisions of Chapter 3 of the Constitution, notably the equality clause (section 8), where they conflict with Muslim personal law. In other words, the question is whether the Constitution will be supreme (section 4) or whether Muslim personal law will take precedence in respect of Muslims. The latter scenario has serious implications for Muslim women since they are accorded a status inferior to men by Muslim personal law, although, significantly, not by Islam itself. In any event, this apparent conflict between the right to freedom of religion and the right to equality is one of the issues that writers of the final constitution will have to address.

**Women under Islamic Law**

Explanation of the legal and social status of Muslim women requires some reference to the Islamic law which evolved in the seventh century of the Common Era (CE) in the predominantly urban environment of the Arabian peninsula and lower Mesopotamia.[21] The two primary sources of Islamic law, *the Qur'ân* and *Sunna*, developed during the 23 years of Muhammad's prophethood. *The Qur'ân*, regarded by Muslims as the literal word of God revealed piecemeal to Muhammad over this period, emerged as a book after his death in 632 CE. It is not considered a book of law, although it contains approximately 80 verses dealing with legal matters, mostly to do with the family and inheritance. The Sunna are the received customs associated with Muhammad, also compiled after his death into a book called *Hadith*. To some extent this can be considered a biography of Muhammad.[22]

Of some 100 verses dealing with women's issues in *the Qur'ân*, only a few are devoted to the Islamic status of women. Thus it is not surprising that varying interpretations of this status have developed.[23] In addition, the fourth chapter or *sura* of *the Qur'ân* is devoted to women, a significant feature when viewed in the context of seventh century patriarchy and misogyny. Indeed, Islam afforded numerous improvements to the lives and rights of women in the Arabian community. However, a flexible and gradual approach was essential if Islam was to survive in the hostile milieu into which it was born, and if the religious bond of comradeship and equality was to replace pre-Islamic paternal and tribal ties.

Modernist Muslim scholars make an important distinction between verses in *the Qur'ân* that are normative or of enduring relevance, and those whose relevance is confined to the context of Muhammad's fledgling community.[24] Their argument is that the moral or ethical norms relating to the status of women contained in *the Qur'ân* are at least as important as its specific legal rules.[25] In other words, their contention is that it is not the spirit of Islam, as revealed in its primary sources, that discriminates against women. Rather it is the practice of an Islam distorted by cultural influences during the centuries of its development and its own early readmission of patriarchy after the death of Muhammad.[26]

The crucial points is that *the Qur'ân* is separated from the classical formulation of Islamic law[27] by processes of legal development lasting more than two centuries. During this period the Qur'ânic norms underwent considerable dilution, often to the detriment of women.[28] In other words, classical Islamic law is not canonical. Rather, it is common law, codified several centuries after Islam came to existence.[29] Not only has the Muslim approach to the issue of women's rights been historically diverse[30] but more significantly, the changes introduced by Islam in relation to women's rights were revolutionary in the context of seventh century Arabia. Faruqi describes four periods: the period of pre-Islamic Arabia or 'Age of Ignorance' the classical period or early centuries of Islam; the period of decline (around 1250-1900) during which a negative picture of the status of women was etched; and the period of reform, which extends from the late nineteenth century to the present. It is irrelevant to an exploration of the original spirit of Islam that these changes do not appear dramatic against the backdrop of modernity, or that the status of Muslim women today compares unfavourably with that of their Western counterparts.

However, it is precisely modern and Western influences that have led to the enactment of legal reform in a range of Muslim countries. Such reforms has been restrictive in some cases, for example in Egypt and Pakistan, less restrictive in Iran and Iraq, and non-restrictive in countries such as Turkey and Tunisia.[31] In some Islamic countries, *Saudi Arabia*, for example, there has been no attempt to reform Muslim personal law.[32]

Various indicators, such as the regulation or abolition of polygyny and the secularisation of inheritance law, have been used to assess whether the status of women in Muslim countries has improved as a result of such reforms. However, close examination reveals that personal law reform in most Muslim countries, especially as it pertains to women's rights, has been minimal and slow, bringing only superficial relief to women, contrary to the clear Qur'ânic injunctions in this regard. Even where reform has been non-restrictive, as in Turkey, it has not delivered substantial improvement to women's lives.[33] This conservatism in the realm of personal law stands in sharp contrast to the liberal adoption of secular commercial and criminal codes.

Thus it is the case that in many respects the position of Muslim women is less favourable today than it was in the early days of Islam. However, this is not to support the contention that discrimination against Muslim women is religiously based. To the contrary, it is, in fact, deviation from the original spirit of Islam, as a result of patriarchal interpretations, cultural or customary influences, illiteracy and ignorance, that is responsible for the oppressed position of Muslim women.[34]

That this oppression may appear most dramatic in the domestic sphere is the result of the tendency in Islamic states towards secularisation in the public sphere, while at the same time leaving the private realm to regulation by Islamic law. Under the influence of the modern trend towards recognition and protection of human rights, constitutions guaranteeing equal rights to all citizens exist in many countries with Muslim communities and even in some Islamic states. Obviously this sets up contradictions and tensions since such constitutional provisions conflict with the Muslim personal law codes that privilege men over women.[35] The following comment in respect of the awkward dichotomy experienced by Egyptian women, in their roles as citizens of modern states and members of a religious community, could apply to all Muslim women:

> "In a division that was never precise, the state increasingly came to influence their public roles, leaving to religion the regulation of their private or family roles. The structural contradictions and tensions this created have to this day never been fully resolved."[36]

Reaction to the challenge posed by modern concern with human rights, particularly as it relates to the status of women, has divided Muslims into three main camps: Modernists conservatives and fundamentalists.[37] The modernist minority is reformist, embracing western ideals of emancipation. Their views is that Islam itself, properly understood, establishes complete equality between the sexes in all spheres, public and private. Conservatives and fundamentalists, between whom there is not much ideological difference, take the view that Islam restricts equality between the sexes to the sphere of religious belief and observances such as prayers, fasting, charity and pilgrimage. Such observances are essentially what determines whether a person is Muslim, and it is this part of Islam that remains practically static, creating a kind of umbrella identity which unifies Muslim people of various cultures.

In India, where Muslims constitute a minority, Muslim personal law is governed by the Muslim Personal Law (*Shariat*) Application Act of 1937 and enjoys statutory recognition as a separate code. Although in force at the time of the commencement of the Indian Constitution and clearly inconsistent with it, Muslim personal law was construed by the Indian courts to be exempt from constitutional scrutiny on the basis that it was not among 'laws in force'.

Thus, for Muslim women in India it is of little help that article 13(1) of the Constitution stipulates that all laws inconsistent with the fundamental rights it guarantees in Part III will be void to the extent of such inconsistency. Nor does the right to equality before the law and equal protection of the law afforded by article 14, or the article 15 prohibition of discrimination on grounds of sex and religion, among others, mean a great deal in practice.[38] Muslim personal law enjoys a large degree of immunity to state interference and regulation in India, creating a 'deplorable situation' for Muslim women.[39]

In Pakistan, appart from the Dissolution of Muslim Marriages Act of 1939 and the Muslim Family Laws Ordinance of 1961, there has been no codification of Muslim personal law.[40] However, unlike their counterparts in secular India, Muslims in theocratic Pakistan have made slow but steady progress in reforming Muslim personal law.[41] Nevertheless, the same pattern of constitutional subordination to Muslim personal law is evident. The 1973 Constitution of Pakistan itself exempts the Muslim Family Laws Ordiance of 1961 from challenge in any court and from article 8 of its Fundamental Rights, which provides that laws inconsistent with those fundamental rights will be void. Thus, constitutional guarantees of the equality of citizens and freedom from discrimination on the basis of sex, are meaningless for women in Pakistan.

In Malaysia, a federation of 13 states with a 50 per cent Muslim population, the federal Constitution is based on a Western model and concept of democracy. However, the commitment to human rights that is part of this model is subverted by constitutional recognition of Muslim personal law and provisions enabling its regulation by state governments. As a result there is little uniformity, except in so far as most states have opted to codify rather than reform Muslim personal law. What is uniform however is the fact of conflict and contradiction between constitution and Muslim personal law.[42]

Indonesia, with a 90 per cent Muslim population, is an exception to this pattern, at least in respect of national marriage laws which were unified in 1975 for all sections of the population, regardless of religion. Although there was resistance from Muslims, these marriage laws changes resulted in modifications to Islamic law. To the extent that Islamic law is part of the new marriage laws, it is part of the positive law of Indonesia and the state is therefore established as an authority in the administration of such law and as an arbiter of its legitimacy.[43]

## Modern Constitutions and Muslim Personal Law

The pattern of conflict between modern constitutions and Muslim personal law outlined above, and its resolution in favour of Muslim personal law, applies also to the position of Muslim states in relation to international human rights instruments such as the United Nations Charter of 1945 and the Universal Declaration of Human Rights (1948). While both documents provide for both religious and women's rights, neither foresees a conflict between these two kinds of rights. In respect of more recent and explicit instrument, such as the 1980 United National Convention on the Elimination of All

Forms of Discrimination Against Women (Cedaw), the strategy of Muslim states and those with significant Muslim communities has been to become signatories but with reservations in respect of articles that conflict with Muslim personal law.

The Egyptian stance on article 16 of Cedaw provides an example. The article requires complete equality between men and women in all matters relating to marriage and family relations during a marriage and upon its dissolution. While Egypt has become a signatory to Cedaw, it is with the explicit reservation that its obligations in terms of article 16 should not prejudice Islamic shariah provisions.[44] Similarly, India has placed a reservation on its signature of Cedaw in respect of both article 16 and article 5, which requires states party to the convention to work towards eliminating prejudicial cutomary practices that maintain inequality between the sexes. The reservation subordinates Indian compliance with the convention to its "policy of non-interference in the personal affairs of any community without its initiative and consent", rationalised on the basis of 'India's desire to safeguard the rights of its religious and ethnic minorities."[45] Pakistan has not yet become a signatory of Cedaw but the government has indicated that it intends to sign the document with similar reservations.[46]

In summary then, it appears that the Cedaw goal of equality between the sexes is unlikely to be realised in Muslim countries, even in those that have signed the convention, since it is a goal in direct conflict with Islam as it is practised today.[47] This is true also in respect of those Muslim states which claim that equality between the sexes has been achieved, as is evident from a cursory inspection of both personal and public law in these countreis.[48]

### Muslim Women in South Africa

The interim Constitution of South Africa includes a Bill of Rights which, among other things, outlaws discrimination on grounds of sex (section 8). The question is how such safeguards of fundamental rights might coexist with recognition of Muslim personal law. Put differently, one might ask what the chances are for Muslim women in South Africa to reap the benefits of the Bill of Rights, given the failure if similar instruments to afford protection to Muslim women elsewhere. Finally, the question could be formulated in terms of conflicting rights: will the right to equality take precedence over the right to religious freedom?

There is of course, another fact for women to contend with: there is no guarantee that legal reform, whether constitutional or statutory, will deliver real equality between the sexes. For Muslim women, the achievement of real equality lies on the other side of reformation of Muslim personal law in line with the true Qur'ânic spirit. The worst that could happen for Muslim women in South Africa is that Muslim personal law remains unrecognised and therefore unproblematised.

Section 35(1) of the Constitution provides that, in interpreting the provisions of the Bill of Rights, a court of law 'shall... have regard to public international law' of relevance to the protection of human rights. Clearly, Cedaw would qualify as relevant in relation to the rights of women and it could be argued that this is so irrespective of ratification of the convention by the South African government.[49] However, the Women's Charter adopted by some 100 women's organisations participating in the National Women's Coalition and handed over to the Constitutional Assembly on National Women' Day in 1994, seeks more explicit recognition for Cedaw in the final constitution.

Submitted in the hope that it will be attached as a supplement or interpretive guideline to the final bill of rights, the charter provides in article 9 that "Custom, culture and religion shall be subject to the equality clause in the Bill of Rights". Representing a distillation of the Cedaw requirement of state signatories "to embody the principle of the equality of men and women in their national constitutions or other appropriate legislation... and to ensure, through law and other appropriate means, the practical realisation of this principle,"[50] such a provision, if adopted, would settle the questions posed in the first paragraph of this section.

However, even if the Women's Charter does acquire constitutional status, a word of caution would be in order, since "the record of equality litigation in countries as diverse as... India and the USA, reminds us that a bill of rights is not always translated into justice."[51] And, in the absence of an explicit settlement of the conflict between the Bill of Rights and Muslim personal law, it may be that, despite the equality clause, the Commission for Gender Equality provided for in the interim Constitution, and Constitutional Principle V,[52] Muslim women will continue to suffer subordination. Indeed, this has been the case not only in Muslim countries but also in secular India, notwithstanding election promises made to women.

There are, in fact, pointers to the possibility of such an outcome in the interim Constitution itself. Section 4(1), while making the Constitution "the supreme law of the Republic", also allows for the possibility that laws or acts inconsistent with the Constitution may be permitted if so "provided expressly". It could also be argued that section 33(1) opens the way for subordination of the equality clause to Muslim personal law by providing for limitation of the rights entrenched in Chapter 3 by 'law of general application', which would include customary law[53] and, by implication, Muslim personal law once it is recognised.[54] However, the provisos attached to such limitation would appear to make this argument untenable.[55]

More difficult to dismiss is the argument that Muslim women will be among the victims of the fact that the Bill of Rights appears to operate only vertically, that is, enforceable only against the state.[56] If this is true of the final constitution then it is difficult to see how challenges to an unreformed Muslim personal law might enjoy constitutional support.

In the light of the fact that neither international human rights instruments nor egalitarian provisions incorporated into the constitutions of Muslim states have been effective in providing relief for Muslim women, it is clear that legal reform is not necessarily the total answer. It may be that gradual social reform within the Muslim community is the only hope for Muslim women. In this regard it is necessary to emphasise again that the supposed androcentric nature of Islam is nothing more than a fiction sustained by ignorance. Therefore, although some Muslim personal laws are in clear conflict with the principle of gender equality, it would be wrong to conclude that Islam itself is antipathetical to equality between the sexes. Indeed, "as women become effective participants in Muslim society, Islam will be better able to cope with the realities of the twenty-first century."[57]

The best option for the recognition and application of Muslim personal law in South Africa lies in the codification of Islamic law and enactment of a comprehensive bill or "uniform Muslim code" applicable to Muslims. Such a code should address variations in the four major schools of Muslim legal thought as well as the desirability of reform to existing Muslim personal law. A secular civil code, intended to apply uniformly to all citizens, would be rejected by the Muslim community. Moreover such codes, where they do exist, have failed to offer significant redress to Muslim women.

It is too ambitious to expect the process of reform of Muslim personal law to be set in motion by a call for the reinterpretation of Islam and *the Qur'ân*, as suggested by some academics at a conference on 'Islam and Civil Society in South Africa" held at the University of South Africa in August 1994.[58] Instead, reform must be addressed in line with the true *Qur'ânic spirit* and in the context of an evolving South Africa.

The relationship between constitutional law and Muslim personal law must be very carefully considered. The constitution cannot protect Muslim personal law if the necessary justification and legitimation for it is lacking. Arguments to the contrary notwithstanding, it is all but certain that freedom of religion will be guaranteed only in so far as it does not violate other fundamental rights.

Although there are opposing voices the general hope in the Muslim community of South Africa seems to be for Muslim personal law to be included in the ambit of the final constitution and in accord with the provisions of its bill of rights. The challenges facing the Muslim Personal Law Board of South Africa in this regard are enormous. Unless it succeeds in its task, the result will be continuation of the status quo, namely the functioning of Muslim personal law independently of the South African law.[59]

At the very least, the board should enable Muslim women to exercise a choice. In reality, however, the vast majority of Muslim women are subject to men and male-dominated religious bodies who continue to regulate their lives in accord with the traditional interpretations of Islamic law. Subordinating Muslim personal law to the bill of rights will ensure that, whatever the final shape of a code of Muslim personal law, it will provide for equality between the sexes and, moreover, in Muslim terms. It is in this regard that the following poignant judicial rumination seems appropriate as conclusion:

> "I often wonder whether we do not rest our hopes too much upon constitutions, upon laws and upon courts. These are false hopes; believe me, these are false hopes. Liberty lies in the hearts of men and women; when it dies there, no constitution, no law, no court can save it; no constitution, no law, no court can even do much to help it."[60]

N. MOOSA

## REFERENCES


1. N. Moosa, "Comparative study of the South African and Islamic law of succession and matrimonial property with special attention to the implications for the Muslim woman", unpublished master's thesis, University of the Western Cape, 1991.
2. J.H. Garvey and T.A. Aleinikoff, *Modern Constitutional Theory: A Reader,* Minnesota, West Publishing Company, 1991, p. 409.
3. A. Davids, *The Mosques of Bo-kaap: A social history of Islam at the Cape,* Cape Town, South African Institute of Arabic and Islamic Research, 1970, p. xv.
4. *Ibid.,* note 4 at xxi.
5. *Demographic Statistics,* 1993, p. 9.
6. This figure is approximated at 500 000; see F. Cachalia, 'Legal Pluralism and Constitutional Change in South Africa: The Special Case of Muslim Family Laws", paper presented at seminar on 'Approaches to the Study of Islam and Muslim Societies', University of Cape Town, 17-19 July 1991.
7. The four major Islamic schools of law were established in the eighth century and named after their founders, namely Hanafi, Maliki, Shafi'i and Hanbali; see J.L. Esposito, *Women in Muslim Family Law,* New York, Syracuse University Press, 1982, p. 2.
8. J.A. Naude, "Islam in South Africa: A General Survey", *Journal Institute of Muslim Minority Affairs,* 1985, p. 25.
9. Project 59, on Islamic marriages and related matters.
10. South African Law Commission, *Twentieth Annual Report 1992* (1993), p. 42.
11. Moosa, *op. cit.,* note 1 at 169.
12. A.K. Toffar, 'Muslim Personal law in a Non-Muslim State', paper presented at workshop on 'Islamic Personal Law in South Africa: Its Future Position', Islamic Unity Convention, Cape Town, 16 October 1994.
13. Moosa, *op. cit., note* 1 at 172-88.

14. Naude, *op. cit.*, note 9.
15. Act 200 of 1993, hereinafter referred to as the Constitution, See J.C. Bekker & G. Carpenter (eds.), *Butterworths Selection of Statutes and Constitutional Law,* Durban, Butterworths, 1994; D. Basson, *South Africa's Interim Constitution,* note 16 at xxiii.
16. Basson, *op. cit.*, note 16 at xxiii.
17. Board gets established and prepares to draw up MPL bill, al-Qalam, 1994, p. 4.
18. These draft bills are based on traditional interpretations of Islamic law and leave much to be desired as far as women's rights are concerned. Viewed from a gender perspective, it is essential that the board should have at least 50% female representation. It is highly unlikely that traditionally oriented *ulama* will be able to formulate and codify Muslim personal law so that both sexes will be treated equally.
19. S. Dangor, "Muslim Personal Law: Interpretation and Application", *Muslim Views,* 1994, p. 12.
20. G. Paleker, "MPL Board Under Attack", *Muslim Views,* 1994, p. 4.
21. B.F. Stowassser, "Religious Ideology, Women, and the Family: The Islamic Paradigm", in B.F. Stowasser (ed.), *Islamic Impulse,* London, Croon Holm, 1987, p. 290.
22. M.F. Rateb, *Civil rights in the light of Islamic legislation,* Cairo, Aalam Al-Kotob, 1988, p. 3.
23. Stowasser, *op. cit.*, note 22 at 262.
24. F. Rahman, "The Status of Women in Islam: A Modernist Interpretation", H. Papanek & G. Minault (eds.), Separate World: *Studies of Purdah in South Asia,* New Delhi, South Asia Books, 1982, p. 302.
25. N. Coulson & D. Hinchclife, "Women and Law Reform in Contemporary Islam", L. Beck & N. Keddie (eds.), *Women in the Muslim World,* Cambridge, Harvard University Press, 1978, p. 37.

26. W.M. Watt, *Muhammad at Medina,* Karachi, Oxford University Press, 1981, p. 272; A. Hibri, "A Study of Islamic History: Or how did we ever get into this mess?", *Women's Studies International Forum,* 1982, pp. 207-12.

27. Islamic law or shariah is the reinterpretation and application of the primary sources by early Muslims. It is common for shariah to be mistaken for Islam itself.

28. Coulson and Hinchcliffe, *op. cit.,* note 26 at 38.

29. F. Shaheed, "The Cultural Articulation of Patriarchy: Legal Systems, Islam and Women", *South Asia Bulletin,* 1986, p. 39.

30. L.L. Faruqi, "Women' Rights and the Muslim Women", *Islam and the Modern Age* 76, 1972.

31. Beck and Keddie (eds.) *Muslim World, note 26 at 15; Coulson & Hinchcliffe, note 26 at 48; B.* Sivaramayya, "Equality of Sexes as a Human and Constitutional Right and the Muslim Law", in T.Mahmood (ed.), *Islamic Law in Modern India,* New Delhi, Indian Law Institute, 1972. p. 75; M. Charrad, "State and Gender in the Maghrib", *Middle East Report,* 1990, 21; NJ Austrin, "Modernisation, legal Reforms and the Place of Women in Muslim Developing Countries", unpublished doctoral thesis, Southern Illinois University, 1987, p. 46.

32. E.H. White "Legal Reform as an Indictor of Women's Status in Muslim Nations ", in Beck & Keddie (eds.), *Muslim World, note* 26 at 54.

33. A. Afetinan, *The Emancipation of the Turkish Woman,* Paris Unesco, 1962, pp. 51-53; F. Mansur Cosar, "Women in Turkish Society", in Beck & Keddie (eds.), *Muslim World,* note 26 at 124–40; D. Kandiyoti, 'Women, Islam and the State", *Middle East Report,* 9, 1991, p. 11.

34. N. Honarvar, 'Behind the veil: Women's rights in Islamic societies" *The Journal of Law and Religion,* 1988, 365; F. Shaheed, 'Cultural Articulations', note 30 at 38 D.C. Gordan, *Women of Algeria: An Essay on Change,* Cambridge, Harvard University Press, 1968, p. 31; A.A. Engineer The Rights of Women in Islam, London, C. Hurst and Company, 1920, pp. v-vi.

35. Kandiyoti, "Women, Islam", note 34-5.

36. M. Badran, *Competing Agenda: Feminists, Islam and the State in Nineteenth- and Twentieth-Century Egypt,* London, Macmillan, 1991, p. 201.

37. Gordan, Women of Algeria, note 35 at 29; Stowasser, "Religious ideology", note 22 at 260.

38. S.A.H. Rizivi, "Book Review: Muslim Law and the Constitution by A.M. Bhattacharjee", *Islamic and Comparative Law Quarterly,* 1987, p. 84.

39. H.A. Gani, *Reform of Muslim Personal Law: The Shah Bano Controversy and the Muslim Women (Protection of Rights on Divorce) Act 1986,* New Delhi, Deep and Deep Publications, 1988, p. 161.

40. R. Patel, *Islamisation of Laws in Pakistan?,* Karachi, Faiza Publishers, 1986. p. 92.

41. Gani, Reform, note 50 at 27 and 158.

42. Z.A Wahid, "The Muslims in Malaysia: A Political and Constitutional Analysis", Ethnic Studies Report, 1990, pp. 9-10; J. Connors, "Malaysia: Responding to Religious and Cultural Pluralism", *Journal of Family Law,* 1988-1989, pp. 203-04.

43. A.H. Johns, 'Indonesia: Islam and Cultural Pluralism", J.L. Esposito (ed.), *Islam in Asia: Religion, Politics and Society,* New York, Oxford University Press, 1987, pp. 217-18; M. Cammack, 'Islamic Law in Indonesia's New Order', *International and Comparative Law Quartelry,* 1989, p. 56.

44. A.A. An-Na'im. *Toward an Islamic Reformation: Civil Liberties, Human Rights and International Law* (New York, Syracuse University Press, 1990) 178-9.

45. A. Rahman, "Religious Rights Versus Women's Rights in India: A Test Case for International Human Rights Law", *Columbia Journal of Transnational Law,* Vol. 28/1, 1990, pp. 473-98.

46. Women & Law, *National Report, Pakistan,* Lahore, Shirkat Gah, 1994, p. vii.

47. M.K. Bruce, 'Work of the United Nations Relating to the Status of Women', *Revue des droits de l'homme,* 1971, pp. 365-66.

48. N. E. Saadawi, 'The Political Challenges Facing Arab Women at the End of the 20th Century', in N. Toubia (ed.), *Women of the Arab World: The Coming Challenge. Papers of the Arab Women's Solidarity Association Conference,* London, Zed Books, 1988, p. 11.

49. Cedaw was signed by the previous South African government in January 1993. The convention has not been ratified by the new democratic government but there have been calls for such ratification to be given soon and without reservation.

50. Part 1, article 2 (a), GA Res. 34/180, 1979.

51. C. Albertyn, 'The Limits of Equality: Women's Issues in a Bill of Rights', *Rights,* 1922, p. 23.

52. This principle reads: "The legal system shall ensure the equality of all before the law and an equitable legal process. Equality before the law includes laws, programmes or activities that have as their object the amelioration of the conditions of the disadvantaged, including those disadvantaged on the grounds of race, colour or gender."

53. T.W. Bennett, 'The Equality Caluse and Customary Law', *South African Journal on Human Rights,* 1994, pp. 123-4.

54. It appears that customary or indigenous law is erroneously equated with Muslim personal law which, although influenced by custom, is essentially religious in nature; see "Muslim marriages will be 'legal' in new SA', *al-Qalam,* 1993, p. 9.

55. Limitation of the rights enshrined in Chapter 3 is permissible, provided that such limitation 'shall not negate the essential content of the right in question', and only to the extent that it is "reasonable and justifiable in an open and democratic society based on freedom and equality".

56. See Bennett, "Equality Clause", note 64 at 125-6 and L.M. du Plessis, "The genesis of the chapter on fundamentalist rights in South Africa's transitional construction" *South African Public Law,* 1994, 13 and 19, for discussion on the horizontal application of human rights.

57. Rahman, "Religious Rights", note 56 at 498.

58. "Conference calls for 'rethinking' Islam", *al-Qalam*, 1994, p. 5.

59. S. Poulter, 'The Claim to a Separate Islamic System of Personal Law for British Muslims", in C. Mallat & J. Connors (eds.), *Islamic Family Law*, London, Graham & Trotman, 1990, pp. 147, 159.

60. J.D. van der Vyver, "Constitutional Options for Post-Apartheid South Africa", *Emory Law Journal* 1991, p. 772.

# SUDAN

- Challenges Faced by Sudanese Feminist Liberation Movement
- Gender Maternity and Morality in Sudanese Community in Egypt
- Feminist Movement and Fundamentalist Resistance
- Sexist Matriculation Policy in Sudan
- Female Circumcision in Sudan

# 41

# CHALLENGES FACED BY SUDANESE FEMINIST LIBERATION MOVEMENT

As in many Muslim countries, in Sudan the Feminist liberation movement has been controversial in the sense that, on one hand there is a general tendency to deny feminism and its existence in the Third World Countries. On the other hand, some writers suggest that Sudanese women suffer from a rigid and oppressive value system, and that this only began to change in the process of contact with the west.[1] Neither view is historically correct. Women enthusiastically campaign in defending their rights and freedom. Moreover, women's struggles in the Third World, including the Women's movement in Sudan, emerged with the national movement and struggle for independence, a phenomenon common to many former colonies. Throughout history, Sudanese women have resisted the oppressive values. Although the roots of the Sudanese women movement reaches back the last century, but its formal existence go back to the 40's of this century, when the first women's organisation was formed in 1947.

The Sudanese feminist movement has achieved a number of important successes for women's liberation. Indicators have shown the women's movement has been committed to achieving social, economic and political justice for example, the Women's movement with support of the Trade Union Movement in 1951 succeeded in getting equal pay for equal work, maternity leave and other employment rights, and by 1954 the right to vote and stand for election. They felt the necessity to take on these issues. Other related issues came from the realisation of their subordinate position in the Sudanese society.

In Sudan, women have been viewed as subordinate in both public and private spheres. One can recognise political, economic and ideological dimensions of women's subordination. More specifically, the voice of the Sudanese women in political, economic and ideological spheres has been determined by voices of women which mostly reflect male domination. Evidence to support this can be drawn from the statistical data: Sudanese women have low level of literacy and educational attainment high fertility and high maternal mortality, low participation in modern industry and the formal labour force, and low participation informal organisations and political parties.[2]

Sudanese women could be perceived as being a unheaded lot, robbed of their will and freedom, and judged by a number of misconceived notions.[3] This image of Sudanese women is widely held by social reformers, government organisations, development planners, religious leaders and, to some extent, by women themselves. But ultimately, understanding the position of Sudanese women must involve an analysis of a whole complex of laws and attitudes, Ideals and realities, rights and obligations, and traditions. To uncover of the Sudanese women's really the above factors and forces must be taken into account.

One can not deny the fact that, there have been changes, and of course these changes took place in different ways for different women in different places, taking into considerations class, race, political background and education. In order to assess the process of social changes and the role of women's movement in encouraging and motivating women's liberation, one have to look to what went on before, that is, the history and the tradition of the Sudanese community. However, how difficult it was for Sudanese women to fight and get their social, economic; political and legal rights, still they succeed to attain some of them, e.g. The following case illustrates how the ordinary woman as that time perceived her oppression: the case was presented to the Governor of Khartoum Province, August 20, 1932:

> "Respectfully I beg to state that a Shari'a judgment of Obedience to my husband, who I have not seen before the wedlock, has been passed. Marriage was made against my will, after 3 days of continual beating; I accepted the same to save myself. But owing to the disease of consummation with which he is afflcated. I prevented him from entering my room, and therefore I am still a virgin. Moreover I am a Khartoum citizen and he is from the Blue Nile Province and owing to his sickness has not work and is supported by his father who is penniless and about to ask for alms. Owing to the above circumstances which do absolutely prevent me from accompanying the said husband, I heartily protest my leaving Khartoum and proceeding to Blue Nile Province.
>
> The only point I am aiming at is that your Excellency will permit me to remain in Khartoum Province and live amongst my family, no doubt without being divorced, if the above said husband refuses to divorce me.
>
> Its not a difficult matter for our religion which allows a man to marry 4 wives at one time to find that I am disobedient'... I wish that I be adjudged as such and I assert that I do not claim any alimony from him."[4]

As a result the Bat eta'a, the Shari'a legal principle which could force the woman to return to her husband using the police force if necessary was abolished. (The new personal law, 1992, the code of House of Obedience has been legalised again). Generally, 'women are viewed to be inferior to men, although in Sudanese society, with its diversity in culture, traditions and religion, subordination takes different forms. In the North (which dominates Sudan administratively, economically, governmentally... etc.) many basic attitudes are based on Islam. It is popularly supposed and practiced that Islam dictates a subordinate position for women. Whether it really does is a controversial question.

A highly patriarchal reading of Islam predominates in Sudan. Zeniab El Tatih, in commemorating International Women's Year, draws attention to what *Qur'ân* actually says about women, stressing its provisions for inheritance, child custody, and the general esteem in which women should be held. Abdel Mahmoud, Minister of Social welfare, during 1970, argues that, Islam has honoured women more than any other religion does, according to them equal treatment and rights regarding different matters. But also reflects on how there is clearly an ideal in Islam that women should not be involved in the public life. Those who claim to be 'progressive Muslim thinkers' refer to the notion of 'motherhood' as women's chief profession.[5]

Zenaib El faith who is considered to be one of progressive Muslim thinkers explains that, since not all women can marry, and since widowhood is likely for some women, women need to have some basic livelihood besides motherhood. El Sheikh Mohammed El Gizoul, head of the Sudan's Supreme Shaira Court, in 1977, supported this argument by stressing that Islam provides for a woman—if she is a mother, or a wife to a sister to be fully supported by the man responsible for her, so that does not need to work. But if she does have to work, Islam allows her to work only among women and serve only women in the community.

He ignored the fact that 87% of the country population live in the rural areas, where women always have been socially and economically active. Sudanese women likewise African women have always worked. Traditionally the vision of women's contribution in the social and economical aspects in the rural areas explains the prestige that Sudanese women hold. They have been perceived as a peace makers, health keepers, bread providers, cultural conveyers, social consultants, home protectors, etc.

Moreover, the views of contemporary Islamic fundamentalists maintain that the scope of action available to women should be limited, ensuring women's continued subordination to men. While women are accorded a secondary and marginal status, they are made to believe that their status is a great honour and distinction. It seems to me that the basis for understanding the potential for women's social emancipation is an analysis of women's subordination e.g., of the forces external and internal to a society which determine women's access to education, decision making and social reforms which have strengthened patriarchal structures, it also relates to a number of social, culture, religious and political factors, and the way in which women's mobilisation within a certain existing political organisations have tended to minimise, devalue and degrading the aspiration for women's liberation.

Tradition, culture and religion all say that women should be respected, but also stipulate that their position be protected by male relatives. For instance, until 1933 Sudanese women could marry herself, where after that when the more conservative Maliki School of Thought rules were adopted a woman's guardian is essential to the validity of the marriage contract.[6] In the other words, women can not in and of themselves command respect—it must come through connection with a male relatives. This realises maintaining women's inferiority to men. The degree of despotism exercised by men (politicians, religious leaders and male relatives) obviously depends partly on how society maintains male superiority. From childhood on wards, girls are thought obedience, passivity, and the duty to be a good housewife and mother by society, religious teaching and the educational system.

In this education can have double roles. It has an important role in raising awareness, developing organisations and empowering women. But within the dominating patriarchal structure of society it also can function by re-enforcing the subordination of women. Doleib in his article on 'some aspects of discrimination between boys and girls in Sudanese Elementary Schools Curriculum' shows that:

> "Despite the fact that we took a random sample of the set of text books and teachers' guides, still they were enough to prove the existence of aspects of inequality and they ascertain the suffering of girls in quantity and quality."

We summarise that in the following points:

- Syllabuses incline to the side of males. Some of them were written without taking into consideration the existence of females. The person addressed always is the male, and he is always meant by the example and the lesson.
- The aspect of the inequality has its social depth. Girls' education was considered for a long time a marginal thing, because the girls's role was limited to the house. This idea will continue for long until the Sudanese woman is recognised by the society to be a working force, producing effectively in the process of progress, and promoting the social and cultural development in the a distinct form.
- The contents of some syllabuses do not provide enough freedom for the girl to verify her identity and asset herself. Instead of this the syllabuses present a negative and marginal role of the women which may not be remembered."[7]

Moreover, these factors make it very difficult to create space for a 'feminist consciousness'. The dominant patriarchal reading of Islam in Sudan has penetrated women's lives, in ways apparently accepted among women themselves. Nevertheless, women try hard to break the silence. Moreover, the nature of the political structure throughout different periods of the Sudanese history, has blocked the emergence of an autonomous movement, as have difference in culture, class, religion, and political interests among Sudanese women.

These differences have at times led to conflicting different actions, dividing Sudanese women's groups along political, cultural and religious lines. Expressively and aggressively, was made very clear in 1964 when two women had left the Sudanese Women's Union which was formed in 1952 accusing the demands raised by the Union of being un-Islamic. Another examples of this split of the women's organisations occurred in 1969 when the May Regime seized and dissolved the Sudanese Women's Union replacing it by a governmental body called Sudan Women's Union. The Sudan Women's Union was affiliated to the Sudan Social Union bringing it automatically under Nemlri's control.

In addition to that, the triple role of women make it very difficult for them to attain and develop themselves in order to get their rights. As it has been observed by a teaching assistant at the University of Khartoum:

> "I chose my work because it suits my circumstances, having to take care of a home and family. I only work four hours a day. As a Sudanese woman, I still have social obligations."[8]

Moreover, Sudanese women required by the society, religion and culture to fulfil their duties as mothers, wives, and in the present economic situation as a worker, e.g. Amna Farah showed that the women, who were also involved in agricultural work, did spend 8-10 hours daily on domestic activities. This brings us to a 60-70 hours weekly. (Women's Studies Course, Ahfad University for Women); This notion of being Super women can be observed every where in the Sudan. A useful subdivision which better shows the character of the women's activities, female students argue and recommend that if women have to work in the out side sphere:

they must make balance between their work inside and out side family household and this includes:

(*a*) Not neglecting the children and domestic activities;

(*b*) They must go early and return early.

(*c*) They have to concentrate in educational aspect of children in order to increase their academic level.

(*e*) They should not neglect their social obligations and duties towards relatives.

(*f*) They have to contribute with high percentage from their monthly income in home activities.

(*g*) They should dress according to the *Islamic teaching* (*hajab*).

One of the most widely held assumption to be found in the literature is that the political significance and the civil role of women has been insignificant. To enter into this argument, a brief historical background is needed. During the colonial period Sudanese women were subjected to a double form of exploitation. Firstly, with the rest of the population they were oppressed by the colonial administration and the various policies pursued by the colonisers, the second form of oppression arises from the specific position of women within the private, family sphere.

Colonial policies in association with patriarchal structure of the Sudanese society made no attempt to improve the position of women. Their policies were directed at women intended either to preserve their subordination within the family and the Sudanese society, or to create new forms of subordination, e.g., when a small midwifery school was established in 1920 no attempt was made to teach the illiterate young women who studied there to read and write. Instead much effort was directed towards training the girls to differentiate between drugs by sights and smell.[9]

The same policies were continued after the independence. National programmes for economic and social development submitted by governments since independence in 1956 have not fully recognised the importance of women's participation in the development process and accordingly not in the private field e.g., rights and obligations. And when this is recognised, it is still filtered through patriarchal society and a capitalist mind. For instances, all the political parties started to have women's wings in their political parties.

Despite their difference, one can say all these organisations and political parties aim to guarantee voices and women's votes. No attempt and support was given by any political parties when recently the government declared the Islamic dress as compulsory dress for women. The Communist party which works underground, in its newsletter made a very vague noise on the issue. In other words, when the policy makers feel the need to integrate women into the development process, there will be many hidden reasons for that e.g., cheep labour, passive personnel who can work without making criticism or trouble. Not just the policy makers but this also include religious leaders.

The current Sudanese Government which can be described as a patriarchal conservative Muslim Brother's government tries to penetrate their oppression on women through very rigid Islamic Teaching and School of Thought. The Sudanese Personal Law is based on the Hanafi School of Thought, while people follow Maliki School of Thought, but recently a few codes from Maliki School of Thought (known as a very rigid school of thought) have been made to coincide with the legal system of Sudan.

Despite the fact that Prophet Mohammed recognised the rights of women. The original Qur'ânic injunctions were intended to provide general rules of modest conduct applicable to both men and women. During the life of the Prophet Mohammed, women are believed to have enjoyed a relatively large measure of freedom, associating with men and regularly attending the mosque to pray for example; how this was may be open to question from the perspective of feminism. In any case, over time the mosque, like other public places, became a male preserve and women generally performed their prayers at home.

Sudanese women did not lose their independence and freedom overnight; instead this was a gradual process, related to other socio-economic and cultural changes as well as the absorbtion (to varying degree) of foreign influence as the Islamic Empire expanded. When the harem system, imported from Persian tradition, was adopted, it became tied to notion of respectability, and women of the better classes were segregated from men and made to remain within the percents of the home.

The value of self respect and piety became closely linked to women's seclusion, which naturally limited their ability to act in any public sphere. Despite this, throughout Islamic history there were women who became scholars, attaining great heights and able to play a part in the diffusion of culture. Nevertheless, for the majority of women, enforced incarceration had the effect of eroding the rights which were given by the Islamic concept.

Thus while the doctrine of Islam in its essence undoubtedly protects women, the improvements which the Prophet intended in the 17th century for the advancement of women were not expanded and built until this century, when certain aspects of family law were modified as a result of the activities of Muslim reformers who believed that many of the ancient laws were both out of date and not in line with original Islamic thought. They saw that a patriarchal social structure had a major role in eliminating favourable legal provisions, thereby undermining women's interests. For example, slight modifications made to the men's right to divorce in most Muslim countries were resisted by the women's movement, and women now can ask for divorce (although Muslim men can still divorce without using the courts). This was also to some extent applicable in the Sudanese case. The family laws in force in Sudan basically follow the same general pattern as in many other Muslim countries, although differences among schools of legal thoughts mean that the legal systems are in no way uniform.

Those who argue that 'countless women enjoy a highly honoured and powerful position within the family circle and live for a lifetime without being subjected to the rigours of divorce and polygamy,'[10] including some Sudanese women themselves, have not realised that this notion of respect and honour, and the status of the Northern Sudanese women in her married life depends to some extent, as it does in other societies, on the ability of the individual woman to command respect and to ensure that her opinions are recognised. At the same time, it grants and undermines women's position in society, and holds the hidden agenda of male patriarchal society. It also ignores the fact that the male partner regards his private life as separate from the public sphere and that this separation gives him a place where he is entitled to exercise authority.

Some Sudanese women feel deeply that many of the archaic laws which still affect the daily lives of countless women run counter to the requirements of modern society. They understand that as long as laws and misinterpretations of women's rights in Islam exist in Sudan which award them subordinate status, they need to maintain, improve and fight for their economic, and educational rights in order to be emancipated. Critical questions have to put forward to the Sudanese women: How do they perceive themselves within the social structure? Do they realise their oppressive situation and if so how could they challenge the dominant value system? How far can they organise themselves under the shadow of these oppressive conditions?

A.H. HAMZA

## REFERENCES

1. Kamier El Wathig, Zeniab El Bakri, Idris Salim and Samiy El Nagar (ed.), *The State of Women's Studies in the Sudan. Khartoum: Development Studies and Research Centre, Faculty of Economic and Social Studies*, University of Khartoum, 1982, p. 5.

2. B. Badri, *A Profile of Sudanese Women, the Long Term Perspective Study of Sub Suharan African*, Washington DC: World Bank, 1990.

3. Fatima Abdel Mahmoud, 'A Women Place', *Sudanow*, November, 1977, pp. 26-27.

4. Carolyn Fluehr, "The Women's Movement in the Sudan and its impact on Sudanese Law and Politics, *Ahfad Journal, Women and Change*, Vol. 2/1, 1985, p. 56.

5. Abdel Mahmoud, *op. cit.*

6. Sheik el Din, *Maliki School of Thought*, 1985, p. 5.

7. *Ahfad Journal*, Vol. 4/2, 1987, p. 8.

8. Abdel Mahmoud, *op. cit.*, 1977, p. 27.

9. Slot, Corry, Women's Studies Course: A manual. Ahfad University for Women, Sudan, 1990.

10. Kenyon, Susan (ed.), *The Sudanese Women. Khartoum*, Graduate College Publications, University of Khartoum, 1987.

# 42

# GENDER MATERNITY AND MORALITY IN SUDANESE COMMUNITY IN EGYPT

Social identity, particularly in the Arab world, is often enacted through gendered norms of behaviour and bodily modifications. For Arab Muslim Sudanese, the practice of infibulation[1] is paradigmatic of the cultural concept of the 'enclosed', and therefore fertile, female body.[1] Scholars have noted the stubborn perserverance of infibulation and other less severe forms of female genital cutting in Sudan despite awareness campaigns, rapid social change, and most recently, a government ban. However, the continued displacement and exile of Sudanese from their country to Egypt and, for many, to final resettlement in the West, has led to significant challenges to cultural norms, particularly as these intersect with gender. For many Sudanese in Cairo, whose disrupted histories and newly imagined futures are represented here by way of ethnographic field-work, cultural identity is no longer unimaginable without reference to the rite of passage that previously defined not only fertility and sexuality but an essentialised Sudanese morality.

This article is a qualitative interpretive analysis of the transition of gendered embodiment of Sudanese ethnic identity in a situation of political and social flux. Specifically, I explore the meaning of FGC for several Sudanese communities residing in Cairo in the context of changing gender norms brought about by displacement. I present this process using the anthropological motion of embodied culture[2] and drawing heavily on the multiple ways gender is negotiated by women and men. I interpret ethnographic data gathered through two different research processes; fieldwork for my doctoral dissertation and a collaborative research project under the aegis of the Population Council. I suggest that the process of rethinking gender roles and relations among Sudanese is reflected in the debate over FGC that opposes 'modernity' and 'tradition', and that FGC has become a contested boundary marker for Sudanese ethnic identity in Cairo.

### Sudanese Ethnic Identity in Egypt: Gender, Propriety, and Displacement

Displacement has become a feature of life for growing numbers of Sudanese over the last twenty years, with hundreds of thousands of forced migrants from Sudan's enduring civil war joining existing communities of labour migrants in several capital cities in Africa and the Middle East.[3] Cairo, long a destination for Muslim Arab Sudanese (and more recently for African-identified Sudanese) for study, medical treatment, summer holidays, and business, has more recently become a center for the Sudanese opposition movement and a cultural and political hub of the far-flung Sudanese diaspora in general. The ease with which Sudanese traditionally entered and resided in Egypt reflects the long history of entanglement between Egypt and Sudan, but tensions in political relations have created widespread uncertainty and resentment in the various Sudanese communities. This instability has led to a unique identity discourse that I have termed elsewhere 'ambiguous ethnicity'.[4]

Muslim Arab Sudanese in Cairo share broad cultural similarities with Egyptians, who officially assert that Sudanese are their brothers in a unified Nile Valley. Yet in fact Sudanese nationals are not able to attain Egyptian citizenship and, since the 1990s, have lost many of their previous legal and political privileges due to deteriorating relations between Egypt and Sudan. These negative experiences, which call into question the state rhetoric of Sudanese-Egyptian unity, have led both Sudanese settlers and recent immigrants to use the cultural concept of *adab*, or 'propriety'—a concept shared by their Egyptian hosts—to construct an ambiguous ethnicity that allows them to assert both unity with and difference from the Egyptian mainstream according to circumstances. Of special import in this discourse are notions of proper gender relations and the debate over 'traditional' values such as sexual modesty, and specifically the related practice, in both Egypt and Sudan, of female genital cutting.

No term for the practice of surgically removing some or all of a woman's external genitalia, a profoundly political act, is neutral. However, the Sudanese who shared their experiences with me used a broad range of terms that reflected their stance toward the practice. On one end of the spectrum was the term *sunna,* a term for that which is sanctioned by Islamic tradition which, in Egyptian and Sudanese cultural discourse has long included the practice of cliterodectomy. On the other end is the concept of 'female genital mutilation', a term coined by non-African activists who associate the practice with causing harm. My own stance is closer to the notion of the latter, though I believe that we should consider the individual choice to circumcise with sympathy and understanding even while viewing the hegemonic cultural discourse as harmful to women. Thus I have chosen to use either 'female genital cutting'[5] or the Arabic (but no less political) terms *tahara* (purification), *khitan* (circumcision), or *khitan al-anaath* (female circumcision).

This article looks at shifting Sudanese attitudes toward female genital cutting, finding that both conservative and transformative rhetoric stem from changes in gender norms.

For Sudanese in Cairo, gender norms and gender relations are a fundamental expression of propriety. Both mainstream Egyptians and Sudanese draw their concepts of propriety from the same pool of cultural knowledge, their shared Islamic heritage and Arab identity. Propriety for Muslims and Arabs is a dynamic set of norms that is constantly, contextually, and consciously negotiated and renegotiated. However, cultural norms are situational as well, and in Cairo Sudanese have transformed these norms into an ethnic vocabulary used privately to distinguish themselves from Egyptians, while publicly calling upon meta-narratives of shared identity to include and be included by Egyptians. The common bonds of history, religion, language, and other building blocks of this shared identity also shape gender ideology for Sudanese and Egyptians. While gender and propriety are not synonymous, propriety, like other cultural concepts, is gendered and is often expressed in terms of gender ideals for men and women.

I use the term 'gender' to refer to systems of culturally constructed roles for men and women and relations between men and women, keeping in mind that these categories are never absolute and dichotomous and that gender and gender construction are fluid processes.[6] 'Making' gender refers to the culturally specific ways in which ideals of femininity and masculinity are enacted, challenged and held up for inspection through social interactions and relationships.[7] Sudanese absorb and express the attributes of propriety that sustain their identity through gendered relationships with each other.

During my research in Cairo, Sudanese enacted and reinforced propriety norms through child rearing, rituals and ceremonies, religious practice, and daily conventions such as meals and visits at the household level. Sudanese continue to perform and transform cultural understandings of propriety as courting couples, husbands and wives, children and parents, and through other types of gendered relationships embedded in a broader social, economic, and political context. As gender intersects with other processes, such as fragmentation of households and shifting economic opportunities for women and men due to displacement, changes to gender roles have thrown propriety norms into confusion. This has had the effect of rendering 'proper Sudanese behaviour' even more central to Sudanese identity in Cairo.

Though not monolithic, shared gender ideals, and the common norms of propriety they imply, bring Sudanese and Egyptians together while serving as a moral counter for Sudanese identity. Experiences of displacement and diaspora have altered Sudanese gender relations. Propriety norms, while represented by Sudanese as an unchanging ideal, have also been affected by these changes, and so represent lines of conflict and contention among and between Sudanese communities as well. I specifically examine conflicts involving men and women regarding sexuality and morality in the current crisis situation. Through personal narratives, I show how individual Sudanese are reinterpreting propriety by challenging gender norms and in the process, reinterpreting their identity. Exploring changing attitudes toward the cultural practice of FGC gives us insight into the shifting balance of power between women and men in the Sudanese diaspora, and ultimately the negotiation of Sudanese identity itself.

**Displacement and Changing Gender Roles**

Women and men of different generations, educational and class backgrounds, and length of stay in Egypt have all experienced changes in their lives due to the crisis in Sudan and their relocation in Cairo, albeit of varying degrees. The instability and increasing hardships affecting northern Sudanese in Cairo have challenged social ideals and the structures invested with maintaining 'proper traditions', such as kinship relations and gender roles. Networks of kin increasingly extend over long distances.

People's economic circumstances in Cairo are deteriorating. Opportunities for work and study have fallen off drastically since the early 1990s. For Sudanese who remain in Cairo, expectations that men provide financial support and women maintain responsibility for the domestic realm are increasingly overwhelmed by such circumstances. As gender roles shift, expand, and transform to accommodate fragmented households, unreliable finances, and social interactions that bring men and women together in 'non-traditional' ways, the core values that comprise Sudanese propriety are subtly, and not so subtly, undermined.

Perhaps the most obvious challenge to Sudanese gender relations and the order they impose on behaviour is the concept of gender 'complementarity' outlined by Boddy.[8] This mainstream Sudanese ideal draws on Islamic prescriptions of separate but complementary gender roles in families, stereotypically portrayed as the father/husband earning the household income and the mother/wife keeping house and rearing the children.[9] The 'natural' differences between men and women have been a focus for much of the Islamist rhetoric coming from the regime, and as such are already being resisted by Sudanese still living in Sudan.[10]

In Cairo, the unstable situation and infrequent opportunities for people to improve their lives propels women and men into new roles. Sudanese male graduates of Egyptian universities, for example, have resorted to labour migration to the Gulf as a way to contribute to the finances of their parents, siblings, and if married, their wives and wives' families. For Sudanese exiles, labour migration also offered employment possibilities to men, but with restrictive travel laws in and out of Egypt and the diminishing of contracts in the Gulf, many Sudanese men in Cairo have spent months or even years living on remittances from a family member, refugee subsidies from the United High Commissioner, or whatever they are able to scrounge from associations with NGOs, friends, and the like.

Women's employment opportunities in Cairo, on the other hand, have not been as severely affected. In Ain Shams, a neighbourhood in Cairo where many long-term Sudanese immigrants reside, I met many young Sudanese women who had received university degrees and found jobs as secretaries, schoolteachers, and receptionists despite the Egyptian labour laws restricting the number of foreign employees in an office or institution. Young men from this community asserted that they were much less likely to find work in Egypt despite similar educational backgrounds. Not only do these new circumstances influence gender relations, but they also lead to challenges to older ways of doing things from the younger generation.

Displacement and job shortages mean that family members may live in two or more different countries. Young men leave their wives and children in Cairo to work in the Gulf while their parents remain in Sudan. Individuals or several members of a family may be offered asylum in the USA or Canada while their relatives or fianancé(e)s may be left behind in Egypt or Sudan to wait for visa. The fragmented nature of the Sudanese community in Cairo makes it less likely that a person will live in an arrangement that supports the ideal of gender complementarity. In the small sample of Sudanese families in Cairo with whom I have relations, I know of married Sudanese men in Bahrain, Saudi Arabia , Oman, the United States, Canada, Asmara, and Addis Ababa who are supporting their wives and children living in Cairo. Since children most often go to Egyptian schools and see their fathers only rarely, the burden of socialising children to be 'Sudanese' falls to these mothers.

Displacement in Egypt and its effect on children's identity has recently become a topic of some interest to members of the exiled community. Salim, a lawyer with an interest in displaced children, described Egyptian manners as 'not honourable', something that he hoped Sudanese children would avoid. He told me 'girls have more problems, because they see Egyptian girls behaving in a 'dishonourable' way. The families are all very worried and scared for the girls' sake.' At least three separate projects to open schools for northern Sudanese children with northern Sudanese teachers came to my attention during the period of my fieldwork, and at this writing at least one has been established. This is one of the many strategies employed by Sudanese in Cairo to preserve what they feel to be Sudanese values in the absence of strereotypical role models based on gender complementarity.

Dislocation and mobility also make finding marriage prospects for men and women problematic. I had long discussions with Layla, a 30-something secretary at a private firm, who yearned to get married but felt caught between Egypt and Sudan. Layla had spent ten years working in Sudan. I asked her 'Why didn't you get married there?' She said, 'Really, there were many suitors, but God was not smiling on me. Either they were old, or they had a first wife and children, or if they were young they did things like drink alcohol, implying that this was unacceptable behaviour. All she was asking for, she said, was 'a normal man, not too rich, just a regular guy'. In desperation, she returned to Cairo, where she was born, to seek a husband, but rejected most of the displaced Sudanese men she met as economically unsuitable. I asked Layla, 'Why aren't you successful here? 'She responded, saying,' well, for ten years I haven't been in Cairo and haven't been working on [developing] relationships.' The closest she came to betrothal, in the time I knew her, was a flirtation with her elderly Sudanese boss, who was divorced and had several children with families of their own.

Northern Sudanese men, particularly those with more formal education, feel that working as labourers, peddlers, or domestic servants means an unacceptable affront to the respect they hold in the eyes of the Sudanese community. Some Sudanese in Cairo have begun to talk about the phenomenon of young educated men who make it to Egypt only to *'ga' ad fil bayt'* (stay at home). In essence, this is a gendered insult, since according to the gender norms that Sudanese share with other Arab societies, women should 'stay at home' while men provide the family's income. I knew several married men who could not find work 'in their field' and instead lived off the income of their wives. Maisoon, a lawyer and political activist, remarked that these men were 'not serious. Women are more serious than men. Men here have a problem of sleep and drunkenness—they get up at 12 pm, have nothing to do,' and spend their time watching television and drinking with friends.

The fact that so many men 'stay at home' further undermines the gender complementarity ideal espoused by Sudanese society. Wives of unemployed men are often able to find work as *hennanas* (women who decorate brides and married women with *henna* paste) or in other, 'less' 'respectable' professions in order to support the household financially.Yet this strategy opens the possibility for tension between husband and wife. Not only is she providing for her husband, thus undermining the masculine ideal, she is also forced into situations that compromise her own respectability— visiting the houses of strangers at a late hour, for example.

## Propriety as a Discursive and Cultural Concept

In Egypt and Sudan, the Arabic word *adab* pertains to 'good manners politeness,' 'which includes the notion of morals and morality for both men and women.[10] In my interactions with both Egyptians and Sudanese in Cairo, I have understood their usage of the term *adab* to mean 'propriety' in a holistic sense. Therefore, the concept is not only limited to ideals of sexual propriety. *Adab*, in my interpretation, is closer to Nordenstam's definition of an individual's ethics of virtue as 'the sum total of his conceptions of what one should be and have and do in order to be good in the different roles one comes to play in life'.[11]

Nordenstam posited that the main components of Sudanese ethics are 'the ideas of courage, generosity and hospitality and cluster of subtly interrelated notions of honour, dignity and self-respect,' and a good Sudanese is thus 'a man [*sic*] who exemplifies these virtues to a high degree'.[12] In Cairo, Sudanese will say of a person whose behaviour is perceived as improper that he or she has no manners, *ma fi adab*, or that the person is *ma muaddab* or *muaddaba* {feminine}, impolite. Through analysing Sudanese identity discourse in Cairo, I have come to understand that 'proper' behaviour comprises a set of related ideals—hospitality, generosity, modesty, dignity, respectability, and social equality that are expressed at all levels of social interaction. Though the interrelated characteristics of propriety are gendered, the concept as a whole encompasses generalised behaviour that pertains to upholding the virtues of Sudanese society. In the following discussion, I suggest that gender ideals for Sudanese in Cairo, as self-identified members of the Arab world, extend from this broader meaning of propriety.

For the purpose of this article, however, I focus on the aspect of 'modesty' as it incorporates 'proper' gender roles for women and men. Modesty, often thought of in terms of sexual propriety, is not solely a concern for women, despite overt gender symbols like female modesty garments and the social expectation that holds women accountable for maintaining social and physical distance from unrelated men. Sudanese men are expected to be discreet about their personal wealth, family connections, and success. Both men and women in Cairo's Sudanese communities consider modest dress an Islamic prescription and assert that drawing attention to oneself in any way is a breach of modesty. By defining Egyptians as 'immodest,' Sudanese go beyond modesty as a function of a woman's behaviour to viewing it instead as a fundamental marker of Sudanese identity. It is in this context that the Sudanese debate over FGC is being framed.

Over the course of my research, I began to recognise the northern Sudanese propriety ideal through the behaviour, commentary, and transgressions of the people in the two communities with whom I was working. The Sudanese represented by my study were generally in agreement about the main, idealised tenets of propriety drawn upon the cultural and religious norms outlined above. Problems in their communities and changes in Sudanese—Egyptian relations that conflicted with their understanding of proper behaviour were a common topic of conversation—indeed, the *adab* discourse loomed large in my interactions with Sudanese in Cairo, and I believe I am representing an acknowledged cultural ideal.

I realised, however, that while members of both long-established expatriate and more recent exile communities wholeheartedly embraced the propriety ideal characterising their behaviour as Sudanese, some exhibited contradictions and deviations from the standard Sudanese propriety discourse. Although I did observe gender differences in the expression of 'proper behaviour', both men and women shared many of the Sudanese behaviours and beliefs around propriety in Cairo. As I will demonstrate, the use of propriety as an ethnic boundary marker has profound implications for the continued practice of FGC.

## Gender and Propriety in the Sudanese Diaspora: Tradition versus Change

Gender ideals for both Egyptian and Sudanese Muslims draw heavily on Islamic concepts norms linking modesty with sexual propriety and Arab cultural beliefs associating honour with marriage ability, particularly for women.[13] As a social category, gender in the Arab world shares certain themes, glossed as honour and shame, patrilineality, polygyny, and gender segregation,[14] that have customarily been the focus of scholars and lay persons alike. These themes permeate the *adab* concept as well, since proper behaviour for Arabs and Muslims often hinges on their social interactions as men or women.

Anthropologist of northern Sudanese communities have identified gender ideologies that relate Sudanese behaviour, especially that of women, to specific cultural codes of modesty, chastity, hospitality, and dignity.[15] Boddy in particular links gender norms and the enactment of propriety with her informants' 'firmly moral sense of identity'.[16] Her analysis of the symbolic underpinnings of reproduction and human fertility as the framework of this identity is based on her understanding that her informants see men and women as wholly complimentary, and that the social structure binds men and women together on the basis of kinship. The main expression of this cultural logic, according to Boddy, are combined in marriage, as a central framework for the production and reproduction of gender ideologies. She writes that, 'Hofrayati's world is suffused by gender: gender constructs permeate the fabric of meaning and inform the idioms of daily life.'[17] Boddy suggests that propriety is a key concept for the Sudanese community she studied, since transgressions of propriety' subvert the complementarity of men and women'[18] and thus undermine society.

However, in addition to assertions of cultural ideals by northern Sudanese and other self-identified Arabs, the particular histories, contexts, and processes that may shape gender as well must balance these themes. Scholars have warned of the dangers of conceptualising Arab societies, and their gender norms, as uniformly shaped by 'gender segregation, tribalism, and Islam'[19] because of the real possibility of neglecting equally important local specificities. Certainly, the tendency to gloss Arab culture as dichotomised into male/female; public/private; traditional/modern; orthodox/heterodox, and other appositions overlooks the diverse experiences and strategies of Arab men and women.[20] Yet in the case of Sudanese in Cairo, the reality of rapid change and dislocation gives added weight to the importance of Sudanese 'traditions,' including FGC and other aspects of propriety. As in all situations of flux, the tension between real and ideal gender roles increases the potential for conflict.

Gender is not a fixed construct even in stable times, since political, economic, and social processes at national, regional, and even global levels constantly interact with gender systems. Through the impact of war, labour migration, new technologies, and ideologies of social change, 'traditional' roles men and women play may change in subtle or dramatic ways. The literature on gender and migration in the Arab world illustrates the various and sometimes unexpected result of large-scale population movements on gender roles and household decision making,[21] which often affect norms of propriety. In Egypt, for example, educated women make a trade-off between securing their family a place in the middle class by working outside the home—ideally constructed as the male domain—even while losing the power associated with control of the domestic—female—arena.[22] Establilshing their sexual propriety through Islamic dress was one way these women could present themselves as unambiguously feminine even while departing from the widely held female ideal in Egypt

The term 'family' needs to be problematised, not only in response to the current situation of flux. Tucker points out the need to contextualise families in history, since our ideas about the importance of family in the daily construction of traditional gender roles and relations are rarely questioned in discussion of change.[23] For the study at hand,, readers should be alert to the historical construction of the Sudanese family. The people of northern riverian Sudan continue to participate in the dramatic changes that have swept the Region in the twentieth century, including war and conquest, changes in labour opportunities both locally and abroad, and natural disasters like floods and drought. Sudanese families have had to cope with the effects of these changes and cannot be uniformly characterised despite folk assertions of unchanging and continuous family structures.

As I noted earlier, Sudanese in Cairo derive their propriety ideals from the interaction between social norms transmitted through learned roles and actual examples against which to measure their own behaviour. Sudanese women and men have learned codes of behaviour through the social institutions—the family, the household, marriage, and the mosque, among others—accorded the responsibility for producing and reproducing gender. These institutions, as well as the norms they transmit, are idealised by Sudanese, despite the dynamic circumstances of Sudanese displacement in Cairo. The specificities which have shaped Sudanese choices around living arrangements, employment, raising and schooling children, and so forth often work against ideal patterns of behaviour ascribed to 'proper' men and women. This is exemplified by changing norms surrounding FGC among Sudanese in Cairo.

## Propriety, FGC and Mobility

Sudanese women and men play a variety of social roles—daughter, son, wife, husband, friend—over the course of their daily routines in Cairo. Their ideas of femininity and masculinity are enacted, challenged, and held up for inspection through their interactions and relationships with one another and with members of Egyptian society. Propriety, or more precisely, the bundle of norms that Sudanese believe mark their identity in Cairo, has become the language of social relations and the standard against which they can measure their behaviour. But changing circumstances due to displacement and the political and economic hardships brought on by ongoing crisis have affected gender and other social relations, with consequences for propriety as a Sudanese ideal.

This is especially apparent in changing attitudes toward FGC. Challenges to Sudanese gender ideals emanate from a complex mix of factors including displacement, reverberations from the Islamist consolidation of power in Sudan, and public campaigns in Egypt and Sudan like those against female circumcision. Generational tensions, including those presented by the opening of new oportunities and the passing of older ones, have also challenged gender norms, particularly in terms of employment and marriage. Sudanese are both accommodating and resisting these changes, and their personal strategies in Cairo often call on 'our traditions' while creating space for challenging them.

**FGC in Sudan as a Paradigm of Embodied Morality**

The literature on female genital cutting has long viewed Sudan as the paradigmatic case of embodied morality. If morality and sexual propriety are fundamental to a Sudanese woman's gendered identity, then female genital cutting represents the embodiment of those cultural ideals. Csordas describes embodiment as process in which meaning is taken upon the body, where the body should not be viewed as an object but as a subject that embodies lived experience.[24]

It is important to note that gender norms for Sudanese are not monolithic, and that many cultural ideals exist in this nation of diverse ethnic and religious identities. However, FGC is associated with the dominant élite of Sudan and accordingly, has become a marker of ethnic belonging and class status for Sudanese minorities[25] even as official efforts to eradicate it gather steam. As recently as the mid-1990s, an estimated 89 percent of people in the Muslim Arab north of Sudan practiced FGC.[26]

Scholars writing on FGC as a rite of passage focus on the cultural paradigm of gendering androgynous children. Boddy, for example, analyses FGC in Sudan as the need to inscribe female identity on the body by cutting off the clitoris so that it cannot turn into a penis.[27] This cultural belief is prominent in other societies practicing FGC, including Egypt.[28] Scholars have asserted that the gendering of both women and men according to biological sex is essential to all interaction in an

Islamic society.[29] Sanders, for example points out that in medieval Islamic societies:

> no aspect of life was free from considerations of sex. The boundary between male and female was drawn firmly and was deeply embedded both in views of the cosmos and in social structures. The most visible expression of this boundary, the social segregation of men and women, was only a particularly concrete demonstration of the notion that male and female were opposites, and that an ordered human society depended on maintaining boundaries that had been ordained by God.[30]

However, Ghannam notes, as substantiated by the anthropological and sociological literature, that the female body rather than the male body is central to gender distinctions in the Middle East.

FGC has often been presented as an issue of more immediate concern to women than to men in societies that practice it. Indeed, Wassef and Mansour in their study of male sexuality and FGC, find the literature very thin indeed on the topic of men's attitudes toward the practice.[31] This is often due to the observation that women are by and large the main decision makers around FGC as a 'rite of passage', determining the age at which their daughters or granddaughters are to be circumcised and deciding on what form the operation should take. It should be noted that most of the practitioners of FGC, whether *dayas* (midwives) outside the realm of biomedicine or nurses within it, are women.

## Modesty and Sexual Propriety: Sudanese Discourses on FGC in Displacement

In my experience, expectations of a Sudanese woman's behaviour often hinges on her ideal domestic role and her sexual propriety. In a mixed gender household, women take responsibility for preparing food and beverages for men and guests, even if they are employed outside the home. In their public interactions with men, women ought not to express sexual interest; their clothing should not be revealing (though head coverings are a personal choice) and they should not linger in public places frequented by men nor return home alone late at night. The modesty ideal for women requires specific behaviour and comportment aimed at sexual propriety.

Dress seems to be a less important component of female modesty than 'appropriate' interaction with men, along with an awareness of the male gaze as a restraint on 'inappropriate' behaviour. Modest dress, in the Islamic sense, is a highly personal decision, and among Sudanese women in both settled and exile communities, dress runs the gamut from the completely covered young married woman on her way to study at an American university, through long skirts and long-sleeved blouse accompanied by varieties of head coverings including the 'Egyptian-style' *hijab* and the *tarha,* a filmy piece of coloured material loosely draped over the head and shoulders, to western-style jeans and T-shirts.

Modest behaviour for women, on the other hand, derives from the cultural norm of segregation by sex, though Sudanese in Cairo by no means practice this in a regulated way. Rather, it involves selecting the venues where one will be seen, and not being overlay forward with men. The Sudanese do not feel that 'brazen' behaviour in men's presence, such as talking in a loud voice or obvious flirting is appropriately modest, since it calls attention to oneself and undermines a woman's respectability.

Female genital cutting, *khitan,* is particularly gender-specific tenet of propriety. Although northern Sudanese have expressed multiple cultural explanations for the continued practice of female circumcision[32] including hygiene and beauty, religion, and chastity, its role in maintaining women's sexual propriety accounts for much of the continued cultural pressure to operate. The explanation most common in Ain Shams, where I conducted research on female circumcision among settled Sudanese[33] was maintaining sexual propriety. Hanin, a young woman from the neighbourhood told me,

> "They [parents] say that it prevents excessive sexual feelings, that taking away just a little helps a girl control herself and behave properly."

Many Sudanese believe that uncircumcised women are more likely to engage in immodest behaviour, since their natural sexual appetite has not been 'tamed' through the operation. This is reflected in jokes and teasing aimed at uncircumcised girls, that it drives them to talk with boys, for example.

However, there are other discourses surrounding the issue of FGC as it regard propriety, sexual or otherwise. The upper-class Sudanese women studied by Bukhari maintain a fundamentally different attitude toward sexuality, and oppose the practice of FGC as a matter of pride in their cosmopolitans.[34] While they are familiar with mainstream expectation of Sudanese women's behaviour, they are scornful of the notion that their morality is related to their sexual behaviour. Their dismissal sexual propriety as a function of an 'outdated' Sudanese tradition is reflected in their active rejection of FGC. Women interviewed for this study were adamant about the harm that FGC had caused them in their own sexual life and were determined that their daughters should not repeat the experience. Unlike the Sudanese women in Ain Shams, these cosmopolitan women did not plan to circumcise their daughters. While this group explained their rejection of FGC as being tied to their education and experiences in western countries, it is important to note both that there are indigenous voices of dissent in the Sudanese FGC discourse and that these voices are still a minority.

This assertion is amply demonstrated by the research of Muhammad Osman Al-Obeid, who interviewed a group of displaced Sudanese men, largely students or older professionals, over a period of a year (1997). Most of these men, when queried directly about *khitan*, felt that FGC was a marginal issue compared to others facing Sudanese communities. Yet when discussing their own sexuality and masculine identity, a different story emerged. Several of the men interviewed expressed their personal opposition to the practice but felt that the peer pressure surrounding feminine propriety, male sexual prowess, and cultural traditions were too much to bear. Only "if I am going to live with my family somewhere else like Florida surely I am not going to circumcise my daughters, but as far as I am going to live among my relatives there is no question about circumcising them," said one man.[35] Others were concerned that by not circumcising their daughters, they would be considered *ma kwayisat* (bad girls) in the eyes of fellow villagers. Others confessed to a realisation that greater sexual pleasure was to be enjoyed from sexual intercourse with non-cicrumcised women, but that they did not want their sons-in-law to enjoy such sexual pleasure with their daughters and therefore intended to circumcise them.[36] Finally, since sexual penetration of an infibulated woman is physically difficult, a discourse of sexual prowess is tied to the continued circumcision of women. One interviewee expressed this concern, saying, 'What does it mean someone's daughter is being circumcised? Are you not man enough to reopen her?'[37]

This anxiety with emasculation is significant as well when considered together with the emasculating effects of displacement for Sudanese men. One might expect that a similar kind of anxiety as that expressed by Egyptians men[38] regarding their potential impotence in the face of the perception of an all-powerful female sexuality might be magnified by the social problems facing Sudanese men due to loss of their breadwinner role in the household. Furthermore, the growing sense of alienation and embattled identity among Sudanese living in Cairo might lead us to conclude that FGC, as a clear marker of sexual propriety, would not only be maintained but actually promoted as a marker as well of an ethnic boundary between Sudanese and their Egyptian hosts. Surprisingly, this does not seem to be the case among Sudanese in Cairo. Indigenous voices of dissent appear to find fertile ground among Sudanese of all social classes for whom the decision to perform FGC on their daughters is a choice made under social duress.

Living in Cairo makes it easier to overcome social expectations that Sudanese girls should be infibulated or even subjected to cliterodectomy. Asia, a woman who had fled Sudan with her husband and two daughters told me that, had she stayed in Sudan, family and social pressure for her to circumcise them would have been too much for her to resist. Despite her opposition to the operation, Assia told me, "*maybe* in Sudan there would be pressure from my mother and grandmother, so here in Cairo I'm free of the kind of pressure." The cosmopolitan women of Cairo's upperclass Sudanese women also acknowledge the importance of the absence of family and neighbourhood pressure in maintaining their stance against FGC. The willingness of these women:

> "To discuss FGC and their decisions not to do so to their daughters is a forgone (conclusion). There is no doubt in their minds that this is a harmful practice and yet they realise that the distance between themselves and the older members of their families and peers is a major factor in their changing behaviour."[39]

## Morphological change in the 'language' of FGC

One of the questions asked in the course of research on changing Sudanese attitudes towards FGC was, if women have not been circumcised by their relatives, who are they and how have they been able to maintain their Sudanese identity outside ideal norms of propriety and gender? A cross-section of these women reveals a wide variety of reasons. Some have grown up outside of their communities, or have lived in societies that do not practice *khitan*. Others had 'enlightened' parents, or had one parent who came from a culture where *khitan* was unknown. Overall, these women reported that they are happy with themselves, with their relationships, and felt able to withstand the peer and social pressure they experienced 'back home'.

An important group of Muslim Arab Sudanese who do not circumcise their daughters as a matter ideological commitment are the Republican Brothers, a progressive Sudanese Muslim movement established in the 1930s by the charismatic religious leader Mahmoud Muhammad Taha. Mai, a young mother who had not been circumcised by her Republican Brother parents, was a staunch believer in the right of a woman to sexual pleasure, and described her marital relations as 'very, very good.' Nevertheless, Republican Brother families are susceptible to the same social pressures as other Sudanese, and one woman descended from Taha himself still found it easier to stick to her anti-circumcision beliefs far away from relatives and neighbour in Sudan.

Growing up at a distance from the cultural borders of Sudanese society may not free a woman from social expectations entirely, but in the case of Salwa her youth in Egypt, Saudi Arabia, and Kuwait is one reason she gives for her parents' decision not to circumcise. They never raised the issue, but she grew up believing that being uncircumcised was normal. Salwa learned about *khitan* on visits with relatives, where she grew to associate the word with pain but also thought that there must be a good reason for why it is practiced. She remembers being frightened when her circumcised cousins told her, during her visit to Sudan, that she would be unable to have children, and she has had periods of doubt when she thought perhaps it would have been better if she had been circumcised, but they passed.

Moving away from the relatives and neighbours who see their responsibility as upholding traditions such as *khitan* seems to have been a significant reason for some of the women we spoke with not to circumcise their daughters. One family, seeking refugee status in the West, has two daughters who are nearing the age where, had they lived in Sudan, circumcision would be the norm. Being away from the pressure exerted by grandmothers, in particular, was an important reason cited by this and other families who did not circumcise their girls. Had they been in Sudan, they asserted, they doubted that they would have been able to resist. Even in Ain Shams, the Cairo neighbourhood settled by Sudanese in the 1940s, *khitan* is the norm. But campaings and publicity carried out by activists, NGOs, and the Egyptian government about the harmfulness of FGC have clearly reached the settled Sudanese population as well.

I came into contact with several women who made it quite clear to me that their Sudanese identity, with its acknowledged focus on propriety norms as ethnic boundary markers, was by no means inconsistent with their firm belief that girls should not be circumcised. Heba, a television director, was raised in Ain Shams but moved out of the community to an Egyptian neighbourhood where many professionals live. Heba has strong feelings against FGC and has not circumcised her daughter, a decision she says she came to by herself. She remained active in a Sudanese NGO promoting women's empowerment until her untimely death in 1997. Abeer, a woman in her twenties who still lives in Ain Shams, is, like Heba, university-educated, but maintains that she has questioned the importance of FGC since she was a young girl. She has placed women's empowerment at the center of her work on behalf of the Sudanese community in Cairo. She has no plans to circumcise her future daughters, and is a forceful voice against FGC among her Sudanese peers in Ain Shams.

These women and their families are at the vanguard of the social change that other Sudanese suggest is inevitable. There is clearly a relationship between geographic or cultural distance from a social environment that shapes and perpetuates people's attitudes toward *khitan*. There are example of the effect of mobility on the practice of FGC for other groups. Izett and Toubia cite anecdotal evidence suggesting:

> "the majority of families migrating to Europe, North America and Australia from countries where FC/FGM is prevalent choose not to circumcise their daughters. This could be because they want to fit into the new society, because of the absence of family and community pressure, or simply because it is not easy to arrange a circumcision in these countries."

Despite the tension between a Sudanese identity discourse that promotes propriety as an ethnic boundary marker and the apparent relationship between displacement and the declining practice of FGC, creative and empowering options for women do seem to be included in the circumstances of Sudanese displacement.

The characteristics that underpin Sudanese identity in Cairo, expressed through the propriety discourse, have gained more importance for this community in crisis in being harder to fulfil. It is more difficult, and thus more respected, to extend hospitality to guest when one's pockets are empty and when one's neighbours are living in equally straitened circumstances. Ideals of modesty are harder for working women to maintain when their jobs keep them late or force them into contact with 'immoral' activities such as brewing or drinking alcohol. A Sudanese person who is able to maintain his or her 'Sudanesenese' in Cairo through adherence to the propriety ideal contributes to the belief that Sudanese are different from Egyptians and have a unique identity that is worthwhile preserving.

At the same time, Sudanese in Cairo have a certain freedom to buck social norms. A political exile and concerned father of two, Yousif had been waiting for resettlement to Canada for over a year. He told me that even if Sudan became safe again, he would not return for the simple reason that his 5-year-old daughter might choose to be a ballerina, a profession that would be unacceptable for girls in Sudanese society. He wanted to ensure that she could make choices unavailable to her in Sudan that did not conflict with her 'respectability.' The cultural concept of propriety is not unique to Muslim Arab Sudanese; indeed, the propriety discourse in the contemporary Middle East, which traces its roots back to pre-Islamic times, developed in conjunction with Arab and Muslim cultures over centuries of interaction. In the Region, it also enjoys popular recognition among diverse societies as an idiom for good manners and proper behaviour.

Propriety also encompasses gender norms, though is not limited to the concepts of sexual propriety, honour, and other shared aspects of ideal behaviours for men and women drawn from the same pool of cultural knowledge. Nevertheless, despite the similar characteristics of both gender expectations and propriety norms in the Arab world, variations of cultural practices and beliefs arise as prescriptive ideals interact with and rub against specific circumstances.

In this article, I have dealt with both generalised propriety as a boundary market of Sudanese identity in Cairo, and gendered attitudes toward morality and FGC as a fundamental aspect of that boundary. Sudanese have been profoundly affected by the ongoing political crisis in their home country, by the displacement triggered by political and economic collapse, and by their deteriorating legal and social status in Egypt. The dramatic changes in the circumstances of Sudanese residence in Cairo have challenged the cultural norm of gender complementarity as men 'stay at home' for want of work while women seek and find new opportunities for themselves. This unstable situation has led Sudanese to place more emphasis on 'proper' ways of behaving and being, an assertion that helps define the ethnic boundaries of the Sudanese community in Cairo. Finally, I have demonstrated the discrepancies between discourse and reality through ethnographic data while analysing how Sudanese have found new ways of asserting their identity and resisting the practice of FGC.

A.H. FÁBOS

## REFERENCES


1. Kaomce Boddy, '*Womb as oasis*; the symbolic context of Pharaonic circumcision in rural Northern Sudan,' *American Ethnologist*, Vol,. 9./4, 1992, pp. 682–98
2. Thomas J. Csordas, *Embodiment and Experience: The existential ground of Culture and self*, Cambridge & New York: Cambridge University Press, 1994.
3. Anita Fabos, 'Community and Change in Ain Shams—The Place of Khitaan, Women's Rights/People's Rights,' *A quarterly Women's Human Right Journal* Published by the Legal Research and Resource Center, Cairo, Egypt, No. 6 June, 1997.
4. Anita Fabos, Social 'Ambiguous ethnicity: propriety (*adab*) as a situational boundary marker for Northern Sudanese in Cairo', Doctoral Dissertation, Boston University, 1999
5. Sandra D. Lane and Robert A. Rubinstein, *Juding the Other: Responding to Traditional Genital Surgeries*, Hastings Center, 1996.
6. Andrea Cornwell and Nancy Lindisharne, 'Dislocating masculinity: gender, power anthropology' in A. Cornwall and N.Lindisfarne, editors, *Dislocating Masculinity: Comparative Ethnographic*, 1994.
7. Sherry B. Ortner, *Making Gender: The Politics and Erotics of Culture*, Boston, MA: Beacon Press, 1996.
8. Boddy, Social *Wombs and Alien Spirits: Women, Men, and the Zar Cult of Northern Sudan*, Madison, WI: University of Wisconsin Press, 1989, pp. 6-7.
9. Ellen Gruenhaum, *The Islamist State and Sudanese Women*, Middle East Report, November 1992, 179, p. 29; S. Hale, 'The Rise of Islam and Women of the National Islamic Front,' *Review of African Political Economy*, No. 54, 1992, pp. 27–41.
10. El-Said Badawi, and Martin Hinds, *A Dictionary of Egyptian Colloquial Arabic*, Beirut; Librairie Du Liban, 1986.
11. Tore Nordernstam, *Sudanese Ethics*, Uppsala: The Scandinavian Institute of Africa Studies, 1968, p. 74.
12. *Ibid.*, p. 75.

13. Boddy, *op. cit.*, 1989; F. Malti-Douglas, *Woman's Body/Woman's Word: Gender and Discourse in Arabo-Islamic Writing*, Princeton, NJ: Princeton University Press, 1991; Leila Ahmed, *Women and Gender in Islam: Historical Roots of a Modern Debate*, New Haven. CT: Yale University Press, 1992.

14. Lila Abu-Lughod, *Writing Women's Words; Bedouin Stortes, Berkeley*, CA: University of California Press, 1993; Judith Tucker, 'The Arab family in History: 'otherness' and the study of the family' in J. Tucker (ed.), *Arab Women: Old Boundaries, New Frontiers*, Bloomington, Indiana University Press, 1993; Suad Joseph, 'Gender and Family in the Arab World,' *Middle East Report*, No. 190, 1994.

15. Ellen Gruenbaum, *Patterns of Family Living: A case Study of Two Villages on the Rahad River*, monograph Series No. 12, Development Studies and Research Center, University of Khartoum, Sudan, 1979; Ellen T. Ismail, *Social Environment and Daily Routine of Sudanese Women: A case study of Urban Middle Class Housewives*, Berlin: Dietrich Reimer Verlag,1982; Anne Cloudsley, *Women of Ombudrman; Life, Lovre, and the Cult of Virginity*, New Yjork; St Martin' Press, 1983.

16. Boddy, *op. cit.*, 1989, p. 48.

17. *Ibid.*, 1989, p. 57.

18. *Ibid.*, p. 96.

19. Lila Abu-Loughod, 'Zones of theory in the anthropology of the Arab world' *Annual Review of Anthropology*, No. 18, 1989, p. 281.

20. Sondra Hale, 'Anthropology constructs the woman: Sudan studies' *Sacramento Anthropological Society*, California State University, No. 16, 1983, pp. 63–71.

21. Elizabeth Taylor, 'Egyptian Migration and Peasant Wives,' *MERIP Reports*, 14/5,1984; Soheir Morsy, *Familial Adaptations to the Internationalization of Egyptian Labour, Family, Law and Change in the Middle East*, Tuxedo, NY: Social Science Research Council, 1985; Andexian, *op. cit.*, 1986; Diane Singerman and Homa Hoodfar, *Development, Change and Gender in Cairo: A View from the Household*, Bloomington & Indianapolis, Indiana: Indiana University Press, 1996.

22. Homa Hoodfar, "Egyptian male migration and urban families left behind: 'feminisation of the Egyptian family' or a realfirmation of traditional gender roles?" Singerman and Hoodfar, *op. cit.*, 1996.
23. Tucker, *op. cit.*, 1993.
24. Csordas, *op. cit.*, 1994, p. 10.
25. Paul Doornbos, 'On becoming Sudanese' in Tony Barnett and Abbas, 1988, p. 671.
26. Lindy Williams and Teresa Sobieszcyk, *Attitudes Surrounding the Continuation of Female Circumcision in the Sudan: Passing the tradition to the Next Generation*, PSC Research Report, Ithaca, NY: Cornell University, 1996, p. 626.
27. Boddy, *op. cit.*, 1988, p. 748.
28. Lane, *op. cit.*, 1996, p. 525; Farha Ghannam, *Fertile, Plump, and strong: The social Construction of the Female Body in Low-income*, Cairo: Population Council, *Reports In Reproductive Health*, No. 3, 1997.
29. Janet L. Bauer, 'Sexuality and the moral ' construction' of women in an Islamic society,' *Anthropological Quartely*, Vol. 58/ 3. 1985, pp. 120–9; Evelyn A. Early, *Baladi Women of Cairo; Playing with an Egg and a Stone*, Cairo: The American University in Cairo Press, 1993; Ghannam, *op. cit.*, 1997.
30. Paula Sunders, 'Gendering the ungendered body: hermaphrodites in medieval Islamic law' in N. R. Keddie and B. Baron, editors, *Women in Middle Eastern History*, New Haven, CT: Yale University Press, 1991
31. Nadia Wassef and Abdallah Mansour, *Investigating Masculinities and Female Genital Mutilation in Egypt*, Cairo: Female Genital Mutiliation Task Force, 1999.
32. R. Oldfield Hayes, "Female genital mutilation, fertility control, women's roles, and the patrilineage in modern Sudan", *American Ethnologist*, No. 2, 1975, pp. 617–33; Cloudsley, *op. cit.*, 1983; Boddy, *op. cit.*, 1989; Hanny Lightfoot-Klein, *Prisoners of Ritual*, New York: Haworth Press, 1989; Nahid Toubia, *Female Genital Mutilation: A Call for Global Action*, New York: Women, Ink, 1993; Samia El Hadi El. Nagar, Sunita Pitamber, and Ikhlas

Nouh (ed.), *Synopsis of the female Circumcision Research Findings*, Babiker Badri Scientific Association for Women Studies, 1994; William and Sobieszczyk, *op. cit.*, 1996.

33. Fábos, *op. cit.*, 1997.
34. Bukhari, *op. cit.*, 1997.
35. Al-Obeid, *op. cit.*, 1997, p. 14.
36. *Ibid.*, p. 13.
37. *Ibid.*, p. 16.
38. Wassef and Mansour, *op. cit.*, 1999.
39. Bukhari, *op. cit.*, 1997, pp. 17–18.

# 43

# FEMINIST MOVEMENT AND FUNDAMENTALIST RESISTANCE

Details are emerging which indicates that the military government of Lt-Gen Omar al Bashir, which took power in a coup d'etat on 30 June, has embarked upon a policy of undermining women's status in Sudan, under the banner of the alleged demands of Islamic propriety. Africa Watch is concerned about developing policies to dismiss women from public service, restrict their access to higher education and the legal profession, and curtail their freedom to travel. A number of women have also been detained on account of their alleged involvement in politics. Africa Watch is also concerned about a crackdown on women street vendors in the informal sector.

## Dismissals of Professional Women

Sudan has a tradition of progressive policies towards female emancipation and participation in society. A large number of students at the University of Khartoum have been women, and women have held senior positions in many government departments. Previous governments included women cabinet ministers.

Since the June coup d'etat, members of the fundamentalist National Islamic Front (NIF) have been in control of the government, despite attempts by the military leaders to conceal this fact. One of their policies has been the systematic dismissal of women from public employment. This has not been announced formally, and in fact the government has been careful to present alternative reasons for its actions. For instance, the dismissal of women has been defended as an economy measure in line with Sudan's economic austerity programme. In January 1990, the Minister for Presidential Affairs, Lt-Col Tayeb Ibrahim, accused some women dismissed from the Ministry of Foreign Affairs of having "won a prize for wine-tasting"—a deliberate slur intended to discredit them in a country where alcohol is considered contrary to the requirements of Islam.

In addition, most dismissals of women have occurred during wide-ranging purges of civil servants believed to be unsympathetic to Islamic fundamentalism. Attending a government conference on the role of women in January, President Omar al Bashir made his position clear. The ideal Sudanese woman, he said, took care of herself and her reputation, cared for her husband and her children, did her household duties, and was a devout Muslim. One report suggests that government policy intends that women should remain in only the two areas of public employment considered "suitable for women": primary school teaching and nursing.

Africa Watch believes that the government has been making a relatively small number of dismissals of women in order to test public reaction, with the aim of later proceeding with more far-reaching action. Africa Watch also believes that the campaign against women is only one part of a general attempt to remove people with sympathies for a secular state, so that Sudan's civil service, police, universities, unions, and professions will be dominated by men with an ideological commitment to fundamentalist Islam.

Africa Watch has received reports that one of the first women to be removed from her post was the Deputy Under Secretary for Employment Affairs in the civil service, Badiaa Abdel Rahman. This was a particularly critical dismissal as Badiaa had held this post for more than seven years, and had played an important role in overseeing the enforcement of the civil service regulations which ensured equal treatment for women. An unknown number of women have been subsequently dismissed from the civil service. One of these is Mrs. Mahasin Abdin, an employee at Khartoum Municipal Authority. She was also detained, and Africa Watch has been unable to discover whether she has been released, and where she has been held.

Many women in the legal profession have been dismissed. For example, sixty dismissals from the Attorney General's chambers included a disproportionate number of women—almost half. The government attempted to justify this on the grounds that many married women were frequently absent from work. However, those dismissed have included women of the highest professional calibre and commitment, such as Asma Kisha, Deputy Director in the Department of International Public Law. Nineteen women lawyers in the provincial town el Obeid were detained in December and held at the prison location of Khor el Abyad, outside the town, because of the lack of facilities for women in the town prison. The government has also insisted that all female recruits to the legal profession are mu'minaat—rigorously devout Moslems. This condition—which is applied more stringently to women than to men—serves to exclude candidates who incline towards secular law, as well as members of Sudan's large non-Moslem minority.

The medical profession has been active in opposing the government's policies, notably in organising a strike in November and December 1989, as result of which one doctor, Mamoun Mohamed Hussein, was sentenced to death. His sentence has not been carried out, but has also been officially commuted. Even before the doctors became militant, women in the medical profession were subject to arbitrary dismissal and harassment. In September 1989, Dr Majda Mohamed Ahmad, Director of the Diarrhoeal Diseases Unit at the Ministry of Health and also an active member of the Sudanese Medical Association was summarily dismissed, and subsequently detained for a day while being interrogated about her supposed political activities. Dr Majda is widely regarded as a physician of the highest professional standards. A nurse, Buthaina Dowka, was arrested on September 4. She was badly beaten, kept in detention while tied by ropes, and released in November without having been charged. Two nurses at Khartoum hospital, Niemat Malik and Nahla Abdel Wahad were detained for a day in January 1990, and warned against any involvement in political activities. Niemat was then prevented from travelling to Great Britain, where she was due to attend a course. In February, Dr Amal Gabralla, wife of the detained journalist Siddig el Zeilai, was arrested in the hospital where she worked. On the way to prison she was not allowed to pass by her home to pick up her one year-old son, who is now being taken care of by a neighbour. Dr Amal was dismissed from her post. She remains in Omdurman prison at the time of writing.

The government has introduced severe censorship, imprisoned a number of journalists, and purged employees at the Ministry of Information and the National Council for Arts and Literature. Africa Watch has learned of six women who were dismissed from their posts in these organisations, for their secularist sympathies or simply on account of their sex.

There has been discussion about limiting women's access to higher education, in particular about restricting the number of women able to study medicine, pharmacy, veterinary science, agriculture and engineering in Sudan's universities, presumably on the basis that these subjects are best left to men. While these restrictions have not been implemented, an ominous sign is the dismissal of all university Vice-Chancellors and their replacement with people sympathetic to the government on 31st March.

The Student's Union at the University of Khartoum, which is dominated by members of the pro-government National Islamic Front, proposed that all female students should compulsarily wear the hejab, the Islamic veil. For the time being, this proposal has been dropped in favour of the provision of veils at a subsidised price, in an attempt to encourage more women to buy veils. Africa Watch has also received a report that three girls attending Omdurman higher Secondary School have been expelled for allegedly belonging to the Democratic Front opposition group.

Women with any involvement in politics, past or present, have been harassed and detained. Three women who held positions in the previous government or the then-ruling Umma Party were detained on September 5, 1993. They were released, rearrested, and released again. They were Rashida Ibrahim Abdel Karim, former Minister for Social Welfare, Sara el Fadil Mahmoud, wife of the previous Prime Minister Sadiq el Mahdi, and Sara Abdullahi Nugudallah, daughter of a former Secretary-General of the Umma Party. The wives and sisters of members of opposition organisations which are working clandestinely have also been subject to harassment. Africa Watch believes that the government's actions against these and other women go beyond the simple harassment of political opponents but are based on opposition to the participation of women in politics in any way.

One measure against women that causes particular problems is the introduction of a measure which insists that any woman who travels is accompanied by a muharram—a close male blood relatives, who acts as a guardian. There is no basis for the requirement of a muharram in Sudanese Law. However Islamic Law as applied in Sudan includes an article known as ijtihad or 'free interpretation', which means that an Islamic juror can apply any prohibition for which he can find basis in *the Qur'ân* or *Hadith. The ijtihad* has been used in the past to obtain convictions for apostasy and to prevent women from working in hairdressing saloons, and is the basis for the new muharram rule.

This has prevented women from travelling, and subjected those who do to harassment and verbal abuse by officials. In one instance in December 1989, a distinguished academic and former lecturer at the University of Khartoum, Mrs Suad Ibrahim Ahmad, who is in her late fifties, was due to travel to a conference on 'Alternative Development Strategies for Africa' in Dar es Salaam, Tanzania, where she was to give a keynote address. She was prevented from going on the grounds that she needed a muharram. A more recent case is that of Mrs Fatima Ahmed Ibrahim, aged sixty and a prominent member of the Sudan Women's Union, who was due to attend a conference on Women in Africa to be held at the Africa Centre, London on 2-3 March 1990. Fatima was prevented from travelling for the same reason.

**Harassment of Women Petty Traders**

Many Sudanese women engage in petty trade in the marketplace, making an income through such activities as selling peanuts, making tea, etc. These activities have always been permitted and fill a niche in the urban economy. The social and economic crisis of Sudan has resulted in more than a million destitute people living around the capital Khartoum alone, many of them displaced from outlying rural areas by drought and war. For many for these families, women who work as street vendors or in other casual employment are the sole breadwinners.

Shortly after seizing power the military government began to clamp down upon this informal sector. This was part of a campaign, headed by the Deputy Commissioner of Khartoum,

Col Yusul Abdel Fatah (Known as 'Rambo' on account of his aggressive energy), to beautify Khartoum and make it into a capital city to stand beside those of the oil-rich Arab state—not by addressing the causes of mass poverty, but by cosmetic measures alone. The less draconian measures included the repainting of all facades of shops and houses on main streets in green and white, the building of fountains at major roundabout and the segregation of men and women on public transport. (According to a recent report, a young boy was lashed for entering a bus through the front door—the women's door—when he boarded a bus with his mother).

The principal measure has been an attack on what the government calls ribih haram, or 'forbidden profit'. This term is applied not only to the black market but to all unlicensed workers in the informal sector. The government's economic thinking fails to recognise that the informal sector makes a positive contribution to the economy, and appears unaware that many women who are prevented from working as street vendors may often have no alternative but to turn to crime or prostitution. Another justification for this attack was that women selling cooked food did not meet requirements of sanitation. However, an equally important reason appears to be the belief that women should confine themselves to the home, it being allegedly against Islamic propriety for them to engage in trade on the streets.

Whether or not the clamp-down on the informal economic sector has been deliberately directed against women, the principal victims have been women.

The clamp-down started with alleged liquor-brewers (alcohol is illegal under Islamic Law), street vendors and prostitutes, who came from peripheral regions in the west of Sudan, or who were refugees from Ethiopia. Between July 21 and 24, 1989, about 2000 people were evicted from their homes in the Saad Gishra, Deim Bahri and Mazad area of Khartoum North. Most were women. They were thrown out at short notice, some were beaten, and some of their furniture and possessions were broken. After a few days living in the streets, the victims were forcibly transported in rubbish lorries to a nearby football pitch. Subsequently, a standard fine of 1000 Sudanese pounds has been imposed on people convicted of alcohol offences: a vast amount for the impoverished women who typically engage in this trade.

Street vendors are frequently arrested in Khartoum. They are summarily tried in makeshift "Public Order Emergency Courts". These courts, which are set up in tents in the main marketplaces, consist of three junior or army officers, and have no respect for due process of law. One court is in United Nations Square in central Khartoum. The vendors' equipment is then confiscated or smashed. For a poor woman whose main source of income is selling tea, the loss of her kettle, teapot, glasses, spoons, stove, and stools represents a major loss of capital. The offenders are then flogged on the spot, usually face-down in the dust. Men normally receive twenty-five lashes, and women a variable amount depending on the whim of the policeman or security officer responsible.

This is not only physically dangerous but also humiliating and painful. Africa Watch has received a report of how in November 1989 one woman died after having been lashed in the public Order Emergency Court at Shajara, one part of Khartoum. An army officer then intervened in the Shajara court and insisted on the presence of a doctor to oversee the floggings. However, Africa Watch has not received any information which indicates that medical personnel are normally present for these lashings. Flogging is a cruel, inhuman, or degrading punishment, and as such is prohibited by the Convention against such forms of punishment, which Sudan ratified in June 1986. Africa Watch also considers that unlicensed street vending cannot be considered on offence warranting such severe punishment.

In one case which Africa Watch has learned of, a Nuer woman from southern Sudan was detained for allegedly brewing beer. She was whipped and otherwise maltreated, and forced into making a confession as to her 'accomplices'. One of those she named was Magdalena (not her real name), another Nuer woman who was nine months pregnant. Magdalena was then arrested, lashed, and taken to prison. Her relatives collected bail money of 400 Sudanese pounds which they offered to the court officer to obtain her release. The court officer said that no bail was possible. Magdalena gave birth in prison, unattended, without water or any other facilities. After the birth her clothes were bloodstained—and for this alleged impropriety she was lashed again. She spent a total of three months in prison with her baby, which she named 'Sijin'—Prison.

Africa Watch has received an unconfirmed but indicative report of another case in the town of Wad Medani on the blue. Nile. A man asked for tea from a woman street vendor, who in turn asked him: "Sadiq el Mahdi tea or Omer al Bashir tea?" The man asked to know the difference. The woman explained: "Sadiq tea has sugar, But Omer tea has only dates". (Dates are used as sweetener when sugar is unavailable). For this joke, the woman was arrested and lashed.

The actions of the Sudan government do not yet amount to a wholesale reduction of women to the status of second-class citizens. However, they are an ominous portent. Africa Watch believes that powerful individuals within the military government fully intend to reduce the status of women to that of legal minors, and end their active and equal participation in public life.

P. RAMET

# 44

## SEXIST MATRICULATION POLICY IN SUDAN

With its different quantitative and qualitative perspectives, the concept of the democratisation of education is profound. One of the primary bases of this concept is student access to education, regardless of sex; conviction, religion, etc. The situation of education regardless of sex; conviction, religion, etc. The situation of education varies from one society to another according to the political, economic, social and culture systems and relations existing in a certain society.

This article gives a picture of the situation concerning education in Sudan. It is one of the under-developed countries influenced by Arabic-Islamic culture, especially in its Northern regions. In one of its recent issue Al-Midan, a daily newspaper issued in Khartoum, capital of Sudan, interviewed a number of persons holding different political and ideological ways of thinking. The issue revolved around female access to higher education in Sudan. We hope this will provide an active discussion about the different forms this problem takes in other places.

A policy, or a general trend, seems to be taking shape in our institutions of higher education, namely to slowly and gradually reduce female student's chances for admission to the University and high institutes under various pretexts. If we keep silent, this will serve to perpetuate the present status of Sudanese women. Indeed, it will even drive them back to a position they have overcome since the sixties.

**Phenomenon of Female Students**

In recent years the phenomenon of female students doing better at the Sudanese entry exams has begun to draw attention. As of late, it has begun to irritate some—as acknowledged by the minister of Education in the transition government. However, it is not merely a question of irritation; some colleges and science faculties have been reserved solely for male students as, for instance, the Department of Surveying at the University of Khartoum, the department of Surveying Technicians at the Polytechnic Institute, the College of Mechanical Engineering in Atbara, the College of Agronomy and Natural Resources in Aby Hraz, the College of Agronomy in Aby Naama and the *Holy Qur'ân* College, Admission to these faculties has been exclusively restricted to male students, a practice dictated by the matriculation policy.

Some colleges have reduced the number of female students admitted to their faculties by demanding higher marks of the fair sex. A case in point is the College of veterinary Medicine—Koko—where 39 male students and only 4 female students have been admitted. The Shambat Institute of Agronomy has set a total of 343 points for the admission of male students, against 368 points for their female counterparts. Accordingly, the institute has admitted 106 male students and only 22 female.

Also the Institute of Secretariat Technicians has set 357 points for the admission of male student and 368 points for female students thus admitting 28 males and 26 females. The Higher Institute of Physical Education has set 351 points for the admission of male students and 345 for female student thus admitting 51 male and only 22 female.

## No Laws Restricting Female Admission

Is this blatant sex discrimination between students based on any recently promulgated laws or bills? An official of the Matriculation Board for University and Higher Education has denied any sexist discrimination in admission. Indeed, he has asserted that there is every year a steady increase in the number of female applicants admitted to the universities and other institutes of higher education. Their share of admission has increased according to him, from 11% in 1990 to 39% at present. In some colleges at the University of Khartoum this share has even increased to about 50%.

He went on to say that the share of female students admitted to the University of Khartoum has reached 41.4% although in some industrially advanced countries their share is yet to exceed 40%. He added:

> "I would like to underline that there are no laws or bills restriciting the admission of female students to the university and other institutes of higher education. Furthermore, the matriculation board takes its decisions with regard to the admission of students not on sex grounds but in the light of academic performance and scientific qualification".

He continued:

> "We should not forget that there are colleges exclusively restricted to females, like to college of Nursing. This college has previously advised that also male students should be admitted but retracted its recommendation later on. There are also the University College of Al-Ahfad and the College of Household Economics which have become exclusively reserved for female students whereas in the past they were open to both sexes. There is also a college exclusively restricted to females at the Islamic University".

He went to say:

> "True some colleges are exclusively restricted to males, but this is so at the recommendation of these colleges and faculties themselves. It is perhaps due to the increased tuition fees at

these colleges or may be in order to have education performing its proper functions. Some specialisations are not suitable to women. Also a number of officials at state enterprises have expressed reservations at the increased number of female graduates employed at their enterprise. The reason is that they cannot work in tough conditions; they have problems moving from one place to another, problems in field work; problems of women giving up their jobs due to family burdens, etc".

## Surveying and Women

The Department of Surveying at the University of Khartoum is one of the faculties denied to female students. Dr. Abdullah added that 'this view is widespread even in developed countries like Britain. We have persuaded many female applicants to switch to any other department to spare them the difficulties they would be facing'. He said that 'all this is not done out of prejudice against women but the meager resources available at present have to be used to train those who are more capable of enduring the strains of this profession. However, we are fully convinced that women are intellectually no less eligible than men".

How does the female engineering student view the matter? Does she have doubts about her ability to endure the stress of study and work? Amal Hassan Samaarait, a graduate of the Department of Electrical Engineering employed at the same department, has this to say:

> "I applied for admission to the University of Khartoum in the academic year 1978-79. I was interested in surveying but my application was turned down because I am a woman and presumably could not endure the stress of study and work. That was the conviction of the decision makers, not mine. As far as I am concerned, I have full confidence in my ability to cope with all strains. I was transferred to the department". She adds: "I find that the matriculation policy at this department is prejudiced against women and fetters their abilities".

Another female student at the Civil Engineering Surveying Department says:

> "I have already done field training at the area of Mount Awliyaa. We had to work all day. As a team of male and female students we, of course, had some difficulties but I did not feel I was not up to it".

She added:

> "The notion that female students cannot endure the strains of study at some Department must be overcome. The Department of Engineering Surveying must be opened up to female students for fear of setting a precedent to deny female students admission to all departments in the future under various pretexts. Testing the ability of female students in practice is the real touch-stone. Moreover, physical and mental abilities vary from one person to another irrespective of sex".

**Planned Matriculation**

Reviewing last year's admission at the Polytechnic Institute we have discovered that the adopted policy is to restrict the chances of female students and reduce their number one way or another. Higher requirements are placed on female students than male students.

Mr. Hafdth Mohammed Otheman, the academic secretary of the Institute, confirms the above mentioned facts. He says admissions requirements are the same for both sexes but the Institute has a definite policy of "planned matriculation". In keeping with this policy, each college announces the number of male and female students to be admitted in the respective year specifying the percentage for each sex. At the Secretariat Department, for instance, it is always set a 50% males and 50% females whereas at the Veterinary Technicians Department it is set at 90% and 10% respectively.

As for why this policy and since when, the academic secretary says that the adopted procedure is high policy implemented by the Institute since the time of Muhi'addin

Sabir. He holds that this procedure safeguards the female student's change of admission. At the secretariat department for example, admission was previously restricted to female, then it was opened up to both sexes. There was a rush of applications by male students crowding out the females. So officials were prompted to set equal shares for the two sexes.

At the Veterinary Technicians Department in Kolo the share of female students has been set a 10% due, he said, to the nature of work at this department. According to him it is hard work at this Institute demanding the presence of students at camps out in the open for many months. It also demands their presence at the live-stock pens and barns where work is hard with animals, something female students cannot cope with. That is why their share of admissions has been set at 10% and they are appointed to certain places only which are suitable to them such as research laboratories and dairy plants.

**Hostels are the Reason**

Professor Hassan Abdul-Noor Dean of the Soba Forestry Institute, says he has no objection to the admission of any number of female students according to the results of free competition. The Institute, he adds, has no discriminatory policy. What blocks the admissions of female students, however, is a shortage of accommodation in the vicinity of the Institute. He pointed out that the institute has received a loan to build female and male student hostels. When these are completed female students will be inconditionally admitted. The Dean says he is about to call for a conference of agronomists to be convened in late January. Agricultural experts will be invited to consider ways of developing the curricula in the interest of the countryside. In the light of the recommendations to be adopted by this conference the agricultural sector's requirements of both sexes will be determined.

The Dean of Abu Hraz College of Agronomy says the matriculation board at the College does not admit female students because it believes that the location of Abu Ghazar and Abu Naama is a hazardous zone for women. He asserts that the administration does not object to the admission of female students. The only obstacle is the shortage of accommodation. The existing hostels are the designed to accommodate only male students. The college thought of building female hostels but the project has not materialised due to the lack of resources. Continuing our investigation into this phenomenon we approached more pedagogues and university professors:

> "Dr. Jalaluddin Taib, the Department of Geography, Faculty of Arts, Khartoum University. He says: "Admission according to sex runs counter to elementary human rights. It is an an extension of prejudice against women and in principal and anomalous, unacceptable attitude".

He adds:

> "We at Faculty of Geography have a surveying course where female students have proved that they are no less capable and diligent than males as far as work and study is concerned. They do field work in inclement weather conditions. They are accommodated in rugged mountainous areas. They do their studies in tents set up in the open. The faculty administration has never felt that this has adversely affected their endurance".

Dr. Jalaluddin goes on to say that he hopes this will not be an exclusive education policy, in recent years the number of female student has increased and their standard has advanced above that of male students. Their share of admission at the university of Khartoum this year was 8-10% which implies a diversity of abilities tendencies and attitudes. Opportunities should be provided on the basis of performance irrespective of sex.

**Better Performance by Female Students**

Dr. Farah Hassan Adam, Dean of the College of Agronomy, Khartoum University, says:

> "Voices have been raised for years now pointing to the increased share of female students in admission. Those upholding such views think that restrictions should be introduced to reduce the number of female students. They claim that this in an attempt to strike a balance whereas opportunities should be given to those with better results".

About admissions at the College of Agronom Dr. Farah says:

> "It is very often equally shared by female and male student were admitted, including 11! females. This year 390 students applied for admission to the college, including 200 females and 190 males. This college, however, can receive only 141 applicants. Admission will in this case be based on performance".

Dr. Farah underlines that 'in some faculties of this college the number of female student exceeds that of male students because they are more industrious than males even in agricultural work where the female graduate has proved her superiority.' Dr. Farah continues:

> "The theme of 'sex differentiation' has been played for many years now. It is part of a growing reactionary trend advocation the 'Islamisation of education'. This will no doubt split up education according to sex."

### What Does the Women's Federation Think?

The view had to be heard of a national organisation leading the struggle for women's equality. Interviewing Fatima Ahmad, chair woman of the Women's Federation, she had this to say: 'The Women's Federation was the first to raise the banner of women's emancipation and equality as well as their participation in the sphere of production. The Federation has campaigned for equal opportunities in higher, academic, technical and vocational education and for equal rights in reality. A hard struggle has to be waged to put these rights into practice a legally established right comes up against barriers and notions opposed to women's quality and rights. It is duty of educated women to contribute to this and expose the case of sexist bias. Using the lax, a victimised woman can go to court to plead her case'. Fatima goes on to say:

> "The role of the Women Federation is to educate Women's Federation is to educate women, who have no faith in their abilities and who are under the influence of these notions. This is carried out along with unmasking dogmatic, rigid thinking through the press and there media. A new campaign has to be launched to eliminate these anti-woman notions."

We have a problem of flagrant discrimination in the admission of students who want to learn. The Universal Declaration of Human Rights, signed also by the Sudan, emphatically comes out against discrimination on sex or religious grounds. We know that social advancement is shouldered by the two sexes. Both are equally gifted. Sexism is alien to learning.

The early female teachers were trail-blazers in devotion and endurance. They had penetrated deep into rugged and remote terrains upholding the torch of knowledge to selflessly carry out their sacred mission. The fact that some women refuse to be transferred to other places should not be used as an excuse to take a prejudiced attitude against female education or employment opportunities. Objection to employment in remote locations is common to both male and female employees. It has nothing to do with sex. It is rather and outcome of the deterioration working conditions in the provinces where usually one has a hard time putting up with inadequate housing and problems of everyday life.

Hence, the preference to stay in the capital is not confined to the State created favourable working conditions in the rural areas to demand that it transfer directives be implemented?

IUS, 1988

# 45

# FEMALE CIRCUMCISION IN SUDAN

Female circumcision (the partial or complete removal of the external female genitalia) is widely practised in the Sudan. It has persisted for centuries because of lack of awareness and knowledge about its adverse physical and psycho-social consequences and because of a firm belief in its supposed benefits of ensuring female chastity and securing marriage and subsequent harmonious family life. In the Sudan, female circumcision has for long remained in secrecy but it is now being brought to the surface by health and medical practitioners, sociologists, psychiatrists, psychologists and others who are all interested in the various physical, psychological and socio-cultural aspects of the practice.

This chapter is primarily presented as a summary of contributions especially prepared for the present Workshop. Additional material to complete the presentation is drawn from other written sources dealing with issues and problems relating to female circumcision in the Sudan. The purpose of this paper is to summarise available information and findings on female circumcision as presently practised in the Sudan and to examine and assess efforts made to abolish it. It is hoped that the paper will be useful in stimulating constructive discussion that lays the foundation for fuller understanding, action, and commitment to eradicate the practice of female circumcision.

**Sources**

Some background material on the Sudan is relevant. The Sudan is the largest state in Africa with an area of about 2.5 million square kilometres. Its terrain consists primarily of an extensive plain rising gradually to highlands in the north-east near the Red Sea coast, and plateau and low mountains near the southern and western borders of the country. In the Sudan the climate is mainly tropical, being equatorial in the extreme south and arid in the north.

The Sudan is sparsely populated with an enumerated population of about 14 million in 1973 and an estimated population of about 14 million in 1973 and an estimated population of over 19 million in 1981. The population in the Sudan is very young, with nearly 46 per cent of the population aged 15 and only 3 per cent aged 65 and over. The current rate of natural growth is estimated to be around 3.2 per cent annually. The Sudan is predominantly rural with less than 20 per cent of its population living in the urban areas.

The educational level of the adult population in the Sudan is low. In 1873 among persons 10 years of age and older, about 32 per cent of males and 12 per cent of females were literate. Recently, there has been rapid expansion in education. About one-half of the boys and more than one-third of the girls aged 7-12 are currently enrolled in primary schools.

The economy of the Sudan is largely based on agriculture; in 1973 about 66 per cent of the economically active people were engaged in agricultural pursuits.

The population of the Sudan falls into several ethno-cultural and tribal groups. In the South there are Christians and Muslims although the majority of people still follow their own traditional religious beliefs and practices. In the rest of the country Islamic religion predominates. Besides Arabic, the lingua franca of the Sudan, different languages and dialects are spoken by various ethnic groups. Politically, from 1899 to 1955 the Sudan was a British colony and it became an independent country on 1st January 1956. From 1958 to 1964, the Sudan came under military rule; from 1964 to 1969 it was ruled by civilian governments, and with the May Revolution of 1969, a single party Presidential system has been instituted, with the Sudanese Socialist Union as a mass political party.

### Forms of Circumcision and its Consequences

While some variations exist, there are three major forms of female circumcision practised in the Sudan. These fall into

(*a*) Infibulation; known in the Sudan as Pharaonic Circumcision, which entails the removal of the whole clitoris, labia minora and either the entire or most of the anterior parts of the labia majora. The two edges are then brought together by stitching or other means and are left to heal. Infibulation is often described as the oldest and most prevalent in the Sudan.

(*b*) Circumcision proper, known in the Sudan as Sunna circumcision, which involves the excision of the tip of the prepuce of the clitoris. The Sunna circumcision is regarded as the mildest form.

(*c*) Intermediate Female circumcision in the Sudan (between Pharronic and Sunna) which entails the removal of the clitoris, anterior parts or the whole of the labia minora and parts of the labia majora. The two sides are then stitched together leaving a variable opening to allow passage of urine and menstrual blood. The intermediate form of circumcision is identified as having various degrees of severity.

### Adverse Medical and Health Consequences

In the Sudan a variety of complications of female circumcision have been reported in the medical literature. Usually immediate and late complication such as immediate shock, bleeding, infection, tetanus, difficulty in passing urine and urinary retention, where as late complications include, among others, vulval swelling, difficulties during labour and delivery, and coital difficulties such as severe pain at penetration and lack of orgasm or sexual gratification. In a nation-wide and cross-sectional survey, Asma El Dareer traced the incidence of both immediate and late complications of female circumcision and their frequency for each of the major types of cicumcision among circumised Sudanese women.

The following is a summary of the main fndings. The immediate complications of all three forms of circumcision numbered 790 cases (25%) of all circumcised females. The frequency for each type of circumcision alone was: Pharnonic 26%, Intermediate 24% and Sunna 8%. Of all the immediate complications, difficulty in passing urine, wound infection, and bleeding were the most common. On the other hand, the delayed complications amounted to 1023 (32%) of all circumcised cases.

The frequency of each type of circumcision alone was: Pharaonic (33%). Intermediate (31%), and Sunna (15%). The most common delayed complications were recurrent urinary tract infections, chronic pelvic infection and results of tight circumcision, namely difficulty in penetration, pain during sexual intercourse and difficulty in menstruation. An interesting result of Asma El Dareer's study is that the pattern of complications of Pharaonic and Intermediate forms of circumcision was found to be the same.

**Adverse Psychological Consequences**

Serious psychological consequences of female circumcision are numerous and most have been reported by students of Mental Health. Material concerning the adverse psychological effects of female circumcision in the Sudan.... Circumcision is not based on extensive surveys but rather it is based on observation and clinical cases. The available information indicates that the immediate physical complications of female circumcision, especially the pain associated with the operation form an instant source of psychological hazards to circumcised female children

It is true that much is done by Sudanese families to lessen the painful effects of female circumcision, but nonetheless the circumcised female child undergoes an unforgettable experience. The clandestine nature of the operation together with the fear-provoking situation associated with it combine to disturb the mental state of circumcised girls to the extent where they cause worry, anxiety sleeplessness, nightmares or even panic. As the girls grow up and the adverse and late physical complications set in, mental injuries in the form of distorted images about menstruation, sex, marriage and childbirth tend to increase.

Moreover, many cricumcised females are most likely to be caught in the web of conflicting expectations and roles. This relates to the fact that in the Sudan circumcised girl is regarded as an adult female and quite often treated as such even though she is just a child trying to play the roles appropriate to early or middle childhood. In such circumstances young girls may experience personality changes; a lively, innocent and friendly child becoming timid and introspective. Again, delayed complications of female circumcision, especially deformity in the female genitalia, swelling and the development of fistulae may cause serious patho-psychological changes and precipitate a series of abnormal psychological disturbances ranging from chronic irritability to reactive depression and psychosis.

**Other Adverse Consequences**

Equally important is that female circumcision has serious negative psycho-sexual effects on women and men alike. Women are most likely, for instance, to meet with lack of orgasm or sexual gratification in intercourse as a result of amputation of the clitoris. This is so because, unlike what is commonly believed in the Sudan, the excision of the clitoris does not reduce desire for sex, but rather it spoils sexual gratification. Among men injury to male sexuality is likely to occur if a man failed to accomplish successful coitus with an infibulated wife. The statistics given by the Sudan Fertility Survey were 79.4 per cent Pharaonic, 16.5 per cent Sunna and 4.1 per cent uncircumcised. The information yielded by Asma El Dareer's survey showed that of 3,171 circumcised females, 2,636 (83 per cent) were Pharaonically circumcised 386 (19 per cent) had had Intermediate circumcision, 80 (2.5 per cent) had had Sunna circumcision and 69 (2 per cent) could not be classified because they were unable to identify which form they had had.

Surveys undertaken among specific population indicated that in more recent years there have been significant changes in female circumcision practices. In particular, surveys carried out among college and high school female students reported a rise in the incidence of Sunna and intermediate forms of circumcision. The statistics given by Gasim Badri, for instance, were 28 per cent Pharaonic, 11 per cent Sunna, 55 per cent, Intermediate, and 6 per cent incircumcised. These figures provided evidence suggesting that there has been a shift away from Pharaonic circumcision among certain categories of females, especially young and urban-oriented ones.

The practice of female circumcision in the Sudan is closely correlated with increasing illiteracy whether this illiteracy concerns those who were circumcised or their parents. Eightyone and 6 tenth per cent (81.6%) of the respondents were illiterate. Again, of all the women interviewed in Asma EI Dareer's research, 43 per cent were illiterate, 84 per cent of their mothers ànd 42 per cent of their fathers were also illiterate. Regional and ethno-cultural differences relating to female circumcision are of some interest, but lack of numerical data precludes detailed statistical analysis. However, different observers noted disparity even within the same region. Thus while in Eastern Sudan the Beja tribes, especially the Hadandowa and Beni 'Amir practice the severest type of infibulation, their neighbours, the Rashaida Arabs, hardly carry out any form of circumcision among their women.

In the Sudan such failure is regarded as a slur on a man's virility and it is likely to breed psychological complications ranging from anxiety to impotence. Moreover, these complications may interfere with marital relationships as when a husband accuses his tightly circumcised wife of his impotence or when a wife is adamant about her husband's failure and ready to declare it. In such situations impotence is likely to result in suicide or homicide—the husband taking revenge on himself or on his wife to defend his honour. It can be seen that female circumcision has serious complex and far-reaching psychological, and social results.

## Nature and Extent of Female Circumcision Practice in Sudan

For a long time female circumcision has been practised in the Sudan despite the harmful physical, psychological and social effects. Among the different groups in the country it is generally associated with much ceremonial and ritual activities. Moreover, female circumcision is characteristically a women's affair and as a deeply-rooted custom it is embedded in a complex set of beliefs and values. On the other hand, the operation of female circumcision is often carried out by non-skilled practitioners under very adverse hygienic conditions. For example, the instrument commonly used is a razor blade and in most instance little or no attempt is made at sterilising it.

Female circumcision in the Sudan is reported to be performed at ages after 6, between 5 and 8 years, or between 4 and 8 years. According to Asma El Dareer's survey 81.4 per cent of the women interviewed were circumcised by the time they were 9 years, with 63.3 per cent having been circumcised between 5 to 9 years of age.

The Sudan Fertility Survey and Asma El Dareer's study provide a broad picture of the prevalence and distribution of female circumcision in the Sudan. These two nationwide surveys indicate that the practice is quite prevalent in the country. Thus, according to the Sudan Fertility Survey, 95.9 per cent of the respondents (ever married females) have been circumcised. In addition, these two surveys provide a useful indication of the incidents of each of the major forms of circumcision currently.

Baggara Arabs continued to practice Sunna circumcision for quite a long time before turning to more drastic forms of infibulation whereas many of the Muslim tribes of Darfur (extreme West) do not perform circumcision on their females. A milder form of circumcision is common throughout the groups inhabiting Northern and Central Sudan as well as among the Kababish Arabs of Western Sudan.

In Southern Sudan female circumcision or any form is not in practice except perhaps where the local peoples come into contact with some Northern groups. In a vast country like the Sudan, these regional and ethno-cultural differences in the practice of female circumcision are scarcely surprising though further research is needed to substantiate them.

**Reasons for the Continuation of the Practice**

In the Sudan numerous reasons are given for the performance and continuation of the practice of female circumcision. First, the operation of female circumcision appears to have been performed with a view to attenuate sexual desire. According to this popular belief, lessening sexual appetite prevents women from indulging in pre-marital sex and from losing their virginity. Loss of virginity and pre-marital sex and deplored and regarded as improper or even immoral in Sudanese Society. However, it has been repeatedly argued that female circumcision even in its extreme form of infibulation (fastening or stitching together the edges of the libia majora) cannot serve to secure women's virginity or to ensure their chastity. This is because it is possible for a female to engage in pre-marital sex and lose her virginity, but through a simple surgical operation get recircumcised shortly before marriage. All this implies that in the light of medical knowledge the view that infibulation protects virginity and ensures continence is certainly invalid.

Secondly, in Sudan female circumcision is performed because of a common belief that a circumcisied woman is 'clean' and un uncircumised woman is 'unclean'. Again, in the light of current medical and health knowledge this reason or rather assertion has no substantial support.

Thirdly, a reason for circumcision most frequently given is that men will not marry a girl unless she is infibulated. The argument for this view is that men derive more sexual gratification from a tightly circumcised woman with a narrow orifice rather than from an uncircumised one. Incidently, it is this kind of reasoning which explains why many Sudanese woman get involved in the vicious series of decircumcision and recircumcision after each successive childbirth. But as mentioned earlier, the various forms of circumcision can only add to women's agony and misery and contribute to men's lack of sexual satisfaction and impotence.

Fourthly, in the Sudan the operation of female circumcision has quite often been performed in the pretext that it is endorsed by the Islamic religion. However, this popular belief has still a strong hold. It has been repeatedly refuted by religious leaders. As Sheikh Hassen Ahmed Abu Sabib has indicated there is no evidence of the Islamic religion favouring female circumcision. The Sheikh also pointed out that Muslim countries associating the practice with religion should revise their stand and that female circumcision should not be practised by any Muslim on the basis of Islam.

Fifthly, in the Sudan, traditionally the operation of female circumcision used to be performed on girls who were approaching puberty. Consequently, female circumcision could be interpreted as an initiation ceremony which functions through certain rites to reinforce and give meaning to the process of psycho-social development from puberty to adulthood. But, now as the age at which the operation is carried out on Sudanese girls varies from one week to about 10 years, the practice of female circumcision may simply create a sense of awareness in the child regarding her future sexual role, but it can hardly prepare her to enact that role. Indeed, with much of its ceremonial and ritual acts being minimised female circumcision can no longer influence the process of socialisation or maturation.

Lastly, many Sudanese families continue to perform the operation of female circumcision on their girls as a tradition or custom dictated by and in line with group norms, values and identity.

**Efforts to Combat Female Circumcision in Sudan**

In Sudan the interest in the practice of female circumcision and concern about its adverse effects were not new. As early as the three decades preceding the Second World War, Sudanese and British Administrators, religious leaders, politicians and other enlightened Sudanese had all been concerned with finding ways and means to abolish the practice. Medical practitioners expended much effort to disclose the extent and nature of the damage inflicted by female circumcision upon its victims.

Religious leaders directed their energies towards dissociating the practise of female circumcision from Islamic religions and making it clear to the public that true Muslims should give up repulsive practices such as excessive excision and infibulation which have no support in the basic principles of Islam. Political leaders and notables gave their blessings and support and the fight against female circumcision went on and eventually culminated in the promulgation of the law of 1946. This legislation prohibited practise of Pharaonic circumcision and made it illegal and punishable by fine and imprisonment.

From the start many serious misgivings were pronounced against these early efforts to deal with female circumcision and against the law that was intended to impose a strict ban on Pharaonic circumcision. The efforts were seen by some Sudanese as a direct interference on the part of the colonial government with intimate practices and values of the Sudanese society and culture and extreme nationalists viewed the whole campaign against female circumcision as a threat to national solidarity as it tended to divide Sudanese people into those for and against anti-circumcision laws.

Moreover, one of the immediate effects of the legislation of 1946 was that many girls were hurriedly taken by their mothers to be circumcised at earlier ages thereby giving those who were trying hard to convince the people to abandon the practice gradually, a serious setback. Indeed, over the years Pharaonic circumcision continued, though less openly, in spite of the fact that the prohibition of 1946 has never been formally revoked. In short, the anti-circumcision legislation has never been fully accepted either in theory or in practice. Nevertheless, the pre-war efforts to deal with female circumcision were not without useful results.

Beside focusing the attention of a relatively large audience of the issue of female circumcision in the Sudan, a number of essential lessons can be extracted from these earlier experiences. First, it is extremely difficult if no impossible, for legislation to wipe out such a deeply-rooted tradition as female circumcision. Second, and most important, is that in introducing laws and similar measures, due consideration should be given to such factors as the political climate and the socio-psychological setting or rather the social-cultural way of life of the people or communities concerned. Finally, if it is deemed necessary to introduce laws to combat a sensitive custom such as female circumcision, a genuine attempt should be made to grasp the full implications of these laws in order to avoid their undesirable results or unintended consequences.

The campaign against female circumcision in Sudan apparently has waned in the two decades or so following the Second World War. However, with the country's rapid change and development over recent decades, interest in female circumcision has been renewed and fresh attempts have been made with a view to eradicating it. Evaluating existing and on-going concerns and action dealing with female circumcision in the Sudan is an onerous task. However, the main features of recent attempts are easy to summarise. On the one hand, considerable and valuable efforts to combat female circumcision have been, and are being made in the country. On the other hand, much of what has been done so far is rather diverse and disparate.

Unevenness and diversity are no doubt the inevitable results of the nature and complexity of female circumcision or the problem itself, the multiplicity of bodies and groups involved in it, and the variety of measures and actions made or suggested for the eventual eradication. These statements are not intended to belittle efforts, past or present, made toward combating female circumcision in the Sudan. They are intended solely to draw attention to the uneven and diverse nature of these efforts and to suggest that there is a need for a more co-ordinated work and a new strategy to do away with female circumcision in Sudan.

Much has been said or implied in this paper about the complexity of various aspects of female circumcision in Sudan. Here it is important to point out that in the last decade or so the number of organisations focusing their attention and interest on female circumcision has increased and that this reflects in a wide range of activities and measures intended to abolish the practice. Indeed, recently many more voluntary organisations, national and international bodies have been actively engaged in work and action-oriented activities with the objective of gaining more knowledge about circumcision-related issues and suggesting appropriate measures to eradicate the practice.

The organisations include medical associations (Obstetrics and Gynaeological Society), Sudan Family Planning Association, Ahfad University College for Women, Babiker Badri Scientific Association for Women's Studies; High Nursing College, Department of Social Welfare, Maternal and Child Health Service of the Ministry of Health, the Sudan Women's Union. University of Khartoum, the National Committee for the Eradication of Female Circumcision of the

Ministry of Internal Affairs and WHO, UNICEF, the Swedish Radda Barnen, Swedish Housewives Association, and the Norwegian Action Group. These organisations articulated their activities and measures through a variety of channels, embracing conferences, seminars, symposia, workshops, discussion groups, radio, T.V., public speeches, books, articles, pamphlets, posters and integrated programmes of all sorts.

The measures themselves include, among other things, emphasis on or call for legislation prohibting all forms of female circumcision, intensification of general education of the public with special emphasis on the hazards of female circumcision, inclusion of courses on female circumcision as part of the curricula of certain educational institutions, intensification of educational programmes for special categories of personnel, e.g., midwives, health visitors, nutrition officers etc., with a view to demonstrating the harmful effects of female circumcision and enlisting the support of these target categories for the campaign against female circumcision and the integration of female circumcision issues with existing health and social programs designed to promote the status of women.

A survey such as the above leads to an apparent paradox regarding the campaign against female circumcision in the Sudan. On the one hand, it appears that a great deal of effort towards eradication of female circumcision has been expended. On the other hand, female cicumcision, as indicated earlier in this paper, is still carried out in many parts of the country. This paradox, however could easily be explained away if it is realised that these efforts to combat female circumcision tend to be on the whole quite space-specific. In a particular, they tend to be limited to the urban complex of Khartoum and other highly selected localities. Again, the recent efforts to eradicate female cicumcision in the Sudan, with few exceptions, are not based on reliable systematic research. All this implies that if efforts to deal with female circumcision are to succeed they should have a much wider geographical coverage and should be based on scientific research.

On the other hand, the lessons learned from the efforts carried out in the urban complex of Khartoum must be of central and crucial concern to the various organisations interested in circumcision-related issues and problems since these lessons can be useful when efforts are extended to the rest of the Sudan.

It is evident that a new strategy to eradicate female circumcision in Sudan must be based on reliable facts and interpretations of certain female circumcision-related problems and issues that should already identified as matters of concern and urgency. The space coverage of these issues and problems should be gradually enlarged to embrace different regions and populations of the whole of the Sudan.

Finally, to the extent that female circumcision is widespread in many African countries, concerned quarters in these countries must seek ways and means to exchange knowledge and experiences relating to this practice with a view to seeing the day it will be completely abolished.

**Research and Work in Progress**

Two surveys were undertaken in the Sudan, one by the Faculty of medicine, University of Khartoum, and the other by the Sudan Fertility Association. Both are nation-wide, and both tackled many aspects of female circumcision (preference for the various types, attitudes toward it, complications ensuing from it, and justification given for the practice).

About 200 pieces of research, of different types, on various scales have also been done, which include dissertations at the first degree and diploma levels, an M.Sc. thesis, and post-graduate professional research. A special project is being undertaken by the Medical Research council to document and classify research on female circumcision and to suggest policies for future research on previous and current efforts to eliminate female circumcision.

1. A national workshop was held in 1981 in Khartoum to discuss female circumcision and to produce

recommendations and stragegies for the elimination of female circumcision.

2. Thereafter a follow-up committee was established as a Sub-Committee of the Babiker Badri Scientific association for Women's Studies. This committee is composed of both men and women and it has provided many public lectures and mass media activities.

3. A book on the proceedings of the Workshop, including all the recommendations made was published in 1983. It has been widely distributed, but there has been no detailed follow-up system to check whether each Ministry has fulfilled its obligations to accomplish the specific objectives of the Workshop.

4. The Babiker Badri Scientific Association has five current projects on female circumcision. Two workshops have already taken place.

5. Before the Dakar Conference took place, a National Committee had been formed which has held two meetings since September 1983. During these meetings it was recommended that a law should be enforced to forbid all forms of female circumcision and that the government should provide a state policy for the elimination of female circumcision.

After the Dakar Conference the two men and two women who attended were supposed to form a National Committee to abolish female circumcision. It was decided, however, that as Sudan has already formed a National Committee, and two of those who went to Dakar were already members of it, there was no need to form another committee. No action has yet been taken by the National Committee.

**Future Strategies**

A.1. The BBSAWS should undertake 6 regional workshops in the 6 regions of the Northern Sudan to sensitise people in rural areas, to select highly motivated leaders from them and then to continue the work of the campaign by forming subcommittees of these to be responsible for the continuation of the work.

A.2. Work should be concentrated on a model area in the three towns of the capital to discover what results can be achieved to eliminate female circumcision, in one specific area. Checks should be made before and after the work in this model area in order to provide an efficient system of evaluation.

A.3. The integrated Women's Development Programmes should be extended to other villages.

A.4. Educational materials should continue to be produced and so should discussion groups continue to take place.

A.5. The project which has already begun should be completed so that midwives become supervisors of the work of motivating others to abolish female circumcision.

B. At the group and individual levels there should be

1. Research on the effects of female circumcision on fertility.
2. Research on the psychological impact of female circumcision children through long term research in rural Khartoum;
3. Other research.

C. A league of university students should be formed for the elimination of female circumcision

D. The National Committee should be re-constituted so as to be smaller in number but to be composed of people really dedicated to the eradication of female circumcision.

E. Although the Sudan Government has no specific strategy, all Ministers concerned should publicly announce that female circumcision should be abolished. The Minister of Health in particular should ask all members of the medical services to take action to combat it. All Public Health Programmes should include education for the elimination of female circumcision.

B. BADARI

# APPENDICES

## I

## Feminist Movement from Ethnic Fundamentalism to Religious Fundamentalism

The article of Stasa Zajovic from the Women in Black-Belgrade rings a bel to all of us who live in multi-ethnic, multi-religious, multi-cultural countries, threatened by growing nationalism or communalism, where the hatred of the other closely entwined with population policies (as a mild form which can evolve into its drastic form of ethnic cleansing) put women at the forefront of these policies. Women in Black-Belgrade is a pioneering organisation which has maintained throughout the war in Ex-Yugoslavia that much needed links between women of different communities and has assisted all multi-cultural, multi-ethnic and multi-religious initiatives of women as well as worked with refugees from all origins in camps. They were the first ones to denounce the atrocities committed by the Serbian regime and the prostitution camps installed for the regime as well as the atrocities committed by the other communities and the brothels installed by the UN peace keeping troops. They also pointed out at the close link between the increase in war violence and domestic violence, thus showing war as an effective brutalisation of the whole society.

Needless to say that Women in Black have faced repressions within Serbia.

In this piece, Stasa, one of the leading figure of Women in Black—Belgrade stresses the similarity between ex-Yugoslavia and Nazi Germany in their involvement of women in a form of motherhood which serves best the interest of a bellicous, expansionist, nationalist and racist regime. It appeared interesting to us to juxtapose to her article two pieces which were distributed at the Beijing NGO Forum at the UN Conference on Women, by women affiliated with fundamentalist groups. The first document, unsigned, reproduced in extenso, shows the proposed model of the Muslim woman in relation to morality and glorification of motherhood. The second document is a statement of the Islamic Research academy Al-Azhar Al-Sharif, published by the office of the Grand Imam, addressed to the Beijing Conference. We have excerpted from it the paragraphs on women and morality, as well as motherhood and war. They illustrate, in the context of religious fundamentalism—the model analysed by Stasa in the context of ethnic fundamentalism.

Muslim women of the world: Keep to your own religion and culture for your own health; reject the disease-ridden proposals to the UN!

Day after day, Muslim doctors all over the world are discovering the great prescriptions for good health in Islamic teachings given to us by our Merciful Creator, *Allâh*, Medically, it has been concluded that all orders and lawful acts in Islam make you healthy, while all acts deemed unlawful and prohibited in Islam make you sick and ill. *Allâh* has said in Al-deemed unlawful and prohibited in Islam make you sick and ill. *Allâh* has said in *Al-Qur'ân*:

> 'We send down in *the Qur'ân* that which is healing and a mercy to the believers" (XVII: 82).

The prescriptions for the good health of women in Islam are comprehensive, including the physical, psychological, social, spiritual and occupational sides of life. For women only Islam prescribes breast-feeding (lactation). Women expose themselves to the risk of cancer of the breast and ovaries if they don't breast-feed their children. Also, their children can suffer from a large number of physical and psychological diseases if they are not breast-fed.

Islam prescribes pregnancy in marriage only. If a woman never has a pregnancy in her life she has an increased risk of contracting cancer of the womb.

Islam prohibits abortion. A woman can get cancer of the breast if she kills her baby through abortion, in addition to the many psychological and medical diseases and problems she may have.

Islam prescribes modesty by covering the skin and body parts in public. Women today develop skin cancer (malignant melanoma) through exposure to the sun while sunbathing naked of half-naked. In Britain alone there are over 40,000 cases of skin cancer each year, many of which are linked to nakedness and exposure to the sun.

Islam prescribes sex only with one within marriage. Having many sexual partners can causes cancer of the cervix, especially if the male partners are uncircumcised. The risk is increased if the woman also smokes.

Islam encourages femininity, womanhood and motherhood when women are prevented from being women they develop hormonal changes, psychosomatic disease, stress, male diseases (especially when trying to compete vigorously with men). Many disturbed children and delinquents will result from the lack of true motherhood.

Islam prescribes a healthy, safe pregnancy. In most pregnancies harm to the mother and baby occurs through alcohol, smoking drugs and sexually transmitted diseases, which are all prohibited and prevented by Islam.

Islam discourages contraceptive pills and devices. People taking contraceptive pills can develop blood clots, thrombosis and other health problems.

Islam optimises the physiology of the body of every woman by utilising all of her organs and not disrupting or interfering with them, as many women do today through a lack of breast-feeding, avoiding pregnancy and lack of motherhood. Islam encourages natural conception, pregnancy and birth free from health hazards.

> *Excerpts from Office of the Grand Imam Statement of the Islamic Research Academy Al-Azhar Al Sharif: Pertaining to the 4th International Conference on the Status of Women to be held in Beijing, September 1995.* Cairo: MWL Press, 1995, pp. 4-7.

"... In their relentless and massive attempts to destroy the family structure, the promoters of the Plan of Action" were not content to stop with casting doubt and confusion on the belief that the family is the basic unit and norm of society, urging parents to close their eyes at the perverse sexual practices of teenagers out of wedlock, considering these practices as individual and private matters, that neither of the parents has the right to interfere. They have the blazing audacity to declare that the concept of family in the sense stipulated by religion is nothing other than a lame concept according to them, because it does not accept or sanction free and unrestricted sexual relations between people of different age groups, lays condition that it should only be between male and female within the framework of Islamic Sharia, does not give these horrible liberties the rights to set up families within their own circles. Al-Azhar completely adheres to the traditional forms of fatherhood, motherhood, and matrimony, while the Plan of Action considers these as a mere set of rules to which people are accustomed all through the ages, so they demand that their practice should be abolished to institute a society free of moral restriction and family ties.

Indeed, the promoters of the Plan of Action went even further than this in pursuit of their whims asking for radical change in male and female relations by sharing out equally the functions between them, including the right of men to maternity leave, like women, and the same equality in inheritance insisting upon changing the laws which present an impediment to that no matter its origin.... Islam has never known what has come to be called woman's problem, which is a secretion of an alien civilisation founded upon exploitation and discrimination which is completely incompatible with the teaching of Islam, that men and women were created from a single soul, ordaining equality of rights and duties between them.

With regard to sexual relations, the promoters of the plan of Action did not find it enough to give liberty to free sex for teenagers, male and female, to indulge in, but they proclaim it loudly in obscene degrading, abhorrent jargon, which implies that it is the right of women and adolescent girls to choose the type of person she wants to assume, whether as a female or male, or in any other shape, that teenagers have the right to indulge in sex with whom they want, whether a man or woman, and that it devolves upon governments and governmental organisations to allow all such practices without let or hindrance, considering that prostitution presents no harm, nor is it illegal unless it is done by force.

By this way, the promoters of the Plan of action have exposed their shameful contradiction to the teachings of all revealed religions, including Islam, which does not permit any sort of sexual relations except inside legitimate wedlock, between a man and a woman, and that is because Islam forbids adultery, fornication, homosexuality and lesbianism, and all what may lead to it, such as immoral gathering between a man and a woman, established equity between male and female without confusion or mixing up their entitles or casting a slur on the nature of either of the two parties.

Anyone scrutinizing the Plan of Action will clearly see a more dreadful violation of the human rights of all nations, and unacceptable tutelage upon states, and this can be clearer still in what the promoters of the Plan of Action have strictly taken religion as an impediment in the way of achieving complete equality between men and women, or can stand as a stumbling block on the way of implementing any aspect of their repugnant aims and objectives, and they force countries to plan educational programs and urge youth to shoulder sexual responsibility, according to their own vision and to satisfy their own ends, forcing governments to cut down military expenditure, reallocating the funds spent on buying weapons to the implementation of their own objectives. They demand governments to forward compulsory periodical reports on the weapons which they possess, whether they are nuclear, chemical, or biological under threat of the rich and developed countries to cut the assistance offered by them converting it instead to the funding of implementation of their objectives. The Plan of Action urges the international Monetary Fund, the World Bank, and many other funding organisations to actively strive towards achieving this goal, and granting non-governmental organisations including feminist, activist movement and among them notorious feminist the ability to exert powerful authority in supervising and reviewing whatever reservations governments may have against the Plan of Action prior to its cancellation whatever its source may be..."

Plan of Action refers to the main discussions and policy document for discussion and adoption by the government representatives at the Fourth International Conference on Women and Development at Beijing in September, 1995.

---

# II

## Women's Take Their Place in the Driver's Seat

Senior women in the Sudanese public service are now allowed to drive cars following the scrapping of decrees prohibiting them from doing so. A source in the state-sponsored Sudanese Women General Union, told IPS that senior women in the public services, army and police are now legally allowed to drive their own or state cars. Several of them have already been spotted driving in the streets of Khartoum. Prominent among them, Dr Ishan Gabshawi, who is the Minister of Health, has been cruising in a government vehicle here.

Women were banned from driving when the strict Islamic Sharia codes were imposed in the Sudan by the country's ousted dictator Gaafar Mohamed Nimeiri in September 1983. It has taken 14 years for women and human rights groups, backed by the Ministry of Manpower, to unite and mount a concerted campaign to persuade the current government, which is also dominated by hardline Islamic leaders, to allow women to drive.

Sources at the Union said women from various sectors had pressed for the lifting of restrictions on them because they had more responsibilities than before and needed to be mobile. The first decree to restore the rights of working women to drive was issued by the Minister of Justice and Attorney General Abdel Basit Sabdarat in September, followed by a more recent decree allowing women to drive private cars. "This is a great victory to us," said Ahaf Abdalla of the Sudanese Women General Union. Abdalla also applauded a decision by government last year to lift restrictions on women travelling abroad. Married Sudanese women can now travel freely without permission from their husbands or elder brothers. However, young girls are still required by law to seek the permission of their fathers or elder brothers when travelling abroad or to rural areas in the Sudan.

Despite government's decisions to dismantle anti-women laws in a piece-meal fashion, women here have complained that they still face a set of barriers erected by male officials. "It took me over one month to get a driver's licence and wherever I drive, traffic police still stop me on the road even if I did not commit any traffic offence," said Sana Ahmed, a freelance journalist here. She accused the police of harassing and discriminating against women, especially when it comes to traffic laws. "They (the traffic police) told me last week that it was humiliating to them (men) to see women driving. It happened when a truck driver bashed my car which I parked on the shoulder of the road. Immediately the police said I was guilty and let off the truck driver without fines or punishments," she recalled. "I think the traffic police refused to pay any attention to me because I'm a woman," she told IPS. Despite the humiliations, she ruled out giving up driving because, she said, her job is demanding.

Commenting on the women's complaints, Colonel Omer Wahaballa, who is in charge of issuing driver's licence in Khartoum State, told journalists here that the lifting of restrictions only allow women to drive at daytime. They are not allowed to drive after midnight for their own safety and also to avoid harassment by male drivers on the road, he said. Despite the lifting of the restrictions, Col Wahaballa said only 5,000 female compared to 700,000 male drivers have been registered in his department since 1996.

The issue of restricting women from driving began soon after independence in 1956, when women were not allowed to drive government cars, including female ministers who served in the past regimes. To go about their work, male drivers were appointed for them. Women only enjoyed a brief honeymoon between 1969 and 1982 before the Nimeiri regime imposed the Sharia, effectively relegating them to the position of second class citizens in their own country. The present government, led by Lt-Gen. Omar Hassan al Bashir, seems selective in dismantling anti-women laws in Sudan.

NHIAL BOL

# III

## The Hidden Politics of Cultural Relativism

Women migrants in Europe or North America have long started to denounce the dangerous softness with which oppressive laws, customs and practices against women, imported from our countries and cultures, are tolerated or encouraged in the host countries, in the name of tolerance, of respect of the other, of the right to difference, of putting at par different cultures or religions, etc... Like our own governments, governments of the countries of immigration are prepared to sell out the well being, the human rights and the civil rights of women, for the sake of giving in to the migrant community solely represented, everywhere in the world, by its male members.

The collusion of patriarchies transcend most of the bones of contention between migrants and hosts. This is why, amongst the many laws and customs that could have been imported from the migrants' culture, only those pertaining to women, the family and the private sphere are viewed with such tolerance.

For instance, no host country will tolerate the amputation of the limbs for thieves (as is the law in countries such as Sudan, Pakistan and the Gulf countries), while, a few years ago, the Dutch Parliament were so far as discussing the possibility of allowing female genital mutilation on the Netherlands' soil for those migrants who practice it in their home country! FGM has been tolerated and performed in hospitals in Italy and in Britain.

One of the major problems women face in their country of immigration is that liberals and progressive people, for fear of being accused of racism and of imposing their own cultural values, fail to take a feminist and human rights stand on such issues—thus unwittingly participating in the construction of Otherness (in our case "Mulismness"). By doing so they fit perfectly in the agenda of fundamentalist forces whose major task at the moment is the construction and imposition of a single uniform (be it religious, ethnic or cultural) identity amongst the migrants.

We present here two pieces: a declaration by Iranian women in Sweden which is an outcry against cultural relativism in Europe. It is followed by a short ironical piece, starting as a tale, in response to a special issue on racism of a German feminist journal published in 1993.

# WEST AFRICA

- Struggle Against Feminine Excision and its Impact on Mother and Child in West Africa

# 46

# STRUGGLE AGAINST FEMININE EXCISION AND ITS IMPACT ON MOTHER AND CHILD IN WEST AFRICA

This topic which is occupying our attention today, I must confess that the problem is real. A study of the problem has revealed that in Togo just like other countries where we operate, that is: Chad, Ghana, Benin, and Burkina Faso (Upper Volta) feminine excision thrives. To speak about Togo, the problem as a traditional practice (excision of clitoris) exists acutely, and at the present moment commission of local groups have been formed to make women commissions of local groups have been formed to make women aware that this tradition should be ignored from all other ancestral traditional practices.

Since the Dakar conference of 1982 on the subject of traditional practices which have an effect on the health of women and children in West Africa, a commission has been formed in Togo. This national commission has already obtained help from Madame Linander and Madame Ras Work, who have agreed to equip it with appropriate visual aid materials to help combat this practice among different social categories of the country. These include religious, political and medical leaders, the population itself (men and women) etc.

Many awareness-raising meetings have been held. The National Union of Togolese Women, through public manifestations which it has organized since 1972 for all women, speaks at gatherings about the bad effects of ritual excision. These women also welcome the resolutions and recommendations of the Dakar conference, and are really ready to intensify the awareness-raising campaigns on the subject.

Also at Sokode, in the Northern part of Togo during the visit of the Inter-Africa Committee members, Mmes. Ras-Work and Linander, there was a meeting of women leaders in the districts, district leaders and muslim religious leaders (because excision here in Togo is practised only by the muslim population, who attach the practice to religion. The resolutions and recommendations of the Dakar conference were highly acclaimed by the participants and they arrived at the following decisions:

1. Excision is a traditional practice which has no source in the Islamic religion.
2. It is the women who like to be excised, as non-excised women were not well thought of in the cultural group.

Our working group organised to this effect has been supported by other organisations of the country. These are:

- L'Association Togolaise pour le Bien-Etre familial
- Les Mouvements de Jeunesse
- Les Services de la Santé Publique
- La Commission Nationale de la Croix-Rouge

As a result of all these meetings the following plan for action to be taken was drawn up:

(*a*) the creation of teams of awareness-raising catalysts

(*b*) the training of these teams

(*c*) the elaboration of a programme for a 1984 campaign for awareness-raising

(*d*) follow-up and evaluation

(*e*) recommendations for 1985

The training of the teams will be undertaken by two midwives, members of the National Committee already created, assisted by teaching aide produced by the working-group on 'Traditional Practices having a bad effect on the Health of Mothers and Children."

To conclude, I believe international cooperation is indispensable in order to support the national action. The Togo working group has already submitted a project by region to the International Committee. We hope that a contribution supporting us will be given in order to enable us to bring our action already started to perfection.

### What Can We Do

Since the beginning of our meeting I hear people talking of hospitals, doctors, experts etc... for the elimination of feminine excision. But how many of these luxuries of our big cities do we have in the rural areas? In many countries, especially in the third world there is only one physician to 300 000 inhabitants. If this is proved to the contrary, the solutions will not come by miracle, and women taking charge of their own problems will surely be indispensable.

The method whereby women take part in the solution of their own problems will lead them to eat things locally produced, in variating what they eat this will enable them to know the functioning of their body, etc. This can suggest to them that they vary their agricultural production. But the precise case which is the subject of our meeting today is that there are certain ancestral traditional practiced, such as excision, that are detrimental to the health of mothers and children. These practices must be abandoned, even eradicated, through a general awareness-raising exercise.

If a mother is in good health, there is no doubt that her child is healthy also. "If women are integrated in the development exercise in a correct and balanced manner, there is no doubt that the future of Africa will be assured", said René Dumont and Marie Moutin in their book entitled *"L 'Afrique Etranglée'* (Strangled Africa). And the future is for children who will be responsible for the world of tomorrow.

If these children are healthy and if the infantile mortality is diminished, our responsibility will only be to increase production all round: building schools, specialised institutions, training leaders, teaching illiterate women to read, making the rural people aware so as to take development in their own hands for self-sufficiency. We are concerned with the problems of feminine excision, but mother and child health, nutrition, and especially family planning, not forgetting food production and training of local leaders, such as volunteers health promoters, traditional midwives (matrons) etc. are also of interest to us.

D. PARKIN

# YUGOSLAVIA

- Islamic Nationalism and Muslim Feminism
- Feminism and Nationalism in Yugoslavia

# 47

# ISLAMIC NATIONALISM AND MUSLIM FEMINISM

This chapter concerns a complex society at a particular, complicated and critical movement in its history, and focuses on one ritual, the *mevlud* (from the Arabic *mawlid*, denoting the calendar date of the Prophet's birthday), as performed by local women at that critical moment during the summer of 1990. Sarajevo was then the capital of the socialist republic of Bosnia-Hercegovina which formed part of the socialist federated Yugoslavia. But multi-party elections were on the way and years of weary contempt, boredom and silence on the topic of politics had been replaced by enthusiasm for the novel recreational activity of comparing political parties and possibilities.

For Bosnia's multi-national population of Muslims, Serbs and Croats (approximately 44 per cent, 31 per cent and 17.5 per cent respectively), the freedom to discuss and the perception of new opportunities were exciting. But with the opportunities came dangers, and with the excitement a tinge of wariness. Streams of disputatious verbiage were emanating from a rapidly multiplying number of the political parties. While several of these included the word 'democratic' in their titles, their exact aims were for the most part ill-defined. All that many prospective voters knew about them was that they were Serb, Croat, Muslim, or non-national in orientation. National awareness was riding high on optimism about economic progress and EC membership, but also giving birth to the new beginnings of anxiety about potentially aggressive nationalisms.

Accompanying the political tension was religious revival. This was true of Bosnia's Serbs, Croats and Muslims, and of their respective faiths, Orthodoxy, Catholicism and Islam. But in Muslim dominated Sarajevo it was Islamic activity that was most in evidence and as part of this general revival the women's *mevlud* rituals were attracting numbers which far outstripped those I had witnessed while doing fieldwork in the mid-1980s. At one level Islamic activity was spreading and uniting the Muslim population, yet underlying this unity of purpose lay the 'mixed motives' of the title. For while all *mevlud*-goers understood their participation as religiously motivated, their understandings of Islam's implications and its relevance to Muslim national identity were varied.

The *mevluds* did not then become a simple banner of national and religious unity vis-à-vis the Serbs and Croats, nor a banner of any particular religious or political outlook; rather they took on a subtle and variegated hue which was sometimes disturbing to their participants. Women who attended *mevluds* in increasing numbers did so partly in celebration of the end of socialist disapproval and partly in search of national/religious unity as a form of new security and meaning in the context of communist collapse. But in the place where they had most hoped to find this unity they also found discord and conflict. What was the revival, who owned it and who had authority to lead it were questions that made the *mevlud* not only a Durkheimian vehicle for the expression of solidarity, but also an arena for clashes over the nature and basis of that solidarity.

One aim of the present paper is to describe something of the emotional texture of a situation full of uncertainty and confusion. Anthropology has become self-critical of a tendency to treat its subject matter a historically, and this criticism has resulted in a tempering of the discipline's traditional study of 'the other' as self-contained and unchanging. Yet while the dynamism of changing times has been increasingly addressed, the anthropology of turbulent times, of major social upheaval, remains a small domain. Given the difficulties inherent in attempting to say anything clear about situations characterised by uncertainty and insecurity this is perhaps unsurprising.

However, the widespread unrest which has accompanied the demise of one-party communist rule in the ex-socialist bloc begs anthropological attention. Where war has found a firm footing, its cultural effects may form the focus of study,[1] but in 1990, Yugoslavia had not yet been subjected to the grim certainties of war.

A second aim is to provide some counterpoise to anthropological studies of women which tend to emphasise the ways in which they express themselves and pursue goals as women. This is perhaps especially notable in anthropological studies of religious and ritual behaviour, and understandably so. Since ritual events more than any other type of event are anthropologically held to say, mean and do things for those who participate in them—rituals reflect social structure, reinforce ideologies, uphold or subvert power structures and so on—women's rituals are most often viewed as events at which women say, mean and do things about themselves as women. Whether religion is used as a direct means of negotiating with men (for example, Somali women's use of spirit possession as a 'weapon of the weal'),[2] or to unite women through a ritual focus on specifically female roles and values (for example, Turkish women's *mevluds*,[3] what many such studies share is an emphasis on the way in which women's rituals are constructed and understood as specifically female, as countermodels, complements or reactions to male ideologies. The stress is on female unity and solidarity and/or on women's negotiation of their gender role in society.

Less emphasis has been placed on gender negotiations and expression in the rituals of Muslim men. This discrepancy need not lie purely in the eye of the anthropological beholder. Given that for many Muslim women rituals represent one of the few occasions for which they can legitimately demand 'time off' from the patrilineal household and their allotted duties within it, it is unsurprising if such events are felt by the participants to be meaningful, at least in part, precisely because they are gatherings at which women and only women come together for an important spiritual purpose. At the same time many such rituals do focus on roles and values felt to be specifically female (and the Sarajevo *mevlud*, like its Turkish counterpart, includes celebration of the childbed and motherhood of the Prophet's mother).[4]

Yet women are not only women, but also people of diverse education, income, occupation, status, belief and temperament and as such, like men, capable of using ritual to assert or negotiate things other than and as well as their role as gendered individuals; and of using ritual gatherings as forums for the expression of conflicting views and values. In the Sarajevo summer of 1990 the prominence of such 'mixed motives' made them hard to ignore.

The misunderstandings and minor hostilities tangible at *mevlud* gatherings occurred against a background in which ethnicity and religion were inextricably, linked, a context in which religious rituals, Muslim, Orthodox or Catholic, were felt to have relevance for national identity and thus at some level a bearing on the political future. They also occurred against a cultural background in which personal and nuclear family autonomy were jealously guarded and open affronts against them avoided. Increased *mevlud* participation drew together women of assorted backgrounds and posed dangers for the preservation of polite restraints.

Thirdly, the presence of representatives of a small, loose, urban network of religiously educated young women caused tension. In the 1980s a quiet brand of Islamic reformism had been attracting small numbers of young people and as the end of one-party rule was pronounced nigh they became more vocal and visible. These reformed Muslims were more knowledgeable about and more inclined towards the wider Islamic world than the non-reformed. The meeting of the two, and particularly of the reformed with older traditional female religious leaders, was problematic.

**Nation and Faith, Town and Neighbourhood**

The Muslims are Serbo-Croatian speaking Slaves of the Islamic faith, descendants of those Bosnians who converted after the Ottoman invasion of the fifteenth century. Under Tito their status as a nation rather than a mere religious grouping was recognised (although this status has been disputed by Serb and Croats voices, and never more so than in the historiographical fevour of the 1990s). In the ordinary language and perceptions of Bosnian Serbs, Croats and Muslims, ethnicity and religion are inextricably linked. A Serb is Orthodox and vice versa, a Croat is Catholic and vice versa, and a Muslim is a Muslim and vice versa. In fact, the terms often applied by Bosnians to Bosnians are Srbin, Katolik and Musliman. While the Communist Party drew a distinction between 'Musliman' with a capital M (national) and 'musliman' with a small m (religious), thus making it theoretically possible to be a Muslim of the Catholic faith or a Serb of the Muslim faith, to the ordinary Bosnian this idea made very little sense.

Islam thus serves to serves to distinguish Muslims from Serbs and Croats but it also potentially ties them to the wider Muslim world transcending the bounds of Bosnia. These two aspects of Muslim identity—distinction from other Yugoslavs and co-identity with the *umma* (community of Muslims)—have been stressed with varying degrees of intensity at different historical moments and by different sections of the population. They by no means exhaust the range of Muslim self-definitions of identity but in 1990 became one axis along which *mevlud* participants found conflict.

Sarajevo's town centre boasts a mixture of Ottoman, Austro-Hungarian and twentieth century architecture and is a domain in which Muslim, Serb and Catholic meet and interact at work, at school and in the shops, markets and cafes. Urbanisation throughout Yugoslavia has meant that the town's population has grown steadily over the past thirty years and the area known as 'New Sarajevo', a wasteland of dreary apartment blocks, is ever-expanding. These blocks are built by business enterprises and inhabited by employees of the firms so that Muslim, Serb and Catholic live alongside each other. In contrast to the town centre and New Sarajevo, the old Muslim neighbourhoods (*mahale*) on the hills of the valley of the Miljacka river are felt to be, and preserved as, Muslim in a way that the rest of the town's space is not.

A mass of steep winding cobbled streets lined with small houses, their courtyards and gardens hidden from the street by high fences and gates, small neighbourhood mosques dotted around, these neighbourhoods are places where people use Arabic and Turkish greetings (*salaam aleikum, merhaba, aksam hajrula*), instead of the standard Serbo-Croatian greetings (*dobar dan, dobar vecer*) of the town outside. For Sarajevans, whether they live in an old style neighbourhood or not, the *mahalas* with their gossip, their old women in *dimije* (flowing, baggy trousers), their Turkish greetings and their constant to'ing and fro'ing are both comical and a prized embodiment of Bosnian and of Muslim tradition.

The neighbourhood is a world apart, and in many ways a world of women. Men work outside the home and are not expected to hang around socialising—they should go out to the cafes and bars. Neighbourhood women attend each other's household rituals such as the *tevhid* (death rituals) and the *mevluds*, drink coffee together, borrow money and goods from each other, help one another with tasks ('you sew my quilt, I'll roast your coffee') and exchange small amounts of cooked and uncooked food. Nonetheless, it is not a 'private' world of women as opposed to the 'public' world of men and the town centre. What distinguishes the *mahala* from the town outside (and particularly so in the mid-1980s) is that it is the domain of Islam and Muslim identity, while the town is where one plays down national/religious identity. It is in such neighbourhoods that most *mevluds* take place, and from such neighbourhoods that many of the participants traditionally come.

## Unity and Distrust

The social, economic and ritual interdependence of neighbourhood women is evoked by the saying *znanje, imanje*, (knowledge is wealth)—if you can't afford a new sofa before the imminent price rise or don't know how to mend a quilt, knowing people who can help is just as good. While no proverb expresses the idea that knowledge is power, the concept is perhaps even more relevant to neighbourhood life. Nuclear family households keep their comings and goings, incomes and courtships secret from one another and even within the nuclear family privacy and autonomy are guarded: husbands and wives may well not reveal the exact state of their finances to each other, daughters will not tell their mothers about boyfriends. This level of secrecy requires skillful gamesmanship and in many respects merits the title of game. Frequently, for example, the woman concealing the cost of her new curtains knows perfectly well that her neighbour knows, and the neighbour knows that the women knows she knows.

The point, however, is that privacy must not be ruptured by an open and offensive statement of the facts. At the same time there are secrets which really supposed to be secret because neighbours, however friendly and helpful, are also potential malefactors who might spread damaging gossip.[5] People are on the defensive, those who 'have to know everything' are roundly condemned—although never to their faces since open conflict and insult must be avoided—and an atmosphere of secrecy, gossip, defence and counter-attack is pervasive.

In examining the witchcraft beliefs of the French Bocage, Favret-Saada (1980) suggests that while Bocage neighbours distrust each other greatly, their sense of co-identity and of distinction from other Frenchmen is profound. The suspicious and clandestine environment of the *mahala* similarly serves to unite its (Muslim) inhabitants *vis-à-vis* Serb and Croat outsiders, tying them together through a web of knowledge and power as well as through the functional interdependence of social coffee visits, lending, borrowing and mutual aid. In this 1980s context outsiders were different, but also distant and therefore people with whom one could have cordial relationships without worrying too much over the consequences. At the *mevluds* of 1990 open disagreement between Muslims lay only millimetres beneath the skin of ritual unity and was, I suggest, perceived as a threat both to personal integrity and to Muslim unity.

### A Diversity of Women

Under the Austro-Hungarians (1878–1918) and within the inter-war Kingdom of Yugoslavia, Shari'a courts had continued to function in Bosnia. However, following the Second World War and the advent of socialism they were abruptly abolished. I have argued elsewhere.[6] that in itself the disappearance of the Shari'a courts had a less disruptive effect on Muslim marriage and inheritance practices than might be expected, partly because many Shari'a provisions such as polygamy and cousin marriage were rarely exploited even under Ottoman rule, and partly because informal arrangements made between kin could circumvent secular legal rulings. The point to be stressed here is that, unlike some of the other women presented in this book, Muslim women neither live under the jurisdiction of the Shari'a nor have recourse to its courts.

In terms of education women vary markedly, the principal determining factors being age and rural versus urban background. Women raised before the Second World War in Sarajevo may have received religious and secular education, while those who were raised in the countryside and later migrated to town are likely to have received religious instruction from parents and the local *hodza* (religious teacher) in Islamic prayer and custom and the life of the Prophet (but not Arabic language), but unlikely to have received much secular education. They may therefore be illetrate or semi-literate. After the second world war, primary education began to be made available and compulsory to all. While some rural parents still keep their daughters away from school, urban Muslims prize knowledge and learning both as a route to a more prosperous future and as intrinsically valuable within an Islamic frame of reference. Most therefore want their daughters to continue into secondary schooling and perhaps even move on to university. The younger the woman and the more urban her background, the more secular is her education likely to have been. On the other hand, standards of religious education have declined. While post-war children may have been sent to the *mekteb* (Qur'ânic school) for part-time instruction in the basics of Islam, it is optional. Children attend after school hours, and few parents are as strict and concerned about success there as they are about success in secular education. The result is that anyone raised before the Second World War is likely to have more religious education than anyone raised after it.

The range of jobs on offer to women is similar to that of any European city—cleaner, shop assistant, clerical worker, secretary, teacher, lawyer, journalist, and so on. But access to such employment depends on qualifications and connections and many women with children prefer to be at home if this arrangement is financially viable. The need for qualifications and the preference for being at home with the children mean that, in spite of the difficulties of finding a first post, overall younger women are more likely to be in formal employment than their seniors. The latter may, however, engage in small-scale income-raising activities such as rearing chickens and selling eggs to the neighbours, rearing goats or a cow and selling the milk, or weaving rugs and knitting traditional patterned socks for sale in the tourist shops or to acquaintances.

The *mevluds* of the mid-1980s were for the most part attended by elderly or middle-aged housewives with variable levels of personal religious observance (from regular prayer and annual fasting to occasional prayer and fasting the odd day of Ramadan), but usually with enough religious education to know of at least some of the relevant prayers (those they did not know they could mumble along to). *Mevlud* holders were relatively well off or considered to be rich (one ritual I attended was held by a family jokingly referred to as the 'Carringtons', in reference to the American TV soap 'Dynasty' which was popular at the time). But the majority of attenders were neither rich nor poor by local standards. They included women married to skilled or white collar workers, owing their own small homes or in possession of company apartments and hoping that their children would rise somewhat beyond them in educational and income terms.

Small grand-daughters, pre-school but old enough not to cry or disrupt the proceedings, were sometimes brought along and always praised and smiled upon in a manner which reinforced their interest in *mevluds* and religion. Young unmarried women, however, were rarely present. Often their college or work commitments would have kept them away, but in any case there was little cultural expectation that they should attend the *mevluds* of any but the closest neighbours and kin. What is appropriate to a *zena* (woman/wife) is not necessarily appropriate to a *cura* (unmarried girl). While the latter was generally expected to have a belief in Islam and to practise Islamic virtues of hospitality, generosity, public modesty and so on, she was not expected to spend much time at rituals. A young woman who did so would be praised, but at the same time most agree that a girl should *hoda* (walk about/have fun) while she had the chance since marriage would put a stop to all that.

Conducting and reciting at the *mevlud* could be anything from five to fifteen *bulas* (female religious leaders, a word of Turkish derivation). *Bulas* were generally middle-aged or elderly women who had no small children to keep them at home and who had for the most part been educated at the female *medresa* (traditional school) before its closure in 1952. They were officially employed by the Islamska Zajednica, the religious establishment which existed under agreement with the socialist authorities. They were, however, a traditional, pre-socialist part of the Sarajevo landscape, and in practice their services at a *mevlud* were very rarely solicited via the Zajednica. Hostesses who knew them personally or by word-of-mouth invited them directly, and paid them handsomely in blue envelopes discreetly slipped into their hands as they left.

The mid-1980s relationship between *bula* and *non-bula* was one in which the former provided religious services which helped to keep Islam alive for women who, caught up by the demands of modern life and of socialism, were less religiously observant than their ideal self-image may have demanded. While there were some caustic comments about the *bulas'* motivation (the blue envelopes contained far more money than a woman could earn from office work or selling eggs), for the most part they were respected figures in front of whom speech was modified to exclude anything too raucous or earthy.

In return, the *bulas* kept Islam alive without trying to rejuvenate it or demand too much religious observance from women unable or unwilling to give it. They provided information on and preached Islamic practices such as Ramadan fasting, the recitation of Qur'ânic texts suitable to particular occasions, the *hajj* (annual pilgrimage to Mecca) and so on, but did not command that women cover their heads in public, avoid seaside bathing or remonstrate with husbands who enjoyed a drink or more (alcohol consumption is high among men). Such practices might be mentioned in a favourable light but were not imperative.

In 1990, this balance was unsettled by the arrival of two new types of women on the *mevlud* scene. Firstly, there were women with less religious knowledge or experience than the typical *mevlud*-goer, women whose enthusiasm was stimulated by a political context in which the disapproval of atheist authorities was no longer relevant, in which religious expression seemed to be an expression of the changing times and of the new freedom which western-style democracy would bring, and in which the assertion of religious/national identity appeared more vital than before. Secondly, there were young women and young *bulas* (or *mu'alimas*, the Arabic term with which the Zajednica wanted to replace *bula* and which many of the young preferred) with a less traditional and more radical vision of Islam than their elders.

**The Reformed**

Everyone had felt that 1980s Yugoslavia was in decline. Tito's death was followed by a decade of rising unemployment, falling wages, massive inflation and a general feeling that the system was going awry and new solutions had to be found. To some of the young within this 'apocalypse culture',[7] Islam, a religion astir in the Middle East, became an appealing solution. As one young woman told me: 'It's modern to be Muslim'.

The female *medresa* had re-opened in 1978 and provided an alternative education to that offered at secular secondary schools. Many of its early pupils were from relatively poor rural families attracted by the fact that the *medresa* provided accommodation, subsidised meals and bursaries. Others were urbanites drawn to Islam. In and around the male and female *medresas* there grew up a small subculture of committed young Muslims, anxious to learn Arabic and as much about Islam and the Islamic world as possible. Some of the young women had adopted Islamic-style dress which displayed their standpoint to the world, and all avoided the revealing sort of Western fashions—short skirts, sleeveless tops—favoured by their fashion-conscious peers.

In socio-economic terms there was no rigid divide between these reformed Muslims and others, but there was a tendency for them to be the offspring either of families of *hodzas, bulas* and dervishes or of families with above average but not high income levels. Parents might be professionals or mechanics, plumbers and skilled craftsmen—people who could earn money moonlighting or in small-scale private businesses. These young Muslims themselves tended to have or aspire to higher levels of education than their peers. Those who were not at the *medresas* or the Islamic Theological Faculty might be at university studying oriental languages, law, medicine, computer technology, architecture or the like.

The principle that Muslim equals muslim was meaningful to and accepted by all. But reformed Muslims placed an additional emphasis on the need to actively choose rather than simply be born into Islam. Thus the strange conversation I overheard between a friend of mine and her nine-year-old cousin. The boy, sensing that the topic was a sensitive and meaningful one to my friend, asked, out of curiosity and mischief it would seem, whether he was a Muslim. The normal answer to such a question from a child would be a simple: 'Yes, of course, what else are you but a Muslim?' But my friend paused and asked him: 'Well, do you think you are?' Curiosity and mischief showed in the reply he gave while scanning his cousin's face: 'No'. 'Well then, you're not', said my friend.

These varying attitudes were also apparent in my own relationships with traditional and reformed believers. The former accepted me as an English Protestant, whatever this may have meant for them, and were occasionally interested in the customs and rituals of my home. The idea that I might convert to Islam was one usually raised in the context of kindly jokes about my marrying some nice Muslim boy and settling in Sarajevo for good. It was more through affection and jest than through any real wish or hope that I would convert; in their eyes I was what I was and was more or less the end of it. For the reformed on the other hand, just as Muslim birth and provenance did not guarantee full Muslim identity, non-Muslim birth and provenance was not a total barier to it. They knew and respected the fact that I was an English Protestant, but Cat Stevens, Boney M and Anthony Quinn had all been Christians too and they had converted. Islam was a universal religion and there was always the possibility, and sometimes the hope, that I too would convert.

The relationship between this subculture and the Muslim community within which it existed was a delicate one. The reformed felt that Islam was theirs in a way that it was not fully the religion of the non-reformed. Thus one male reformed Muslim told me of the Ramadan *bajram* (feast) greeting he had received from a neighbour, scornfully adding: 'How can he wish me a happy *bajram*? 'He hasn't fasted Ramadan, so *bajram* isn't his to celebrate.' Yet since many of the reformed Muslims came from families more traditional and less observant than themselves, they could hardly turn their backs on or polemicise with negligent Muslims. At the same time they had to respect, albeit sometimes grudgingly, those elderly Muslims who, although often believers in bits of what the young saw as superstition, sometimes illiterate and certainly not schooled in Arabic or Islamic theology, nevertheless prayed five times a day and fasted Ramadan. Reformed Muslim women therefore tended to avoid the company of those non-reformed who were neither kin nor neighbour and to look forward to an early marriage (a practice supported by reference to the *Hadith*, the Prophet's sayings) which would take them out of the sphere of their own nuclear family and allow them to create a family environment and lifestyle more in keeping with their beliefs.

From the point of view of the non-reformed it was hard to find anything concrete to object to in the behaviour of the reformed. Unless one was an out-and-out atheist (which very few, even within the ranks of the Communist Party, were), what could one criticise about learning Arabic, daily prayer, and mosque attendance? Such things were self-evidently admirable. However, the reformed Muslims' strictness and seemingly snobbish avoidance of the non-reformed made the latter uneasy and resentful. It led to comments that while these paragons might look perfect on the outside, only God knew what was in a person's heart. And furthermore, some would point out, even if they did not themselves pray five times a day, their grandmother or other kin did, and they could therefore expect to be treated more civilly by reformed Muslims.

It was a tension that I sometimes found myself caught in middle of. My non-reformed friends and acquaintances were unsettled by my relationships with the reformed, worrying about whether the latter were criticising them to me or turning me against them. My reformed friends worried that the non-reformed were giving me an inaccurate picture of Islam which I would then spread abroad. If this made me uncomfortable it was far more unsettling for my assorted acquaintances. In a society where ethnic unity is to be maintained, open hostility to be avoided and where insult is always suspected, conflict over a matter as sensitive and central as Islam was disturbing to all.

In 1990, the tension came out into the open as the predominantly young reformed on the one hand, and the religiously observant or religiously negligent non-reformed on the other hand, found themselves face to face (with the *bulas* caught in the middle). In the 1980s, reformed Muslims had for the most part kept themselves to themselves and left the *mevluds* alone as traditional rituals primarily attended by older women and conducted by older *bulas*. Many non-reformed women raised after the Second World War had left these occasions alone because they felt unfamiliar with the ritual environment, ignorant of the prayers, put off by an atmosphere of socialist disapproval or simply indifferent to this piece of tradition. Now both types of women started adding their *mevlud* efforts to those of the traditional *mevlud*-goers, injecting new and various aspirations, understandings and hopes into the proceedings in a way which threatened the old balance between *bula* and non-*bula*. It made women vulnerable to the sort of open criticism and attack customarily avoided, and questioned the very nature of Muslim religious and national unity.

### Mevluds

As indicated earlier, *mevlud* denotes the calendar date of the Prophet's birthday. In Bosnia, it also denotes the text of a poem celebrating this event and honouring the Messenger (there are several such poems in Serbo-Croatian and in Turkish), and, thirdly, a ritual including recitation of such poems. (For clarity's sake it is only in this latter sense that the term is used here.) By extension the term *mevludski* programme denotes a gathering at which the intention is to celebrate and honour the Prophet through recitations of religious material.

If the word itself has several related denotations, it is also true that no single *mevlud* is identical to another. The rituals vary in textual context as well as in venue, grandeur, pretext and participation. All *mevluds* are held to mark some particular event, be it the calendar date of the Prophet's birthday, the return of a son from military service, the building of a new house, the anniversary of a relative's death or some other occasion. Those organised by men are most often held in mosques, *tekijas* (dervish lodges) or other non-household venues, and are generally open to woman as long as sufficient space is available to ensure some degree of physical distance between the sexes.

Women's *mevluds* are held in the home and open only to female friends, relatives and neighbours of the hostess, some of whom will have been specifically invited, while others who could not be contacted directly hear about it on the grapevine. Invited or not, any woman who has some relationship with the hostess will be welcomed. For the understanding is that she has attended out of respect and affection for her hostess, and in order to join her prayer and thanksgiving with hers. In this respect, the *mevlud* is similar to the other major collective rituals performed by women, such as the *tevhid* ritual held for the recently deceased. But a number of dissimilarities help to illuminate why the *mevlud* is capable of becoming the sort of arena for individual expression and a testing ground for competing views that it appeared to be in 1990

While those who attend the *mevlud* are held to be doing so far the hostess' sake, they are also held to be getting something out of it for themselves. Reflecting this understanding, the *mevlud* sweets given to participants on departure are treated more as going-home gifts than as thanks and payment—the meaning explicitly attributed to the *kifla* (bread loaves) distributed to *tevhid* participants in the closing stages of that ritual. Part of the something *mevlud* attenders are getting is *sevap* (religious merit, deriving from the Arabic *sawab*).

Although local ideas on the nature of *sevap* are sometimes sketchy, underlying all exegesis on the matter is the idea that it accrues to actions which are good but not necessary religious duties. Thus one gets no *sevap* for saying daily prayers, but much from fasting the ten days of *muharrem* (the first month of the Islamic calendar). The *tevhid* is not formally accounted a religious duty, and women say that one might equally well pay for a *hatma* (an entire reading of *the Qur'ân*) to be recited for the deceased at the mosque. However, evidence suggests that the *tevhid* has been growing in popularity in recent years. Newcomers to Sarajevo, and in particular Muslim gypsies, have been adopting the custom.[8]

In practice, most Sarajevo Muslim women treat the *tevhid* as something which should be done if at all possible, for somehow it would be a bit shoddy to opt for the *hatma*. The *mevlud*, on the other hand, is decidedly optional. The cost of hosting such an event is far greater than the *tevhid* and beyond most family's reach, and the returned son, the completed house or the anniversary of death are deemed less in need of prayer than the recent death of a relative.

The *mevlud's* optional nature allows for *sevap* and, along with the lesser sadness and seriousness of the event marked and the greater flexibility of the elements of the ritual, for beauty and enjoyment. Women express a pleasure in *mevlud*-going which would seem out of place in the context of a *tevhid*. In later discussions of the event, they are more likely to classify it as *lijep* (beautiful), and to dwell on the factors that made it so—the quantity and quality of food served, the number of women and *bulas* present, the attractiveness of the participants' clothing, the beauty of the *bulas'* voices, the comfort of the seating and heating/ventilating arrangements, the general ambience and so on.

*Mevluds* vary greatly in these respects from those where almost everyone gets a seat to those where women are squashed together on the floor; from wealthy surroundings in which guests wear silk and fresh, white embroidered or gold-laden headscarves to those with a high proportion of old women in knitted slipper-socks and floral flannel; from those where one is served coffee, some *pita* (cheese or spinach pastry), salad and cake to those where one is regaled with six or seven courses served in relay by young women of the household.

So too does the textual context of the ritual vary. The *mevlud* may last for up to two and a half hours and is led by the *bulas* who take it in turns to recite sections of *the Qur'ân* and passages from various different *mevlud* poems. Among the standard elements of any *mevlud* are the collective recitation of *salavats* (salutations to the Prophet) and prayers towards the end of the formal ritual, a pause for the drinking of sherbet (a cinnamon flavoured beverage) handed round to all participants after the *mevlud* poem section in which the childbed of the Prophet's mother is described (a heavenly bird offered Amina sherbet to ease her labour pains), and the collective chanting of the Serbo-Croatian 'Dobro Nam Dosao, O Pegjamber' (Welcome, O Prophet, a text from a *mevlud* poem) after the birth of Muhammed. These moments at which the guests are required to become active participants are invariable, but from the *bula's* point of view a *mevlud* involves a significant degree of judicious creativity, decision-making and intuition. Without having rehearsed and without distracting on-the-spot discussions as to whose turn it is next, each *bula* must contribute an appropriate bit or bits of recitation. The Prophet's story must be told, but who should tell which bit of it and using which section of which text is a question resolved only as the ritual unfolds.

The optional nature, flexibility and spontaneous creativity typical of mevluds allows for innovation and contrasts relevantly with the tone of the *mevludski* programme mentioned above. In the mid-1980s, I attended *mevludski* events organised by *medresa* students and other committed reform-style Muslims. Held in mosques and thus without hosts, the *mevludski* programmes also differed from *mevluds* in their content and tone. Carefully rehearsed Qur'ânic recitations and Serbo-Croatian hymns rather than *mevlud* poems formed the textual core of the event. Since there was no sherbet and no

'Dobro Nam Dosao', and since few ordinary Sarajevans can recite much of *the Qur'ân*, and the hymns were at that time little known and somewhat suspected outside the circle of the *medresas* from whence they were being spread, the scope for active participation on the part of those attending a *mevludski* programme was limited. Rather than a collective ritual, the *mevludski* programme felt very much like a meeting between performers—the *medresa* young people who sang and recited—and the audience. While the former were the focus of the event and were congratulated on their performances, no one suggested that the attenders had acquired any *sevap*. Although they had attended a religious occasion, they had not actually done anything much that could attract *sevap*. In short, the *mevludski* programmes were controlled, didactic and self-consciously 'modern' in a way that the traditional *mevluds* were not. Four or five years later, some elements of these programmes were to be introduced to household *mevluds* in a way that was partially successful, but also a cause for unease.

### A *Mevlud* in 1990

These changes were apparent during a *mevlud* which I attended at the time of my fieldwork in 1990. The house had three rooms, a kitchen and a courtyard hidden from the street and the neighbours by high walls. Perhaps a hundred women had packed themselves into the available space. Those in the drawing room, where the ten *bulas* sat, consoled themselves that while none of the courtyard breeze could reach them there, at least they were acquiring more *sevap* than their more comfortably seated companions. As the foreign guest I got a place in the drawing room where I sweltered in my jacket and headscarf until kindly told to take the jacket off and let the scarf hang over and cover my bare arms. At first I resisted the suggestion, since bare arms at a *mevlud*, even covered by a scarf, seemed completely unacceptable in the light of my prior *mevlud* experiences. But when a second woman urged me, and I looked around the room to find any number of women in short sleeves, I gratefully gave in.

We drank our coffee and gossiped until the first *bula*'s reedy voice signalled the start of the ritual. Each *bula* took her turn, while we sat and listened. I watched the company, particularly intrigued by a tall, pale young woman in a black headscarf who sat near the front, deeply involved in the proceedings and silently reciting to herself. The sherbet and the 'Dobro Nam Dosao' came and went, upon which 'black headscarf's' voice filled the room with the mournful tones of a Serbo-Croatian hymn. She had bided her time and let her seniors recite first, but the piece she chose now was a long one, each heart-rending verse followed by a heart-rending chorus. The latter was reasonably easy to pick up after a couple of hearings, and some of the assembled women began to sing along with it, encouraged by 'black headscarf' herself, whose pre-occupation lifted slightly and whose eyes opened to glance at us all in the silent beat preceding the chorus. I realised that the woman must be a *bula/mu'alima*.

Not all of the old *bulas* appeared happy with this innovation to the *mevlud* ritual, and one or two began to fan themselves vigorously and to 'tut-tut'. On the other hand, some of the women present evidently appreciated the hymn enough to join in. Part of their enjoyment probably lay in the fact that they could actively join in, that after sitting quiet and cramped there was something they could rouse themselves for in the same way that they did for 'Dobro Nam Dosao'. At the same time, the sort of suspicious resistance to joining in that had been felt by some attenders at *mevludski* programmes in the mid-1980s had been partially broken down by the spreading fame of the *medresa* choir. Earlier in the year a concert had been arranged at the Zetra sports stadium where popular, commercial singers sang *sevdalinke* (Muslim folk songs), and the *medresa* choir recited religious material. This event, in which national and religious identity were jointly celebrated, had been attended by thousands and then widely distributed on a video cassette that almost everyone I knew had watched.

If 'black headscarf's' success was an example of the reformed reaching the unreformed (but not all of the old *bulas*), what happened in the courtyard after the event suggested the opposite. The formal ritual had ended, we had all been served *pita*, salad, cake and coffee and now was the time for mingling and conversation. I found myself in a small circle of women, including one in her late forties and attired in a just-below-the-knee-length, short-sleeved dress. She, like most of us, had removed her headscarf after the formal ritual ended, but was nevertheless perspiring in the heat. A second woman, around 35 and smartly dressed in long skirt, co-ordinating jacket, silk blouse and headscarf fastened with a pearl pin, stood near her. Out of the blue the short-sleeved woman suddenly and rather aggressively enquired: 'Why are you dressed up like that in all this heat?'

There was a long uncomfortable pause before the proud and yet more aggressive answer; 'Because of *Allâh*!' For a spilt second there was silence as the two stared at each other, then both turned their attention to their immediate neighbours, and some moments later, the smartly dressed woman moved off to another circle. It was a small incident, but everyone felt the tear it had made in the fabric of an occasion intended as one of piety and unity. The contrast between short-sleeved comfort and headscarved elegance (neither of which had been typical of mid-1980s *mevluds*) stands as a visual image of the strain between reformed and non-reformed Muslims.

### A Diffused Conflict

The wary relationship between the groups had developed and changed in the context of the new political freedom and the general Islamic revival. Since the non-reformed felt that they had always been proper Muslims at heart, just a bit lapsed, it seemed to them that their current religious vigour should make up for the lapse and repair the breach between themselves and the reformed. It was certainly the case that my non-reformed acquaintances seemed to feel a new confidence and ownership of their religion. Women who had five years earlier dodged my questions about Islam, mildly teased me about my penchant for hanging around mosques and jovially presented me to each other as someone who 'knows more about Islam than you do!' no longer made these implied denials of religious knowledge, but lectured me on Islamic history and custom in a way that claimed the topics as their own. If they were reclaiming Islam there was no longer a need to feel shifty and resentful about the devout and practising reformed.

Yet from the reformed's point of view, religious observance or enthusiasm was not and never had been the only yardstick. As indicated elsewhere, devout but illiterate old women had always fallen outside the realm of those who could be criticised, but had never been included in the realm of the truly admirable. As for those who had never previously been devout but were making efforts now, they were frequently seen as jumping on a bandwagon. Thus many Muslims took pains to point out: 'I'm not one of these new Muslims who not only just discovered it when it got easy, I was a Muslim years ago when the authorities disapproved'.

At sake in the dispute between the two groups of women was the personal integrity of both. For the old *bulas* both personal integrity and traditional authority were being challenged by the black headscarved *mu'alima*. Her innovative hymn had been take up by some of the *mevlud* participants and what it stood for—reform style Islam—threatened to unhinge the old balance between *bula* and non-*bula* in which the former was revered for her piety and learning and the latter provided with religious services but not with demands for rethinking and rejuvenating Islam.

Behind such immediate threats to the person lay the uneasy feeling that, when it was most needed, religious/ national unity was being threatened. All understood themselves as attending the *mevlud* for the sake of Islam, and for all Islam was intimately related to Muslim national identity and thus of relevance to the political future being debated in every cafe and newspaper and on every street corner and shop floor. All shared certain basic wishes for that future—more jobs, better wages, less corruption, more religious freedom—but the extent to which Muslim identity implied distinction from Serbs and Croats, unity with the wider Islamic world, or any other relationships, was by no means a matter of agreement. The possible political implications of stressing different aspects of Muslim identity were not articulated or debated by anyone. This was not a dispute between defined positions and aspirations (and certainly not a dispute between those wanting a secular or an Islamic state), but a diffused conflict between various far less detailed or explicit attitudes. Striking at the heart of national/religious unity as it did, it was nonetheless profoundly disturbing.

**Postscript**

Since this chapter was written, Bosnia—Hercegovina has been ripped apart by an extraordinarily brutal war for the creation of ethnically pure territories and politics. Its Muslims have become the target of genocide, and Sarajevo itself subjected to a full year of constant shelling. In spite of their 1990 anxieties, as this war drew closer Muslims denied its possibility with increasing vigour, widely insisting that no serious violence could disrupt Bosnia's long traditions of multi-ethnic co-existence (and failing to arm or organise for conflict). The path from summer 1990 to the beginning of the assault on Bosnia in spring 1992 has been a tortured and complex one which cannot be dealt with here. But two points should be made.

This chapter has highlighted two aspects of Muslim identity, distinction from Serbs and Croats and co-identity with the wider Muslim world, but these do not exhaust the number of ways in which Muslims have understood themselves or their situation. As war drew closer in 1991, the nature of Muslim identity as European identity and of Islam as faith in keeping with the spirit of Europe—rational, tolerant and just, as it was perceived in the pre-war period—received increasing stress. So too did the importance of multi-national Bosnian identity as opposed to the identities of Serbia and Croatia. In Sarajevo the onset of war was widely understood as an urban/rural conflict between civilised citizens and barbaric peasants.[9] The European nature of Muslim Bosnian identity and the urban/rural divide were not new ideas coined for the moment, but understandings which had always been present. It is the stress placed on varying perceptions of identity that has changed over time and in response to changing contexts (and this is as true of Serbs, Croats and of all identity groups as it is of Bosnia's Muslims).

The second point concerns the route by which so bloody a war took hold. The conflict has sometimes been presented as caused and fuelled by age-old inter-ethnic hatreds which festered within families and communities until the communist lid was removed from the boiling pot. The example of the 1990 *mevluds* and their context suggests a differing scenario, pointing to fear rather than hatred and underlining communism's legacy and final collapse as significant in themselves rather than merely as the removal of a lid covering something else of decisive significance.

In the 1980s Sarajevans had generally known who was Muslim, Serb or Croat and symbolically guarded the ethnic boundaries, but this had not implied hatred. As noted, in 1990 Sarajevans were both optimistic about the future and anxious that aggressive nationalism should not blight it. This anxiety was reflected in fairly widespread support for a legal ban (later overturned) on the creation of nationally-based political parties. Until the last moment, the reformed Communist Party and the Alliance of Reform Forces (multi-national parties) appeared to have political support in Sarajevo. Overall then the desire was precisely for inter-ethnic peace rather than strife.

The 1990 *mevlud* expressed nationalism of a celebratory, nervous and disunited character, containing no coherent idea of how the future should be organised, merely hoping that it should be better, more prosperous, more liberated, more peaceful than the past. Nevertheless, Muslim religious activities were to become disturbing to non-Muslims, just as, for example, the increasingly heard Serbian patriotic pop songs were disturbing to Muslims. Fear, liberally stoked by the media, helped pave the way for the importing of a wider Yugoslav war, brewed, supplied and originally prosecuted outside Bosnia-Hercegovina, and in this war the Muslims could only be the major targets.

C. SORABJI

## REFERENCES

1 D. Lan, *Guns and Rain: Guerillas and Spirit Mediums in Zimbabwe*, London: James Currey, 1985; R. Wilson, 'Machine Guns and Mountain Spirits: The Cultural Effects of State Repression Among the Q'eqch'i of Guatemala', *Critique of Anthropology*, Vol. 11/1, 1991.

2. I. Lewis, *Ecstatic Religion*, London: Penguin, 1971.

3. N. Tapper, 'Gender and Religion in a Turkish Town: A Comparison of Two Types of Women's Gatherings', in P. Holden, (ed.), *Women's Religious Experience: Cross-Cultural Perpectives*, London, Croom Helm, 1983.

4. *Ibid*.

5. D. Rheubottom, 'The Seed of Evil Within', in D. Parkin (ed.), *The Anthropolgy of Evil*, Oxford: Basil Blackwell, 1985.

6. C. Sorabji, 'Islamic Revival and Marriage in Bosnia' *Journal Institute of Muslim Minority Studies*, Vol. 9/2, 1988.

7. P. Ramet (ed.), *Yugoslavia in the 1980s*, Boulder, Co.: Westview Press, 1985.

8. T. Bringa, 'Gender, Religion and Person: The Muslim Identity in Rural Bosnia', Ph. D. Thesis, University of London, 1991.

9. C. Sorabji, 'Ethnic War in Bosnia?', in *Radical Philosophy*, 1993, p. 63.

# 48

# FEMINISM AND NATIONALISM IN YUGOSLAVIA

In late eighties, with the consolidation of nationalism as the state ideology in Serbia, the propaganda directed against women grew stronger. It is well-known that in periods of acute crisis economic repression or marked repression, women are called to turn back to 'home and family'; they are referred to as "the angels of the home earth", as ideal mothers, as faithful wives... Such propaganda, among other things, aims at postponing or preventing social tensions, outburst of social discontent caused by mass lay-offs of working men and women. Women are the first to be fired; it is demanded that they hand their jobs over to men. At the end of eighties and the beginning of nineties, when over a half of enterprises, were suffering severe economic losses, preparations started for mass lay-offs, mostly of employed women.

For that reason, in early 1990, demographers and physicians, whole-heartedly supported by regime-sponsored mass media and institutions, offered some 'very interesting legal proposals concerning women'. Although these false promises lacked any realistic basis, some of these 'projects' must be singled out for their cynicism and underestimating of women.

## Projects Devoted to Wives and Mothers

In February 1990, Ivan Knajter, a physician and self-proclaimed demographic expert, proposed 'legal innovations designed to help the reaffirmation of the family'. He suggested the imposition of taxes on unmarried or divorced men and women over the age of thirty. According to the explanation of the project author, the tax would consist of 10 percent of the salaries of these unfit persons. The goal of the project was to 'prevent the disastrous decline in birth-rate in Serbia"; it is not clear why it would be so important whether children are born within or outside marriage. The said 'expert' suggests that 'persons who refuse to outside marriage. The said 'expert' suggests that 'persons who refuse to accept voluntarily matrimonial duties should be forced to do so'. This idea never occurred even to Stalin! In his times, the model of the "woman-hero of maternity, under the benignant moustaches of uncle Joseph" was launched. Hitler required German women to place their bodies at disposal for the renewal of the Aryan race. And both of them considered themselves collective fathers, either of the working class or of the nation.

In order to avoid suspicion as to his own 'moral-political pedigree' and due to the necessity of choosing among the possible collective fathers of the nation in Serbia (the president of the Republic, the head of the Church or the commander-in-chief of the Army), Knajter wished above all to win the favour of women. He states:

> "Once she is married, the wife would be considered employed, with all the social security benefits. The marriage would be her working place".[1]

He forgot just a trifle: who would provide the salary? Social security, special state funds, labour unions, the husband, a provider, or perhaps the father of the nation? In the end, he reveals another argument to justify the project, apart from the 'prevention of the disastrous decline in birth-rate': 'This proposal would have opened many new working places'

Of course, working places for men, who would only later be mobilized and sent to the front to defend the mother-nation, while she, is the meantime, would give birth to cannon fodder. In Nazi Germany, on April 7, 1943, the 'cleansing women' started, that is, mass firing of employed women. Fathers and sons of the nations everywhere agree with Hitler in his idea that 'in politics, one has to win the support of women, since men spontaneously follow them'. Unfortunately, this is not true; as a matter of fact, exactly the opposite holds, particularly in militarized societies.

**Maternal Mobilisation—Saving the Nation from Extinction**

The development of this propaganda may be divided into two phases, although they are constantly intertwined. The first phase started as early as the middle of eighties. It consists of the preparation of various projects aimed at the 'suppression of the white plague'. The second phase is the propaganda about child-bearing for patriotic reasons, that is, for the enhancement of national security.

At the beginning of the 'first phase', demographers followed territorial principles, asserting that in central and eastern Serbia, as well as in Vojvodina, the birth-rate was dropping at an alarming rate, while in Kosovo it was rising disturbingly. At this time, demographers had not yet introduced the ethnic criterion. The imbalance of the demographic development was explained instead either by economic factors or by changes in the system of values. As a solution, mostly administrative measures were offered, the model 'ideal family—three children' was popularized, etc.

The demographic discourse—in accordance with the expansion of the nationalist ideology—soon acquired a repressive, racist character. Starting with January, 1990 to this day, all draft bills resort to the 'ethnic principle'. The January 1990 Resolution on the Renewal of the Population, as well as the May 1990 amendments, suggest a double population policy—pro-natality for Serbia and Vojvodina and anti-natality for Kosovo. It was immediately clear that different demographic situations were used, on the one hand, in order to spread nationalist hatred, and on the other as another instrument of patriarchal separation of and discrimination against women on the ethnic basis. Feminists of Belgrade expressed their protest and indignation:

> "Coercive measures of population policy are applied in countries where human rights are violated daily, where the state deliberately encourages ethnic and racial intolerance. The introduction of coercive managements in the already poor network of gynaecological facilities in Kosovo is impermissible, since the right to medical services is a civilisational, not an ideological issue. Such repressive measures fail to bring about the 'desired' results, nor can they serve as the substitute for changes in the economic, social, and educational spheres. If women really enjoyed the opportunity and the right to choose, the population problem would not exist. Instead of administrative measures of population policy, the differences in demographic development should stimulate the creation of conditions where women will win their reproductive rights."[2]

Official documents started multiplying—for example, the resolution on the Renewal of the Population—among which 'The Warning' should be singled out for its neo-Malthusian, racist character, Nine 'significant' national institutions composed this document. The ruling party, the Socialist Party of Serbia, adopted 'The Warning' at its congress as one of the three official documents. 'The Warning' openly points to the 'threat' that minority peoples pose to the majority that is since "Albanians, Moslems and Gypsies, with their higher birth-rate, deviate from national, humane reproduction, [they] threaten the rights of other peoples."[3] That is to say, women of the above-mentioned nations (and not men, who still do not bear children!) participate in the 'general conspiration against the Serbian people'; they bear children out of separatist, fundamentalist reasons, and thus Serbian women should bear children out of patriotic and moral reasons: "The will to bear children should be mobilized"[4].

The newly formed parties joined the appeals of demographers, physicians and state institutions to maternal mobilisation. In relating to women, almost all the parties failed the democracy test; their ideas are imbued with militaristic language. The program of the Association of All Serbs of the World, for example, published before the first multiparty elections, the following proclamation:

> "In these difficult times for our state, not bearing children, as a national behaviour, will be considered treason".

In the same vein, the Serbian popular Renewal suggested the foundation of a fund for Serbian women who have four or more children. In the style of all nationalist moralizing babble, the party's leader Mirko Jovic also urged:

> "To equalize children born out of marriage with those born in it constitutes a form of special war against the Serbian people".

Nationalist are fond of speaking about honesty, going back to the roots, and medieval idyll; thus, the 1990 program of the Serbian Renewal Movement provides that one of the goals of its policy is the restoration of the family, the return to customs, the ensuring of conditions for an honest living. The Serbian Renewal Movement will place its capabilities at the service of the renewal of the Serbian character, striving for the flourishing of those virtues of the Serbian man that will soon become a part of the Serbian moral code. Feminists replied to these Serbian politicians worried about the extinction of the nation with the following:

> "To all the guardians of the Serbian morality we suggest that they examine the model of parthenogenetic procreation (conception without sin) and to clone themselves into innumerable Serbian copies. We suggest cooperative financing of this genetic engineering. It may be assumed that young Serbian fetuses will be immediately christened, then incited

and trained for hatred and war against the numerous enemies of the Serbian people."[5]

## Moral Condemnations: the Extremely Misogynous Character of the Propaganda

Generally speaking, this propaganda is imbued with strong moral condemnations and hatred against women. "The Warning" accuses women of not having children out of 'conformism and selfishness'. Marko Mladenovic, an official demographer, in one of the famous pathetic statements about the 'biological death; the gangrene, the tragedy', reveals the time-old desire of men to usurp women's procreative power:

> "Our man does not have children because happiness for him means having fun, a car, or a summer cottage. This is egoism."[6]

Then this enraged militarist joins cradles and guns together:

> "How to save Serbia! in 15 or 20 years there will be nobody to work, give birth and wage war."[7]

The Church enthusiastically joined the expansion of this 'emotional plague of fascism', as Virginia Woolf termed it in 1940:

> "Those who care for endowments, fun, summer holidays or furniture are more numerous than those who care for having children'.[8]

> Or, 'today many Serbian women kill their children by abortion. Feminists are in favour of killing unborn children. Fortunately, they have nothing to do with the being of the Serbian people".[9]

Some are particularly furious because, in spite of all the obstacles, the connections between the feminists from Belgrade and Zagreb still exist, and these latter are 'gravely' accused: these feminists from Serbia are very well connected with feminists from Zagreb, who propagate the extinction of the Serbian people.[10] Apart from hatred and condemnation, the Church also envisions natural punishments for women who do not bear children:

> "Women who bear children seldom get cancer. And the more children they have, the more they are immune to this horrible disease. Spinsters and women who prevent childbirth are by 40 percent more often afflicted by cancer, particularly breast cancer, than women who have children"[11].

**Patriotic Mobilisation**

The father of the nation (this time embodied in the president of the Republic), Slobodan Milosevic, in his 'historical speech' at Kosovo Polje in June, 1989 declared: 'If we are not very good at working, we are excellent at fighting.' This was the beginning of actual preparations for the war. He had chosen the right place—'the cradle of the Serbian people', but also the place of the great collective defeat. The offended honour of the fatherland will be revenged by military raids, since 'we must not forget that once we used to be an army—large brave, proud. Nowadays, six centuries later, once again we are fighting and more battles are ahead'. At the same place, and after the Battle of Kosovo, the cult of the heroic jugovic mother was born, the mother who offers her sons to the death. War trumpets are heard all over the country, while nationalists demand that maternity hospitals become recruitment centres:

> "For each Serbian soldier who fell in Slovenia, Serbian mothers must give birth to a hundred new soldiers"[12].

It is no longer enough to bear children in order to prevent the extinction of the nation, but sons are now needed for the defence of the fatherland and the struggle with 'enemy peoples'. Nationalist demographers, linking child-bearing to war, accurately calculate the pace of the enemy's advancement:

> 'The last Serbs will defend themselves from the Kalemegdan fortress, in the year 2091. But this last battle may also happen earlier, having in mind pessimistic prognoses."[13]

Later on, the same demographic "mathematician" has come to an even more precise calculation, with an unmistakably admixture of racism:

> "In the Blakians there are nations multiplying at rabbit's rate, with 10 or 15 children per family. In fifty years they will reach Belgrade"[14].

The similarity with Nazi Germany is no coincidence:

> "it must be made possible to each German woman to have as many children as she likes, since. if not, in 20 years the Third Reich would be left without the divisions necessary for the survival of our people."[15]

The racist and militarist logic that, we must be more numerous than them, is also followed in Montenegro:

> "Eastern Orthodox population lives in the municipalities with low birth-rate, while where Albanians, and Moslems are in the majority the birth-rat is high. The issue of birth-rates is all the more important having in mind that Montenegro's neighbours are three states whose intentions are suspicious".[16]

The propaganda is not restricted to mass media. Institutions, lavishly supported by the state, with nothing to offer but repressive measures, keep springing up every day (councils, boards, commissions, committees for the population renewal). Some of them, like the Fund for the Protection of Mothers and Offspring (founded in Belgrade in January 1993) insist most on financial help, that is, membership fee as the best means to 'supress the white plague'. This makes one think that out of this fund "all the Serbian people will arm itself so that finally all Serbs may live in the same state"[17]

Some of them have a more 'modern' point of view and consider the problem in terms of the laws of the market: 'Bearing children is like any other industry: the quantity of output is proportion ate to the amount of capital investments'.[18] Since for this 'eminent' expert the women is a body that is possessed, and the man is the owner of the belly and the children, in his misogyny he forgets about the laws he refers to:

> "Although pregnancy was brought about by the sexual intercourse between the women and the man, talking in the

> capitalist sense, we would say the following: at the moment of conception, the foetus is in the 50 percent the property of the woman and in 50 percent of the man. But as the pregnancy progresses, man's investments decrease since all the invested capital is the property of the woman".[19]

The misogynous attitude of the majority of demographers, physicians and politicians even makes them forget the official opinion of the regime that 'the unjust sanctions are to blame for everything'; 'Poverty and the sanctions are not to blame. We used to be even poorer than we are, and still our predecessors had 7 or 8 children'[20].

A colleague of this demographer, afforded enormous space in official media, wrote: 'The sanctions and the war cannot be an excuse. Earlier, birth and marriage were the most sacred act to every woman. And nowadays mothers advise their daughters not to marry, not to have children, to be egoists. During our 35th Gynaecological Week we ascertained that the reasons why women do not have children are 85 percent egoistic, 26 percent masked egoism, and only 8 percent genuine economic reasons.[21]

But this was too much for the President of the Republic, who corrected them, reminding them that in their national and misogynous trance they must not forget that 'the sanctions are killing our unborn babies.[22] Since in militarist societies it has always been assumed that 'maternity is the counterpart of war, or war is the symmetrical complement of maternity (E. Badinter), all this is accompanied by the appropriate language and rituals. Nicole Laroux illustrates by the example of Sparta how 'delivery is associated with war, the infantry-man with the woman in childbirth. The word ponos, denoting 'pain', is used both for a young man training in strengthening his body and for a woman suffering labour pains. Maternity is seen as similar to battle.[23]

In Nazi Germany, medals were awarded to 'good, fertile mothers' who gave birth to and reared the castle of warriors.

In Serbia, in Kosovo Polje, since June 1993, the Church gives medals to warriors and mothers with four or more children:

> "We have established the jugovic Mother decoration in order to encourage bearing more children in our people."

Last year they awarded 16 golden and 14 silver medals. Since they were not satisfied with the 'performance', they admonished: 'in earlier times, mothers were able to send as many as nine sons to the emperor's army, so that they could fight for freedom of their country and of their Orthodox faith. We have such mothers today, too, but very few.[24] Since in June, 1994 only 27 medals were awarded. Serbian women bear increasingly less children, and Serbian men are increasingly unwilling to go to war.

RADA TRAJKOVIC

## REFERENCES

1. "Borba", "Politika", March, 1990.
2. Open letter to the public from the Second Session of the Women's Parliament, June, 1991.
3. "The Warning", June 30, 1992, p. 2
4. *Ibid*, pp. 5 and 2.
5. The Belgrade Women's Lobby, October, 1990.
6. "Politika", March 5, 1993.
7. *Ibid*.
8. "Borba", June 30, 1993. The statement is by Artemije, the episcope of Rasa and Prizren.
9. "Politika", March 27, 1993. The statement of Vasilije, the Orthodox bishop of Zvornik and Tuzla.
10. S. Adasevic, in the Radio-Belgrade II Channel program "*Reserved* for...", April. 1994.
11. "May God Help Serbs to Unite, Believe in God, and Mutiply", the message by the bishop Nikolaj, placed as posters in the streets of Belgrade, October, 1992.

12. Rada Trajkovic, the president of the association "Homeland", July, 1991.
13. M. Mladenovic, "Politika", March 5, 1993.
14. M. Mladenovic, in the Radio-belgrade program "Reserved for...", April, 1994.
15. Rita Thalmaum, "Etre femme souls le illle Reich", p. 137.
16. "Politika", July 20, 1993. A statement by Radovan Bakovic, professor of the Faculty of philosophy in Niksic.
17. "Vreme", May 31, 1993.
18. M. Mladenovic, radio program, "Reserved for...", April, 1994.
19. Franaces Kissling "Yo aborto, tu abortas, todos callamos", feminist paper "Voz de la mujer", Mexico, May 1990, No. 4, p. 24.
20. Radmilo Jovanoc, physician, 'Politika', May 10, 1994.
21. S. Adasevic, in the radio program "Reserved for...", April, 1994.
22. S. Milosevic, in the text of the abolition of Danica Draskovic and Vuk Draskovic, July 1993.
23. Nicole Lraux, "Le lit et la guerre", in the journal "L'homme", Jan./Mar., 1981, XXXI.
24. "Borba", June 30, 1993 A Statement by Artemije, the episcope of Rasa and Prizren.

# BIBLIOGRAPHY


Abdel Kader, Soha, *Egyptian Women in a Changing Society, 1899–1987*, Boulder, Colo.: Lynne Reinner Publishing, 1987, pp. 137–38.

Abu-Lughod, Lila, "The Objects of Soap Opera: Egyptian Television and the Cultural Politics of Modernity", *Worlds Apart: Modernity through the Prism of the Local*, ed. by Deniel Mille, London and New York: Routledge, 1995, pp. 190–210.

Adamu, Haroun al Rashid, *The North and Nigerian Unity*, Gaskiya Corporation Zaria, 1973.

Adamu, Mahdi, The Economics of Culture Among the Hausa During the Present Millenium, A.D., *Kano Studies*, 1979.

Ahmed, Leila, *Women and Gender in Islam*, New Haven: Yale University Press, 1992, p. 167.

—, 'Feminism and Feminist Movement in the Middle East', *Women Studies International Forum*, 5/2, 1982.

—, "Early Feminists Movements in the Middle East: Turkey and Egypt," *Muslim Women*, edited by Freda Husain, Becehan: Croom Helm, 1984.

Ahmad, Maryan, Interview by author, Kano, Nigeria, 1 July, 1993.

Ajao, O.O., "Female Circumcision: It is Archaic," *Sunday Sketch*, Feb. 6th, 1983, p. 5.

Ajayi, J. and B. Ikara, *The Evolution of Political Culture in Nigeria*, University Press Ltd. and Kaduna State Council for Arts and Culture, 1985.

Aku, Akpa, *Daily Sketch*, October 28th 1983, p. 3.

'Aliyya al-'Asqalani, "Al-Tasallut yudammir al-'alaqa al-zawjiyya: sultat al-rajul fi al-bayt la tu'add add istibadan," *Al-Luwa' al-Islami*, 1995, p. 16.

Amadiume, I., *African Matriarchal Foundations: The Igbo Case*, London: Karnak, 1987.

Amin, Qasim, *The New Woman*, trans. Samiha Sidhom Peterson, Cairo: American University in Cairo Press 1995, p. xi.

Ansari, Hamid N., The Islamic Militants in Egyptian Politics', *International Journal of Middle East studies*16, 1984, pp. 123–44.

Arjomand, Said (ed.), *From Nationalism to Revolutionary Islam*, Albany: State University of New York, 1984.

Asad, Muhammed, *The Message of the Qur'ân*, translation of *the Qur'ân* and notes, Dar an Andaulsu, Gibraltar, 1980.

Ashmawi, Sa'id, *Al Shariah al islamiyya* (Islamic Law), Cairo, 1980 and *Islam al siyasi* (Political Islam), Cairo, 1988.

Atiku, Abubakar, *Ifadat al-murid* (Informing the disciple), Cario: Shukrat Maktabat, 1956.

Aziz, F.A., "Gynaeocologic and Obstetric Complications of Female Circumcision," *Gynaecol. Obstet.* 17/6, 1980, pp. 560–63.

Badamasi, Maryam, Interview by author. Rimin Kebe, Nigeria, 20 August, 1992.

Badran, Margot, "Gener Activism: Feminists and Islamists in Egypt", *Identity Politics and Women: cultural Reassertion and Feminism in International Perspective*, ed. by Valentine M. Moghadam, Boulder, Colo.: Westview Press, 1993, pp. 202–27.

—, *Competing Agenda: Feminists, Islam and the State in Nineteenth- and Twentieth-Century Egypt*, London, Macmillan, 1991, p. 201.

—, *Feminsits, Islam and Nation: Gender and the Making of Modern Egypt*, Princton: Princeton University Press 1995, pp. 139–40.

Barkow, Jerome, Hausa women and Islam. *Canadian Journal of African Studies*, 6/317–28, 1972.

Baron, Beth, "Mothers, Morality, and Nationalism in Pre-1919 Egypt", *The Origins of Arab Nationalism*, Rasid Khalidi, Lisa Anderson, Muhammad Muslih, and Reeva Simon (eds.), New York: Columbia University Press 1991, pp. 271–88.

Bello, Sule, The State and Economy in Kano circa 1894–1960: A Study of Colonial Domination, Ph.D. Thesis, Ahmadu Bello University, 1982.

Bennett, T.W., 'The Equality Caluse and Customary Law', *South African Journal on Human Rights*, 1994, pp. 123-4.

Bhabha, Homi, *The Location of Culture*, London and New York: Routledge, 1994, p. 2.

Bonat, Zuwaqu Abugwon, The Colonial Phase of the Underdevelopment of Zaria Province, 1902–1945, M.A. Thesis, Ahmadu Bello University, 1985.

Boyd, J., The *Caliph's Sister*, London: Frank Cass, 1989.

—, and Murray Last, The Role of Women as 'Agents Religieux' in Sokoto *Canadian Journal of African Studies* 19/2, 1985, pp. 283–300.

Bringa, T., 'Gender, Religion and Person: The Muslim Identity in Rural Bosnia', Ph. D. Thesis, University of London, 1991.

Bruce, M.K., 'Work of the United Nations Relating to the Status of Women', *Revue des droits de l'homme*, 1971, pp. 365-66.

Callaway, Barbara, Women and Political Participation in Kano City, *Comparative Politics*, 19/4, pp. 379–393.

—, 'The role of women in Kano City politics', *Hausa women in the twentieth century*, ed. by Catherine Coles and Beverly Mack, Madison: University of Wisconsin Press, 1991.

—, and Lucy Creevey, *The Heritage of Islam: Women, religion and politics in West Africa*, Boulder, CO: Lynne Rienner, 1994.

Chhaachhi, Amrita, 'Forced Identities: The State, Communalism, Fundamentalism and Women in India', *Women, Islam an the State*, ed. by Deniz Kandiyoti, Philadelphia: Temple University Press, 1991, pp. 144–75.

Clarke, P. and I. Linden, *Islam in Modern Nigeria: A Study of a Muslim Community in a Post-independence State, 1960–83*, Mainz: Grunewald, 1984.

Coles, Catherine, and Beverly Mack (eds.), *Hausa Women in the Twentieth Century*, Madison: U of Wisconsin P, 1991.

—, 'Muslim women in town: Social change among the Hausa of northern Nigeria', Ph.D. diss., University of Wisconsin at Madison, 1983.

—, and Beverly Mack, 'Women in twenthieth-century Hausa society', *Hausa women in the twentieth century*, Madison: University of Wisconsin Press, 1991.

Cook, Robert, "Damage to Physical Health form Pharaonic Circumcision (Infibulation) of Females", *A review of Medical Literature*, WHO/EMBRO Tech. Publ. 2, Vol. 12, 1976, pp. 138-144.

Cruise O'Brien, Donal, *The Mourides of Senegal: The political and economic organization of an Islamic brotherhood.* Oxford, UK: Clarendon, 1971.

Dangor, S., "Muslim Personal Law: Interpretation and Application", *Muslim Views*, 1994, p. 12.

Davids, A., *The Mosques of Bo-kaap: A social history of Islam at the Cape*, Cape Town, South African Institute of Arabic and Islamic Research, 1970, p. xv.

Dekmejian, H., *Islam in Revolution, Fundamentalism in the Arab World*, Syracuse, NY: Syracuse University Press, 1985.

Dessoui, Ali (ed.), *Islamic Resurgence in the Arab World* New York: Praeger, 1982, esp. Saad Eddin Ibrahim, 'Islamic Militancy as a Social Movement: The Case of Two Groups in Egypt':

John Espositio (ed.), *Voices of Resurgent Islam,* Oxfrod: Oxford University Press, 1983.

Diop, C.A., The *Cultural Unity of Black Africa,* London: Karnak, 1989.

El-Messiri, Sawsan, *Ibn al-Balad: A Concept of Egyptian Identity,* Leiden: Brill, 1978; Walter Armbust, *Mass Culture and Modernism in Egypt,* Cambridge: Cambridge University Press. 1996, ch. 2.

Emirate, Kano, *Comparative Studies in Society and History,* 1977, 18, pp. 395-426.

Falola, T., *The Political Economy of Ibadan,* Nigeria: Ife Press, 1984.

Favret-Saada, J., *Deadly Words: Witchcraft in the Bocage,* Cambridge: Cambridge University Press, 1980.

Flegel, E.R., Biography of Madugu Mohamman Mai Gashin Baki, Paper to Fourth Seminar on the Economic History of the Central Savanna of West Africa, Ahmadu Bello University, Zaria, 1885.

Gani, H.A., *Reform of Muslim Personal Law: The Shah Bano Controversy and the Muslim Women (Protection of Rights on Divorce) Act 1986,* New Delhi, Deep and Deep Publications, 1988, p. 161.

Garvey, J.H. and T.A. Aleinikoff, *Modern Constitutional Theory: A Reader,* Minnesota, West Publishing Company, 1991, p. 409.

Gerami, Shahin and Melodye Lehnerer, 'Women's agency and household diplomacy: Negotiating fundamentalism', *Gender & Society,* 15/4, 2001, pp. 556–73.

Al-Ghazali, Zainab, *Ayyam min hayati* (Days of My Life), Cairo: Dar Al Ahurq, 8th printing 1986.

Gibson, Gordon D., Thomas J. Larson, and Cecilia R. McGurk, *The Kavango Peoples,* Franz Steiner Verlag, 1981;

Gilliland, Dean Stuart, African Traditional Religion in Transition: The Influence of African Tradition Religion In Northern Nigeria, Ph.D. Thesis, Hartford, 1971.

Gordon, Robert J., *The Bushman Myth: The Making of a Namibian Underclass,* Westview Press, 1992;

Al-Hajj, Muhammed Ahmed, The Mahdist Tradition in Northern Nigeria Ph.D. Thesis, Ado Bayero College of Ahmadu Bello University, 1973.

Hale, Sondra, 'Anthropology constructs the woman: Sudan studies' Sacramento Anthropological Society, California State University, No. 16, 1983, pp. 63–71.

Harb, Al Ghazali, *Istiqlal al mar'a fi acl islam,* Cairo: Dar Al Mustaqbal Al'Arab, n.d.

Hatem, Mervat, 'Class and patriarchy as competing paradigms for the study of Middle Eastern Women' *Comparative Studies in Society and History,* 29/4, 1987, pp. 811–18.

Herbstein, Denis and John Evenson, *The Devils Are Among Us: The War for Manibia,* Zed Books, 1989.

Hibri, A., "A Study of Islamic Herstory: Or how did we ever get into this mess?", *Women's Studies International Forum,* 1982, pp. 207-12.

Hijab, Nadia, *Woman power: The Arab Debate on Women at Work,* Cambridge; Cambridge University Press 1988, pp. 29–35; Howard Merriam, 'Egyptian Islamic Fundamentalism and the Law', and Sarah Graham-Brown, 'After Jihan's Law: A New Battle Over Women's Rights' *The Middle East,* June 1985, pp. 17–20.

Hill, Polly, *Ruraal Hausa: A Village and a Setting,* Cambridge University Press, Cambridge, 1972.

Hinchliffe, Doreen, The Status of Women in Islamic Law, in G.N. Brown and M. Hiskett (eds.), *Conflict and Harmony in Education in Tropical Africa,* George Allen and Unwin, London, 1975.

Hinz, Manfred and Nadia Gevers, *Koevet Versus the People of Namibia,* Working Group Kairos, 1989.

Hiskett, M., *The Development of Islam in West Africa,* London and New York: Longman, 1984.

Hodgkin, T. (ed.), *Nigerian Perspectives: An Historical Anthropology*, Chaucer Press Suffolk, 1975.

Hoffman-Ladd, Valerie J., 'Polemics on the modesty and segregation of women in contemporary Egypt' *International Journal of Middle Eastern Studies*, 19, 1987, pp. 23–50

Holden, P. (ed.), *Women's Religious Experience: Cross-Cultural Perspectives*, London: Croom Helm, 1983.

Hourani, Albert, *Arabic Thought in the Liberal Age*, Cambridge: Cambridge University Press, 1983, pp. 130–63.

Hussain, Aziza, Inji Ruhdi, Saniyya Salih Awatif Wali, Mervat Ittalawi, Muna Zulficar, Magda Al Muti, *Al Huquq al qanuniyya lil mar'a al'arabiyya bain al nadthariyya wa al tatbiq*, The Legal Rights of the Egyptian Woman: Theory and Practice, Cairo, 1988.

Imam, Ayesha, "The Women's Movement, State, and Democracy in Nigeria," Paper presented at the Akut workshop on Social Movements and Democracy in the Third World, Delhi, India, October 1992.

—, Women's Liberation: Myth or Reality (Paper to Muslim Sisters' Organisation Conference, Kano), *Women's Struggles and Strategies: Third World Pespectives*, ISIS Rome, 1985-86.

Iregbulem, L.M., "Post Circumcision Vulva Adhesions in Nigeria", *Brit. J. Plast, Surg.*, 3/1, 1980, pp. 83–86.

Isichei, E., *A History of West Africa*, London New York: Longman, 1977.

Ismail, Ellen T., *Social Environment and Daily Routine of Sudanese Women: A case study of Urban Middle Class Housewives*, Berlin: Dietrich Reimer Verlag, 1982.

Janjic, D., *Gradanski Rat u Bosni i Hercegovini* (Civil War in Bosnia Hercegovina), D. Janjic and P. Shoup (eds.), *Bosnia i Hercegovini Izemedu Rata i Mira* (Bosnia Hercegovina Between War and Peace), Belgrade/Sarajevo: Forum for Ethnic Relations, 1992.

Jayawardena, Kumari, *Feminism and Nationalism in the Third World*, London: Zed Press, 1986.

Joseph, Suad, *Gender and Family in the Arab World,* Middle East Report No. 190, 1994.

Kabir, Zainab, Women's Liberation: Myth or Reality" *The Muslim Woman in the 14th Hijab,* FOMWAN", 1989.

Kabira, W.M. and A. Nzioki, *Celebrating Women's Resistance,* Nairobi: Women Perspective Publications, 1993.

—, *Our Secret Lives,* Nairobi: Phoenix, 1992.

Kandiyoti, Deniz, Bargaining with patriarchy, *Gender & society* 2, 1988, pp. 274–90.

—, 'Contemporary feminist scholarship and Middle East Studies' in Deniz Kandiyoti (ed.), *Genedering the Middle East: Emerging Perspective,* Syracuse: Syracuse University Press, 1996.

Kani, A., *The Intellectual Origins of the Sokoto Jihad, Iman,* Nigeria, 1985.

Kanogo, T., Kikuyu Women and Politics of Protest: Mau Mau', P. Halden MacDonald and A. Ardener (eds.), *Images of Women in Peace and War: Cross-Cultural Perspectives,* London: Macmillan. 1987.

Kano State Government, *White Paper on the Report of the Kano State Committee* for *Women Affairs,* 1988.

Kisekka, Mere, "Women's Organized Health Struggles: The Challenge to Women's Associations," Mere Kisekka (ed.), *Women's Health Issues in Nigeria,* Zaria: Tamaza, 1992, pp. 105–21.

Koopman, Jeanne, "Women in the Rural Economy: Past, Present, and Future", *African Women South of the Sahara,* ed. by Margaret Jean Hay and Sharon Sticher, 2nd edn. New York: Wiley and Sons, 1995.

Kuhnke, Laverne, 'The 'Doctoress' on a Donkey: Women Health Officers in Nineteenth Century Egypt', *Clio Medica* 9 (1974) no. 3, pp. 193–205.

Lambert, H.E., *A Guide to Women's Organisations and Agencies Serving Women in Kenya,* Nairobi: Mazingira Institute, 1985, p. 100.

Lane, Sandra D. and Rubinstein, Robert A., *Juding the Other: Responding to Traditional Genital Surgeries,* Hastings Center,.

Lan, D., *Guns and Rain: Guerillas and Spirit Mediums in Zimbabwe,* London: James Currey, 1985.

Lancaster, John, "Cloudy Days for Cairo Star: Film Celebrity Sued by Islamic Right, Stalked by Alleged Ex-Lover," *Washington Post,* January 31, 1996, p. 12.

Last, Murray, *The Sokoto Caliphate,* Longmans, London, 1967.

Lemu, Ahmed, The Role of Muslim Women in Politics from 1992, *The Muslim Woman,* 1/1, July 1988, pp. 5–9.

Levojoy, Paul, Plantation Slavery in the Economy of the Sokoto Caliphate, *Journal of African History,* XIX, 1978, pp. 341–68.

Levtzoin, N., *Rural and Urban Islam in West Africa,* Boulder: Lynne Reiner, 1987.

Levy, R., *The Social Structure of Islam,* Cambridge University Press, 1969.

Lewis, I., *Ecstatic Religion,* London: Penguin, 1971.

Likimani, M., *Women of Kenya; Twenty Years of Independence,* Nairobi: Giant Printers, 1983.

Mackeod, Arlene Elowe, *Accomodating Protest: Working women, the New Veiling, and Change in Cairo,* New York: Colombia University Press, 1991.

Maha, 'Umar "Min ajl hayat zawjiyya mustaquira wa hadi'a," *Al-Luwa' al-Islami,* 1996, p. 17.

Mahadi, Abdullahi, The State and the Economy: The Sarauta System and its Role in Shaping the Society and Economy of Kano Emirate With Particular Reference to the 18th and 19th centuries, Ph.D. Thesis, Ahmadu Bello University, 1982.

Malti-Douglas, Fedwa, "A Woman and Her Sufis" Washington, D.C.: Center for Contemporary Arab Studies Occasional Papers, Georgetown University, 1995.

Margolis, D., 'Women's Movements Around the World; Cross-Cultural Comparisons,' *Gender and Society,* Vol. 7/3, 1993, p. 380.

Mayer, Ann Elizabeth, 'Book reviews' *Middle East Women's Studies Review,* 13/5, 1998, pp. 4-7.

Meek, C.K., *The Northern Tribes of Nigeria,* Oxford University Press, London, 1925.

Midibbo, Ahmed Mohammed, European Trading Comapnies and the Under-development of Northern Nigeria 1855–1939: The Case of the Royal Niger Company/United Africa Company, Ph.D. Thesis, Ahmadu Bello University, 1985.

Mohammed, Abubaar, Sokoto, The Satiru Revolt, M.A. Thesis, Ahmadu Bello Universality, 1986.

Mohanty, Chandra Talpade, 'Under Western eyes: feminist scholarship and colonial discourses' in Patrick Williams and Laura Chrisman (ed.), *Colonial Discourse and Post-Colonial Theory: A Reader,* New York and London: Harvester Wheatsheaf, 1994.

Monsted, M., *Women's Groups in Rural Kenya and Their Role in Development,* Copenhagen: Center for Development Research, 1978.

Muhammad Ibrahim, Mabruk, *Mawqif al-Islam min al-hubb,* Cairo: Al-Nur al-Islami, 1996, p. 19.

Mukhtar, Mansur Ibrahim, The Impact of British Colonial Domination on the Social and Economic Structures of the Society of Kano, 1903–1950, M.A. Thesis, Ahmadu Bello University, 1985.

Nasif, Mansur Ali, *Ittaji al Jami Lil Usul,* Beirut.

Noibi, D.O.S., The Role of Muslim Women in Politics from 1992, *The Muslim Women,* 1/1, July 1988, pp. 5–9.

Nzioki, A. and W.M. Kabira (eds.), *They Have Destroyed the Temple,* Nairobi: Longman, 1993.

Nzomo, J., 'The Kenya Women's Movement in a Changing Political Context in S. Khasiani and E. Njiro (eds.), *The Women's Movement in Kenya,* Nairobi: Association of African Women for Research and Development, 1993.

Oduol, W.A., 'Kenyan Women in Politics: An Analysis of Past and Present Trends', G.S. Were (ed.), *Trans-African Journal of History,* Nairobi: Gideon S. Were Press, Vol. 22, 1993, pp. 166–80.

Offen, Karen, 'Defining Feminism: A Comparative Historical Approach', *Signs,* Autumn 1988, no. 14, pp. 119–47 and Gerda Lerner, *The Creation of Patriarchy,* Oxford: Oxford University Press, 1986.

Ofodile, F.A. and J.O. Oluwasanmi, "Post-Circumcision Epidermoid Inclusion Cysts of the Clitoris", *Plast Recenstr. Surg.* 63/4, 1979, pp. 485–86.

Ogunbiyi, A., 'The Position of Muslim Women' as stated by Uthman B. Fudi, *Journal of West African Studies,* Ife University, 1969.

Ogunsola, Albert F., *Legislation and education in northern Nigeria,* Zaria, Nigeria: Oxford University Press, 1974.

Ogundipe-Leslie, Molara, *Sew the Old Days and Other Poems,* 1985.

—, *Re-Creating Ourselves: African Women and Critical Transformations.* Lawrenceville, NJ: Africa World Press, 1994.

—, "Not Spinning on the Axis Maleness," *Sisterhood Is Global,* ed. by Robin Morgan,. London: Doubleday, 1984.

—, and Carole Boyce Davies (eds.), *Moving Beyond Boundaries,* International Dimensions of Black Women's Writing 1, London: Pluto, 1995.

Ojwang, J.B. and J. Mugambi, eds. *The S.M. Otieno Case: Death and Burial in Modern Kenya,* Nairobi: Nairobi University Press, 1989.

Okechi-Owiti, 'Some Socio-legal Issues, in J.B.O. Ojwang and J.N.K. Mugambi (eds.), *The S.M. Otieno Case: Death and Burial in Modern Kenya,* Nairobi: Nairobi University Press 1989, p. 12.

Onimode, B. (ed.), *The IMF, the World Bank and the African Debt,* London: IFAA/Zed Books, 1989

Onwuejogwu, Michael, The Cult of the Bori Spirits Among the Hausa, in Mary Douglas and Phyllis Kaberry (eds.), *Man in Africa,* Tavistock, London, 1969, pp. 279–306.

Orire, Abdulkadir, The Role of Muslim Women in Politics from 1992, *The Muslim Woman,* 1/1, July 1988, pp. 5–9.

Paden, John, *Religious and political culture in Kano,* Berkeley: University of California Press, 1973.

Paden, *Ahmadu Bello, Sardauna of Sokoto,* London: Hodder and Stoughton, 1986.

Paleker, G., "MPL Board Under Attack", *Muslim Views,* 1994.

Palmer, Herbert (trans. and commentary), The Kano Chronicle, *Journal of the Anthropological Institute,* 38, 1908, pp. 57–98.

Parkin, D. (ed.), *The Anthropolgy of Evil,* Oxford: Basil Blackwell, 1985.

Patel, R., *Islamisation of Laws in Pakistan?,* Karachi, Faiza Publishers, 1986. p. 92.

Perchonock, N., "Double Oppression" S. Bappa *et al., Women in Nigeria Today,* London: Zed Books, 1985.

Philipp, Thomas, "Feminism and Nationalist Politics in Egypt", *Women in the Muslim World,* ed. by L. Beck and N. Keddie, Cambride: Harvard University Press, 1978.

Pittin, R., 'Selective Educational Issues in Gender, Class and Ideology in Northern Nigeria', *Review of African Political Economy,* no. 48, 1990.

—, Marriage and Alternative Strategies: Career Patterns of Hausa Women in Katsina City, Ph.D. Thesis, University of London, 1979.

Poewe, Karla O., *The Namibian Herero: A History of Their Pyshcological Disintegration and Survival,* Edward Mellon Press, 1985.

Poulter, S., 'The Claim to a Separate Islamic System of Personal Law for British Muslims", C. Mallat & J. Connors (eds.), *Islamic Family Law,* London, Graham & Trotman, 1990, pp. 147, 159.

Qasim, Amin, *The Liberation of Women,* Cairo: American University in Cairo Press 1992.

Rahman, A., "Religious Rights Versus Women's Rights in India: A Test Case for International Human Rights Law", *Columbia Journal of Transnational Law,* Vol. 28/1, 1990, pp. 473-98.

Rahman, F., "The Status of Women in Islam: A Modernist Interpretation", H. Papanek & G. Minault (eds.), Separate World: *Studies of Purdah in South Asia,* New Delhi, South Asia Books, 1982, p. 302.

Ramet, P., 'Apocalypse Culture and Social Change', P. Ramet (ed.), *Yugoslavia in the 1980s,* Boulder, Co.: Westview Press, 1985.

—, *Yugoslavia in the 1980s,* Boulder, Co.: Westview Press, 1985.

Republic of Kenya, *The Women's Bureau Annual Report,* Nairobi: Ministry of cultural and Social Services, Women's Bureau, 1988.

Rheubottom, D., 'The Seed of Evil Within', D. Parkin (ed.), The Anthropolgy of Evil, Oxford: Basil Blackwell, 1985.

Rizivi, S.A.H., "Book Review: Muslim Law and the Constitution by A.M. Bhattacharjee", *Islamic and Comparative Law Quarterly,* 1987, p. 84.

Robinson, C.H., *Hausaland: Fifteen Hundred Miles Through the Central Sudan,* London, 1896.

Saadawi, N.E., 'The Political Challenges Facing Arab Women at the End of the 20th Century', N. Toubia (ed.), *Women of the Arab World: The Coming Challenge. Papers of the Arab Women's Solidarity Association Conference,* London, Zed Books, 1988, p. 11.

Sadiya, Halima, Interview by author, Kano, Nigeria, 21 October, 1993.

Sahgal, Gita and Nira Yuval-Davis (eds), Refusing Holy orders: Women and Fundamentalism in Britain, London; Virago Press, 1992.

Sambo, Bashir, 'The Role of Muslim Women in Politics from 1992', *The Muslim Woman,* 1/1, July 1988, pp. 5–9.

Schacht, J., 'Islam in Northern Nigeria', *Studia Islamica,* Vol. viii, 1957.

Schildkrout, Enid, 'Widows in Hausa society' *Widows in African Societies: Choices and constraints,* ed. by Betty Potash, Standford, CA: Stanford University Press, 1986.

Shafiq, Duriyya, *Al Kitab al abiyad lil huquq almar'a al misriyya* (The White Paper on the Rights of the Egyptian Woman), Cairo, 1953.

Shaheed, F., "The Cultural Articulation of Patriarchy: Legal Systems, Islam and Women", *South Asia Bulletin,* 1986, p. 39.

Sharpe, Barry, The Armature of Slavery: People and Things in Northern Nigerian Consciousness, Presentation to Social Anthropology Division Seminar, University of Sussex, 1988.

Shenton, Robert, *The Development of Capitalism in Northern Nigeria,* James Currey, London, 1986.

Sorabji, C., 'Islamic Revival and Marriage in Bosnia' *Journal Institute of Muslim Minority Studies,* Vol. 9, no. 2, 1988.

—, 'Ethnic War in Bosnia?', *Radical Philosophy,* 1993, p. 63.

Stowassser, B.F., "Religious Ideology, Women, and the Family: The Islamic Paradigm", B.F. Stowasser (ed.), *Islamic Impulse,* London, Croon Holm, 1987, p. 290.

Sule, Balarabe, and Priscilla Straratt, Islamic leadership positions for women in contemporary Kano society, *Hausa women in the twentieth century,* edited by Catherine Coles and Beverly Mack Madison: University of Wisconsin Press, 1991.

Sullivan, Earl, *Women in Egyptian Public Life'* Syrancuse, NY: Syracuse University Press, 1986, and for a general survey see Ann Mosely Lesch and Earl Sullivan, 'Women in Egypt—New Roles and Realities', *USFI Reports* 22, Africa, 1986.

Tapper, Nancy, 'Mysteries of the Harem: an anthropological perspective on recent studies of women of the Mulsim Middle East' *Women's Studies International Quarterly,* No. 2, 1979, pp. 481-7.

—, 'Gender and Religion in a Turkish Town: A Comparison of Two Types of Women's Gatherings', P. Holden (ed.), *Women's Religious Experience: Cross-Cultural Perpectives*, London, Croom Helm, 1983.

Temsamani, Touria, 'Analyse socio-économique de la condition de la femme au Maroc' Aicha Belarbi *et al.* editors, *Droits de Citoyenneté des Femmes au Maghreb,* Casablanca: Le Fennec, 1999.

Thomas, B., *Politics, Participation, and Poverty: Development Through Self-Help in Kenya,* Boulder: Westview Press, 1985, pp. 7–8.

Thomas-Emeagwali, G., 'Development at Risk', *Woodstock Road Editorial,* St. Antony's College, Oxford, no. 7, 1991.

—, 'Women in Pre-colonial Nigerian Economy', paper presented at the Annual Conference of the African Studies Association, Chicago, 1989.

Tibenderana, Peter K., The beginnings of girls' education in the native administration schools in northern Nigeria, *Journal of African History* 26, 1985, pp. 93–109.

Timothy, Mitchell, *Colonising Egypt,* Cambridge: Cambridge University Press 1988, pp. 111–13.

Toffar, A.K., 'Muslim Personal law in a Non-Muslim State', paper presented at workshop on 'Islamic Personal Law in South Africa: Its Future Position', Islamic Unity Convention, Cape Town, 16 October 1994.

Touhami, Abdelkhalek, 'La pauvreté au Maroc: une approche basée sur la satisfaction des besoins de base' *Pauvreté, Satisfaction des Besoïns Essentiels et Variables Démographiques au Maroc,* Rabat: Institut of National de Statistique et d'Economic Appliquee, 1999.

Tremearne, A.J.N., *The Ban of Bori,* London: Frank Cass, 1968.

Trimingham, J.S., *Islam in West Africa,* Oxford: Clarendon Press, 1962.

Tucker, Judith, E., *Women in Nineteenth Century Egypt.* London: Cambridge University Press, 1985.

Umar, Muhammad Sani, 'From Sufism to anti-Sufism in Nigeria', *Muslim identity and social change in sub-Saharan Africa,* edited by Louis Brenner, Bloomington: Indiana University Press, 1993.

Wallace, Christian, The Concept of Gandu: How Useful is it in Understanding Labour Relations in Rural Hausa Society? *Savanna,* 7:2, 1978, pp. 137–150.

Wassef, Nadia and Mansour, Abdallah, *Investigating Masculinities and Female Genital Mutilation in Egypt,* Cairo: Female Genital Mutiliation Task Force, 1999.

Watt, Michael, *Silent Violence: Food, Famine and the Peasantry in Northern Nigera,* University of California Press, Berkeley, 1983.

Watt, W.M., *Muhammad at Medina,* Karachi, Oxford University Press, 1981, p. 272.

Williams, Frieda-Nela, *Precolonal Communities of Southwestern Africa: A History of Owambo Kingdoms,* 1600-1920, National Archives of Namibia, 1991.

Williams, Lindy and Sobieszczyk, Teresa, *Attitudes Surrounding the Continuation of Female Circumcision in the Sudan: Passing the tradition to the Next Generation,* PSC Research Report, Ithaca, NY: Cornell University, 1996.

Wilson, R., 'Machine Guns and Mountain Spirits: The Cultural Effects of State Repression Among the Q'eqch'i of Guatemala', *Critique of Anthropology,* 11/1, 1991.

Wipper, A., 'Equal Rights for Women in Kenya,' *Journal of Modern Studies,* Vol. 9/3, 1971, pp. 427–42.

*World Bank Participation Sourcebook,* Ch. IV: 'Practice pointers in enabling the poor to participate', Washington, 2000.

Women in Nigeria, *The WIN Document,* Zaria, 1985.

Worsley, A., "Infibulation and Female Circumcision: A Study of a Little Known Custom", British Journal of Obstetrics and Gynaecology, 45, 1938, pp. 686–691.

Wright, Helena, "Medical Dangers of Female Circumcision", IPPF Medical Bulletin, 1980, pp. 1–3.

Yusuf, Ahmed Beita, Legal Pluralism in the Northern States of Nigeria: Conflict of Laws in a Multi-Ethnic Environment, Ph.D. Thesis, University of Buffalo, 1976.

Yusuf, Bilkisu, Muslim Women in Nigerian Politics, Paper to Symposium on Muslim Women in Nigeria, Lehrstuhl fur Islam wissenschaft, University Bayreuth, May 19, 1990.

Yuval Davis, Nira, 'The Bearers of the Collective: Women and Religious Fundamentalism in Israel', Feminist Review, No. 4., 1980.

Zahra, Interview by Hajiya Mario Muhammed, *Uwa Mabada Mama*, Radio Programme, July/August, Kano State Radio, 1984.

Zawiya, S.S. and Sadauki, T.A., *Jigatau Dan Bayero*, Kaduna, Nigeria: Nationhouse Press, 1991.

# INDEX

## D



## E

## F

## G

## H



## I

## J



## K

## L



## M

# O



# P

## T

## Y



## Z